CW00544163

Watermill

Life Story of a Welsh Cornmill

by

David Llewelyn Davies

Felin Lyn: *This watercolour was painted in the early 1950s by Megan Jones in her student days. She is the grand-daughter of the last full-time miller and is now Mrs Dawson. The original is held by the Jeffreys family who were the tenants of the time. All the buildings comprise Felin Lyn, except for the one on the extreme right which is Glyndwr cottage.*

By permission, Bertie & Hilda Jeffreys.

Watermill

Life Story of a Welsh Cornmill

being the history of
Felin Lyn, Dyffryn Ceiriog,
Denbighshire, North Wales.

by
David Llewelyn Davies

in association with
Cymdeithas Melinau Cymru/The Welsh Mills Society
c/o Museum of Welsh Life, St. Fagans, Cardiff, Wales

Published by The Ceiriog Press, Ty Brethyn, Grange Road,
Llangollen, Denbighshire LL20 7BS, Wales, United Kingdom.

British Library Cataloguing in Publication Data.
A catalogue record for this book is available from the British Library.

ISBN 0-9530336 0 0

Typeset by:
Celtic Publishing Services, Ty Brethyn, Llangollen, Wales, U.K.

Printed and bound in Great Britain by
Bookcraft (Bath) Ltd.

Contents / Cynnwys

MAPS: A composite group of eight full-page maps are inserted in the middle of the book on pages 93-100. Other, smaller maps can be found at appropriate places in the book.

Cyflwyniad / Dedication

Cyflywynir y llyfr hwn er côf am felinwyr y gorffenol ai teuluoedd a fu'n gweithio y Felin Lyn drwy nifer o ganrifoedd.

This book is dedicated to the memory of the succession of millers, and their families, who worked Felin Lyn through several centuries.

Prydau Bwyd / Mealtimes

Bendith cyn bwyta
O Dad, yn deulu dedwydd.
Y deuwn, a diolch o'r newydd
Can's o'th law y daw bob dydd
Ein lluniaeth a'n llawenydd.
Amen.

Grace before meals
O Father, bless this family.
We come to thank thee anew
For by Thy hand each day
We receive our sustainance and well-being.
Amen.

This Grace was composed by W. D. Williams (1900-1985) and became a well-known favourite throughout Wales; it is still said today in many Welsh-speaking households.

Backcloth / Cefndir

Oats

If we think, perhaps nostalgically, of watermills as something of the past, we should counterbalance the thought by remembering that man has eaten grain since Neolithic times, is still eating it, and will continue to do so until he destroys this planet. Grain has always been the primary food of the world because it provides a more wholesome diet for a smaller amount of effort than any other product. Each day the inhabitants of the world obtain half their calorific intake from cereals.

Cereals maintain their prime position as a food because of several virtues when compared to other types of food. They are nutritious, easily harvested, can be stored for long periods without deterioration, and are relatively cheap.

Barley

Of the world's surface devoted to crops, over half is occupied be cereals. In descending order of tons produced, the cereals are… *Wheat*, followed closely by *rice* and *maize;* In fourth place is *barley,* followed laggardly by *millet* and *sorghum;* Next is *oats,* with *rye* in seventh place.

Wheat

All this leads to the truism that cereals are an absolute necessity in our daily lives.

The watermill, such as Felin Lyn, was very relevant in its age, and was only superseded by advances in technology and trade – *not by fundamental changes in our diet.*

Comment and Thanks/ Sylw a Diolch

It is natural enough to question why this Welsh watermill, Felin Lyn, was chosen to be the object of this lengthy study.

It was not well-known, beautiful, mechanically unusual, or connected with some famous event, so as to make it stand out in time or place. On the contrary, it was ordinary and commonplace and a most typical example of a Welsh watermill. If it has any merit, it lies in being representative of its age and surroundings.

Felin Lyn was chosen quite simply because it was the nearest building to my boyhood home. My grandfather and then my father owned it for over half a century and when it was falling into ruin at the beginning of the 1980s, it seemed timely to jot down its history. This was done, none too accurately, on seven sheets of paper but such matters have the habit of snow-balling and 17 years later it has emerged in this form.

The text will speak for itself, but there is one aspect of milling that I would like to emphasise. It is that in Britain up to about 125 years ago, a cornmill was vital to the very existence of the people that lived round about it. Almost all food was grown locally and, then as now, cereals formed the dominant part of a person's diet and it was the mill that made them edible. We still need mills to prepare our daily food but now they are distant, unseen, unknown.

Assembling the history of a private building such as a house, farm, or watermill, is obviously difficult. The very obscurity and insignificance of the subject becomes daunting to the enquirer. In the case of Felin Lyn we have been decidedly lucky. Many slender strands have been collected and have eventually been woven into a serviceable rope of local history.

My primary aim has been to place this mill in its natural context – the countryside – and to avoid dealing with it in narrow clinical isolation. That is why there is considerable detail about the neighbourhood, and its people and their interaction with the mill. Much of current milling literature deals mainly with machinery matters and to produce a counterbalance, I have relegated this aspect to Chapter 4.

Needless to say, I have received information, technical advice of all kinds, encouragement and infectious enthusiasm from a wide spectrum of people and institutions, and for this I am most grateful. *'No man is an island'* is as true for literary work as for any other endeavour.

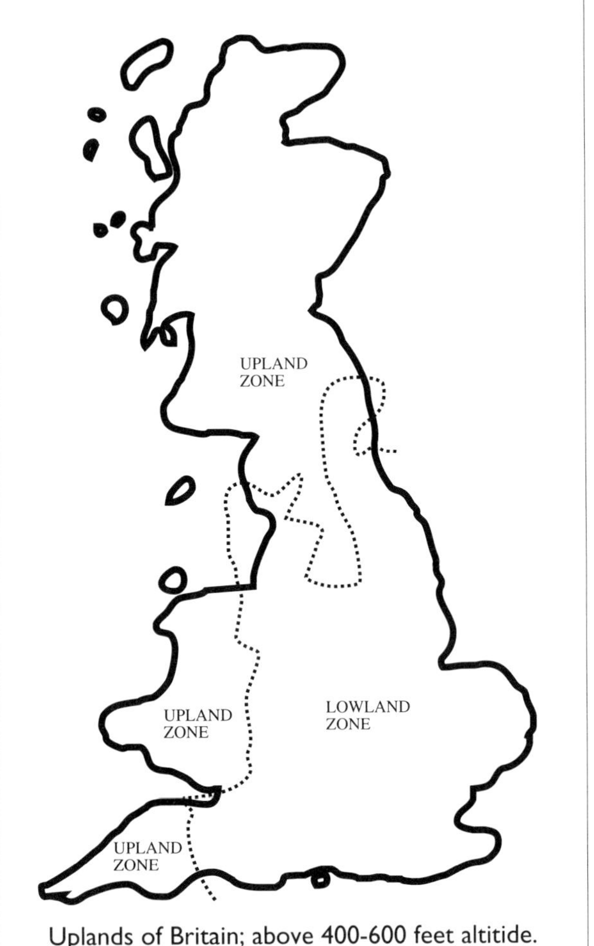

Uplands of Britain; above 400-600 feet altitide.

Five persons must be singled out as having made a considerable impact upon the finished work. First and foremost is the late Mrs Gwladys Jones, a daughter of the last fulltime miller to work Felin Lyn. She was born and raised at the Mill in the early years of this century and supplied me with many milling and domestic details, which have breathed life and soul into the narrative. Her excellent memory and active assistance in the early 1980s were of inestimable value.

The second person to be individually thanked is my local 'field worker' and friend (of same birth year and primary school), Dewi Jones of Llwynmawr, who has lived all his life within a mile of the former mill. It is he who has tirelessly carried out local researches, translated documents and suggested lines of enquiry. Within the Ceiriog he is acknowledged to be one of the current local historians. Without such practical help, this history would have been much weaker.

The third acknowledgement goes to the late Ifor Edwards of Wrexham, who when I first knew him was a headmaster and Denbighshire historian, and latterly President of the Denbighshire Historical Society. It was he who initially encouraged me in the work, examined and measured Felin Lyn in 1980 and fielded many queries over the years. Without his impetus, I might never have started the project.

Next, gratitude to Dr Gwilwym Maelor Davies (no relative), retired member of the Department of Agriculture, University College of North Wales, Bangor. He advised me most patiently on all matters relating to agriculture and its historical development in Wales. Dr Davies was born and brought up at Chirk and has a link with Pontfadog in that his nephew currently farms Tan-y-garth, so he brought both expertise and local knowledge to the subject.

Finally, grateful thanks to a milling expert, Mr J. Kenneth Major. He is an architect, mill enthusiast, past and current officer of British and international mill societies, and author and speaker on many aspects of milling practice and history. He led me by the hand in the early days when I was novice of the subject and later gave advice when the manuscript was in its early stages; he was also of comfort when the first publishing venture aborted in 1990.

With regard to institutions, I have leaned heavily over the years upon the resources of Clwyd Record Office (principally in Ruthin), National Library of Wales (Aberystwyth), and the Welsh Folk Museum (Cardiff) which has recently changed its name to the Museum of Welsh Life. All these three establishments have exuded professionalism and a willlngness to help and have maintained their cool under a flow of correspondence. My gratitude to their staff and archives is profound. To this group, I should add Kamloops Public Library (British Columbia) in my home town; its resources also proved invaluable in 'general' matters.

Tribute should also be paid to two men of the last century, who unwittingly contributed to this history. They are John Hughes (1802-89) and George Borrow (1803-81). The former was born a mile from Felin Lyn and in later life became a recorder of things, great and small, near and far. The latter was the author of the well known travelogue *"Wild Wales"*, which carries descriptions of Dyffryn Ceiriog, including Pontfadog.

It is not possible to list everyone who made a contribution to this work but to all of them go my heartfelt thanks; I would like to mention the following:

Agricultural College, Cirencester; Archer Maps; Brewing Institute; Rev. A. Davies; late Tom Davies; Mrs M. Dawson; George Edwards; Guildhall Library, London; Glyndwr District Council; late George Heald; House of Lords Library; late Mrs E. Humphreys; Institute of Actuaries; Mrs M. James; Stan Jeffreys; Robert Jones; Roger Kidner; Mrs C. Kitton; Mrs M. Lewis; Eric Lloyd; Patrick McIver; Merseyside Maritime Museum; David Myddelton; Oswestry Public Library; A & A Peate Ltd; John Raybould; late Tom Roberts; Rylands Library, University of Manchester; Shropshire Records, Shrewsbury; Society for Protection of Ancient Buildings; late Dick Thomas; Vancouver City Archives; Martin Watts; former Welsh Water Authority; Hugh Wilkinson; Frans Woons.

Having acknowledged all this valuable help, I must make it quite clear that I carry the responsibility for the contents of the book, whether it is presented as fact, supposition, interpretation, opinion or conclusion. Any defects are to be laid solely at my door.

Two other people should also be thanked for their significant contributions. First is Gerallt Nash, who recently examined the text in detail and made many useful suggestions. He is one of the founding members of the Welsh Mills Society and is its current Chairman and also the Honorary Secretary of The International Molinological Society. The other is Tony Cornish of Ceiriog Press who had the critical job of transforming a mass of paper into a book; in my estimation he has done an excellent job.

Bringing up the rearguard of appreciation is a well-deserved tribute to the understanding and patience shown by my wife, Jan, and my daughter and son, Susan and Trevor. To them the project seemed interminable and in fact my children became teenagers and then adults during the process, whilst my wife thought she had lost her dining room table for ever.

My last word concerns trans-Atlantic research and authorship; it is *not* to be recommended. In this instance it was made easier because of motivation, a certain advantage with regard to documents, and some personal knowledge of Felin Lyn, the land and the people thereabouts. Without these advantages, the task would have been well nigh impossible.

David Ll. Davies
Kamloops,
British Columbia,
Canada.
June 1997

Notes

Before you begin to read...

1. All dimensions, measures, volumes, weights, monetary values, etc, are expressed in units then in use when the watermill, Felin Lyn, was working. This has been done consciously to preserve the flavour of times past. Readers wishing to convert to present-day metric equivalents can do so by using the tables listed in Appendix XI.
2. References in the text to areas such as 'Ceiriog' or 'Gwryd' imply terrain covering both valley and hilltop. If the text needs to be more specific, it will say so.
3. All distances are quoted as direct 'crow' miles unless otherwise stated.
4. Place-names are spelt in yesteryear form, most likely in spellings current in the late nineteenth century.
5. Throughout the text, the words 'Felin Lyn' and 'Mill' (with capital M) are used interchangeably.
6. All illustrations are credited to source, where known, otherwise from the author's collection. All tables have been compiled by the author unless otherwise noted.
7. Statements and opinions expressed by the author, may not necessarily represent those of the Welsh Mills Society. The latter organisation supports this historical work in general, but cannot necessarily identify itself with a particular viewpoint.
8. Changes that confuse: Whilst Felin Lyn was working it stood in the County of Denbigh that had been established in 1536. If still working, the mill would have seen radical changes in local government structure. In 1974 Denbighshire and Flintshire were amalgamated (with some minor boundary changes) to become the County of Clwyd. In 1996 all Welsh counties were abolished and were replaced by twenty-two 'Unitary Authorities'. Clwyd was occupied by three of them – 'Denbigh', 'Flint' and 'Wrexham' – and to add to the confusion 'Denbigh' was called 'Denbighshire', though shires no longer exist. Felin Lyn would now be part of 'Wrexham' and not in the much-shrunken 1996 version of Denbighshire.

Classifications for research and cross-referencing

History	19/20th century, Wales, Denbighshire, Dyffryn Ceiriog.
Milling	Corn, watermill, uplands, North Wales.
Food	Welsh diets, grain: growing, grinding, cooking, meals.
Country life	Farming, cornmilling, customs, one local community.

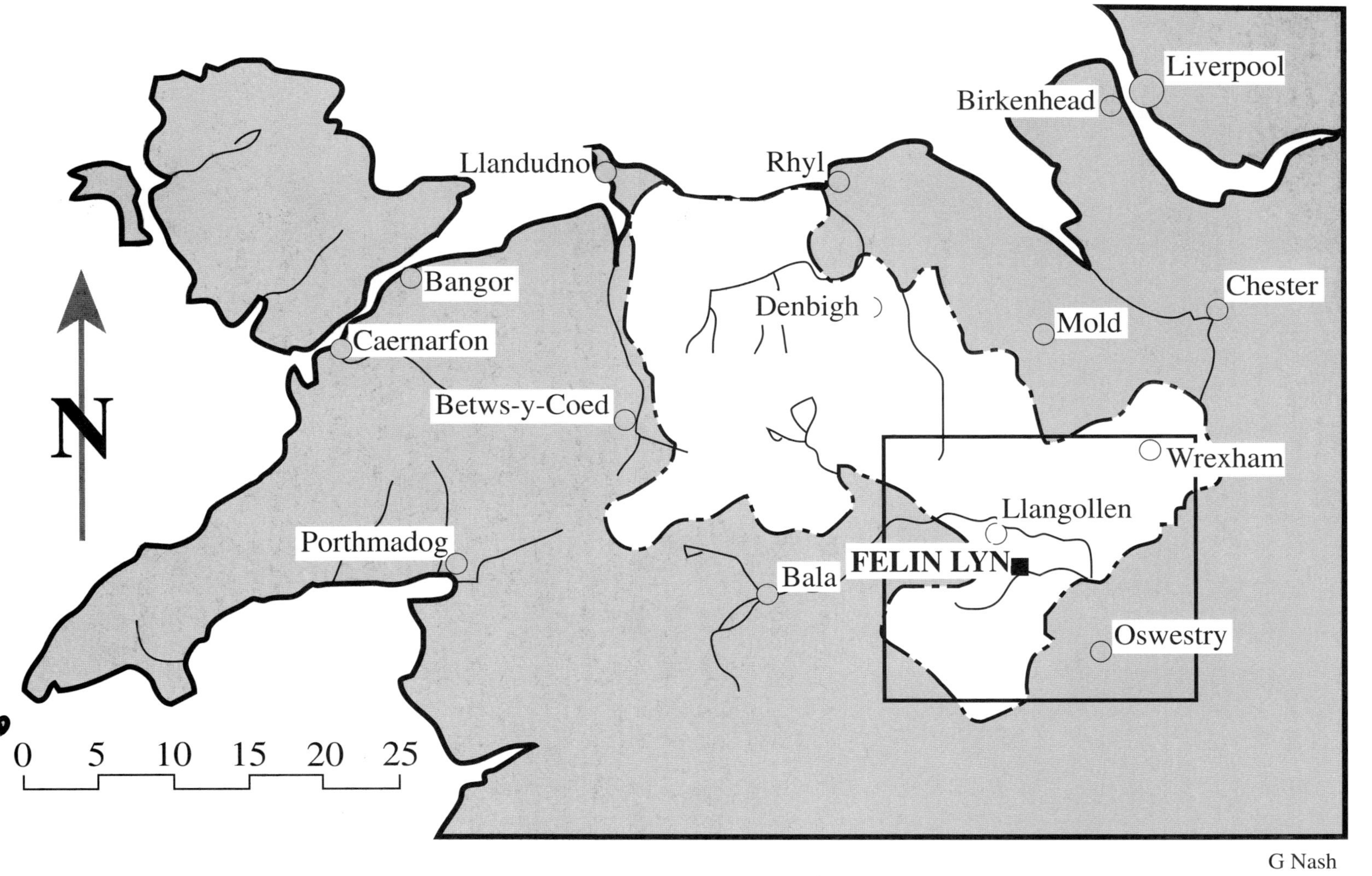
Liverpool
Birkenhead
Llandudno
Rhyl
Bangor
Chester
Denbigh
Mold
Caernarfon
Betws-y-Coed
N
Wrexham
Llangollen
Porthmadog
FELIN LYN
Bala
Oswestry
0
5
10
15
20
25
G Nash

The Mill

Location	Between Llwynmawr and Pontfadog, Dyffryn Ceiriog, Denbighshire (pre-1974), North Wales. [Map reference: SJ 232376]
Year of Operation	From c.1775-1810 to 1936, as Stage III mill.
Function	Production of human and animal food, in form of meals, flours and bruised grain.
Grains processed	Oats, barley, wheat; and after 1880 increasingly maize (Indian corn).
Size of 'territory'	6 to 8 square miles, holding about 550 people living in 110 dwellings.
Grain harvest of the 'territory'	Approximate and estimated: about 100 tons each of wheat, oats, and barley.
Annual milling output (much of 19th C.)	Approximate and estimated: 100 tons of barley, 90 tons of wheat and 50 tons of oats; totalling close to 250 tons.
Milled products eaten by customers	Annually; about 120 tons by humans and about the same amount by animals.
Mill property	Mill itself had three floors, each of about 400 sq. ft plus kiln. Also miller's house, farm buildings and six acres of fields.
Machinery	Overshot wheel, under-gear transmission, and 3 pairs of millstones (2 soft and 1 hard).
Water supply	Afon (river) Ceiriog augmented by Nant (brook) Gwryd.

Chapter 1

th*e* b*asics*

This is the story of a Welsh cornmill in the nineteenth and twentieth centuries, but it is much more than that – it is a tiny fragment of a much larger story about man himself.

After World War II there was much interest in world archeological circles to discover more about man's transition from a nomadic hunter-gatherer to a farmer 'anchored' to a piece of land. This is the greatest evolutionary step that man has ever undertaken and first occurred in the period 8000-5000 BC. Most of the studies were made in the Near East, and one of them was undertaken by an American professor in 1966 in eastern Turkey. (Note 1.1)

He was impressed by seeing dense and almost pure stands of *einkorn*, a variety of wild wheat, growing on the rocky slopes of a volcanic mountain. He decided to carry out an experiment to see how attractive this food source would have been to nomadic peoples. First, he stripped the grain from the stalks with his bare hands and managed to pick $5^1/_2$lbs of grain per hour – and got raw hands. Then he used a 5,000-year-old flint sickle and his productivity increased to $6^1/_4$lbs per hour. After he had cleaned and threshed his *einkorn* grain, he found he had collected 2lbs of edible grain per hour. What was more, it was excellent food with 50% more protein in it than can be found in modern bread wheat.

The professor calculated that during the three-week ripening period, a family of ancient reapers with flint sickles or bare hands could gather more grain than they could eat in a year. This easily-won food, however, had one grave disadvantage to nomads: it could not be carried around on their wanderings, having to be kept completely dry. This posed a threat to their safety when encountering other starving peoples.

There was also an immediate problem of how to break down the hard outside shell of this grain to get at the edible grain inside. We shall stop the story at this point and stride across the centuries to see how this particular Welsh mill, called Felin Lyn, cracked the grain and cracked this problem.

Introduction

The subject of this history was a water-powered corn-grinding mill situated in the hill country of north-east Wales. It lay in the extreme south of the former county of Denbighshire (which became a part of Clwyd in 1974) and was within two miles of the Welsh-English border. It was called Felin Lyn.

Felin Lyn was located between Pontfadog and

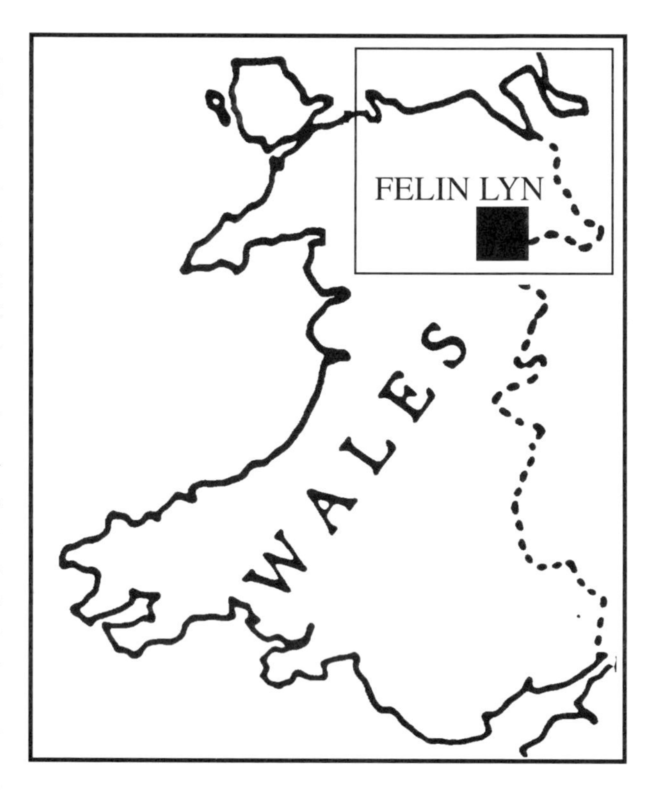

Llwynmawr, formerly both hamlets and now villages, in the valley of the Ceiriog. The nearest large village is Chirk, some four miles to the east, at the lower end of Dyffryn Ceiriog. Neighbouring towns are Llangollen, three miles to the north, Wrexham, ten miles to the north-east, and Oswestry, seven miles to the south-east. The nearest cities are Chester and Shrewsbury, some twenty miles to the north-east and to the south-east respectively. It will be noticed that all these places lie east of a line drawn north and south, because to the west of this line lies the Welsh hill and mountain mass.

Though close to English influences in neighbouring Shropshire, the Ceiriog has managed to the present day to maintain its Welshness in language, culture, and traditions. It has to be emphasised that Felin Lyn was very much a Welsh watermill, worked at all times by Welsh millers who spoke Welsh, and whose customers were almost totally Welsh.

In the 1990s the indigenous residents continue to speak Welsh amongst themselves, whether it be in the kitchen, on the telephone, or out in the fields. This tenacity of the language is encouraging and could be an expression of an emerging world-wide trend that fosters minorities and regionalisation. For an English person this current pervasiveness of the Welsh language in the area may be difficult to detect, since these Welsh people are bilingual and as a courtesy always speak English in the presence of English people.

Felin Lyn has existed since medieval times but this history deals only with the period when the latest mill was built, some time in the latter half of the eighteenth century or at the beginning of the nineteenth century. It then worked until 1936 when it ceased to function effectively as a watermill. Its job was to grind the grains grown in the immediate neighbourhood which were oats, barley and wheat. Prior to 1875-80, when the very localised food chain was broken up, the Mill serviced an area of some seven square miles, which covered both valley floor and hilltop. In this area lived some 550 people, so it meant that Felin Lyn had to supply them with their year-round needs of milled grain for themselves and, just as importantly, their animals.

It is estimated that in its heyday in the nineteenth century, Felin Lyn processed some 225-250 tons of grain each year.

The Mill property included a weir, lengthy millrace, mill and farm buildings, and four fields totalling six acres. Water power came from the Afon (river) Ceiriog and one of its tributaries.

The Mill was known to the Welsh as 'Felin Lyn' and to the English as 'Glyn Mill'. For the benefit of English readers, it should be explained that in certain circumstances Welsh words are affected by mutation and this has happened here. The actual words are MELIN (mill) and GLYN (glen or narrow valley). A further confusion for English people is that 'f' is pronounced 'v' in Welsh and so when spoken the name sounds like 'Velin Lyn'. Typically, in an age when people were not very literate, its name was also written in other ways such as 'Melin y Glyn', 'Velyn Llyn' and 'Felyn Lyn'.

The place was never known as Pontfadog Mill, since Pontfadog is a hamlet or small village largely created after the 1860s when the valley bottom tollroad, now the main road, was built. A possible explanation as to why the Mill was given the indistinctive name of 'glen mill', when much of the valley in which it was located is a glen, is given later in this chapter.

The Ceiriog is a narrow Welsh valley that rises in the Berwyn mountains to the west and runs eastwards for some 17 miles, in typically hilly country. The Welsh have two words for 'valley' which helps to explain the type of terrain hereabouts. One is glyn, meaning a narrow valley and is related to the Gaelic 'glen', whilst the other is 'dyffryn' meaning *wide open valley*.

The upper part of the Ceiriog is relatively open and the head-end village is called Llanarmon *Dyffryn* Ceiriog to

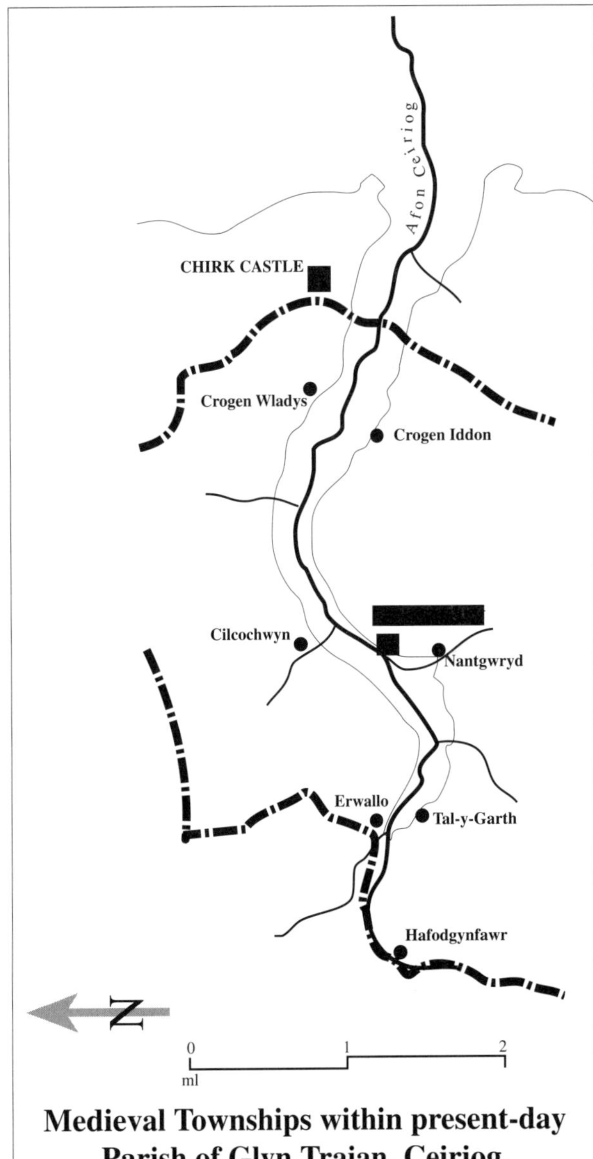

Medieval Townships within present-day Parish of Glyn Traian, Ceiriog.

emphasise this feature. However the lower part of the valley is quite constricted and another village draws attention to this by calling itself Llansantffraid *Glyn* Ceiriog. It is in this lower section of the Ceiriog that Felin Lyn was situated. The very eastern extremity of the valley lies partly in England (Shropshire), and at this point, where the Afon Ceiriog joins the River Dee, the hills fall away and the land becomes a plain. The largest village in Dyffryn Ceiriog is Chirk which lies at its lower end on the northern flank hills and 'looks out' eastward to the English plain. Lines of communication of this and previous centuries follow the Welsh-English border in a north-south sweep of Chirk, straddling the valley on stilts except for the old coach road that hugs the ground.

In order of appearance these transportation routes are: A5 main road (Thomas Telford's mailcoach route linking London to Dublin); British Waterways (Ellesmere Canal of 1805); Britrail (Shrewsbury and Chester Railway of 1848); A483 main road (almost Motorway standard linking Chester with the south in 1991).

Medieval Grist Mill

It is presumed that there has been a watermill on the site of Felin Lyn for at least 500 years. Chirk Castle was built to the orders of King Edward I, between about 1295 and 1310, and with it was created a new Marcher Lordship of Chirk. The supporting lands covered nearly a hundred square miles and for ease of administration were divided into six manors, and one of these was the Manor of Glyn. This Manor of Glyn covered the lower part of the Ceiriog and was in turn sub-divided into seven Townships. The names of these Townships survive to this day as names of farms or houses and all lie in the Parish of Glyn Traian, formerly a part of the Parish of Llangollen. They are:

Township Name in 1391	*Current Farm Name*	*Distance from Mill*
Grogan Wladus	Crogen Wladys	3000 yds east
Kielkychwyn	Cilcychwyn	1000 yds north
Arwallo	Erwallo-isaf	1700 yds west
Talegarth	Talygarth-uchaf	2400 yds west
Havot Kynvor	Hafodgynfawr	3200 yds west
Nant Goryt	Llangwryd-uchaf	400 yds s.w.
Groganython	Croggen Iddon	2400 yds east

Despite the 600 years that separate these two sets of names, one is struck more by the similarities than by the differences. The 'Llan' prefix to the modern 'Gwryd' is a spurious change made only 150 years ago.

An examination of a large scale map will show that Felin Lyn sat about dead centre in this Manor of Glyn, and if there was a medieval mill that serviced the Manor of Glyn, then it would be logical to call it Glyn mill in English, or Felin Lyn in Welsh. This also provides a satisfactory explanation as to how the Mill got its name; otherwise one has to wonder why a 'modern' mill was given such a featureless name seeing that much of the Ceiriog is glen or 'glyn' like.

If this supposition is correct, it is likely the mill was a typically small medieval one and was powered by water from the brook or 'nant' Gwryd. The course of its race can be surmised, probably running in a straight line from the bottom of the then Nantgwryd farmyard (called Llangwryd since mid-nineteenth century) to the mill, and then tailing parallel to the river and the adjoining steep hillside.

Chirk Castle records make reference to a mill at 'Glyn'. In the year 1465-6 it stated; *"£4 of certain rent received of the tenants of Glyn for the repair of the mill and the turning of the water and maintenance of course of same to the said mill"*. However it is not known if this Glyn reference relates to a possible predecessor of Felin Lyn, since Glyn is a fairly common place-name in Wales. A 1795 map shows three houses named 'Glynn' within a mile of Felin Lyn and the upstream hamlet is spelt 'Glynn Ceiriog'. (Note 1.2)

The nearest township farm to Felin Lyn is Llangwryd, but this is a modern name and was well-known until the middle of the nineteenth century as *Nantgwryd.* It is of ancient creation, for a surviving 1391 record lists it as 'Villa de Nant Goryt'. This would suggest an active farming community in the area which would need a mill. So we are left with the quite plausible notion that a medieval mill was required in the immediate area, and Felin Lyn's site was both suitable and central.

Edward Llwyd's *Parochiala* of 1697 lists a 'Velinlyn' as being two hundred yards above 'Pont Vadog' so here is proof that the site was already occupied by a watermill at that date.

Siting and Building Date

Coming from the north, the present border between Wales and England follows the River Dee and then its tributary, the Afon Ceiriog until Offa's Dyke is reached, two miles west of Chirk. At this point the border turns due south and faithfully follows the Dyke, which was built 1,200 years ago to mark the border between Saxons and Welsh. To this day it still marks the real border between the two nations, for most people to its east are Anglicised whilst those to the west were strongly Welsh until the upheavals of World War II.

Felin Lyn lies two miles west of Offa's Dyke (and the present-day border) and despite the close proximity to England was typically Welsh, as will unfold in this history.

The site itself lies in the valley bottom of the Ceiriog four miles upstream from Chirk and about a third of a mile above the hamlet of Pontfadog. Upstream about one mile distant are the hamlets of Llwynmawr and Dolywern and one mile beyond them is the village of Llansantffraid Glyn Ceiriog; this latter village is abbreviated locally to *Glynceiriog* or even plain 'Glyn'.

Felin Lyn is sited on the south bank of Afon Ceiriog and 50 yards away from it. At this point the flattened bed of the valley is 200 yards wide and the Mill was located at the edge of this bed where the land abruptly changes contour. The enveloping side hills immediately climb away to the north and south, steeply at first and then more gradually to rounded smooth summits. These summit hills are bare of trees, are at about 1200-1300 feet elevation, and though in previous times oats, barley and wheat were grown here, they are now largely devoted to pasture or barley.

The Mill was located at National Grid Map Reference SJ-232376 of the 7th Series and stood at an altitude of 435 feet above sea level.

Until the mid-nineteenth century, for the purposes of ecclesiastical and civil administration, Felin Lyn lay in the Parish of Llangollen. This was a throwback to the early 1200s when Cistercians established their abbey at Valle Crucis, two miles north of Llangollen; they had small chapels and farming interests in the Ceiriog. The Parish of Llangollen was subdivided into feudal units of land called *townships* and it is believed the Mill lay in the Township of Nantgwryd.

This is confirmed by the burial register entry for a Felin Lyn miller who died in 1806 and was described as *'miller of the Township of Nantgwryd'*. The 1839 Tithe survey also allocates the Mill to this township. It is possible that the Mill lay at the intersection of three townships because a later legal conveyance gives the location as being *'In the Townships of Nantgwryd, Crogen Iddon and Hafodgynfawr or one of them'*. The Township of Crogen Iddon lay immediately east of Felin Lyn's buildings.

In 1848 the large and unwieldy Parish of Llangollen was broken up and that part of it which had covered the Ceiriog in this vicinity was taken and made into a new Parish of Glyn Traian (Welsh for a 'third part'). The new parish stretched from Offa's Dyke to the outskirts of Llansantffraid Glyn Ceiriog and had as its centre the hamlet of Pontfadog where a church was built in 1847, and a rectory in the early 1880s, by the Church of England. This made it one of 57 parishes in Denbighshire.

When tithes were converted from objects to money in 1840, the concept of townships as an administrative unit died. From then on Felin Lyn quite simply stood in the Parish of Glyn Traian, in the County of Denbigh ('Sir Ddinbych' in Welsh).

Reasonable diligence in researching obvious sources has failed to provide any building date for Felin Lyn. Search of estate papers at Chirk Castle, 'West' papers at Ruthin, and 'Chirk Castle MSS' and 'Longueville Deeds & Documents' at the National Library of Wales, Aberystwyth, yielded nothing.

Since the Chirk Castle Estates had been the dominant landowner in Dyffryn Ceiriog for at least five centuries it is not unreasonable to assume that Felin Lyn was built under the direction of the Estate. Chirk Castle lies two-and-a-half miles to the east of the former Mill.

A field mapping party of the Ordnance Survey recorded the Mill in 1830-31, so this makes for the earliest documentation. The earliest surviving evidence of ownership is given in the Tithe Survey of 1839, where Felin Lyn is shown as being held by the Honourable Frederick West of Ruthin Castle. The large Chirk Castle Estate was sub-divided into three in the late 1700s and part of it went, through marriage, to West who moved to Ruthin in 1826.

The author's guess is that Felin Lyn was built sometime between 1775 and 1815, and he favours the period 1790-1810. The 1775 date has been selected as the earliest date for land improvements and enclosures in the area, whilst 1815 saw the end to the Napoleonic wars. After that date there was economic depression and for at least the next three decades it is improbable landlords would have invested in new mills.

The building itself was two-storeyed which was a nineteenth rather than an eighteenth century architectural development in the Ceiriog. Prior to this most buildings in the area were single-storey, usually of elongated plan. The machinery first installed in Felin Lyn was perhaps of a design newly evolved in Britain in the period 1750-1800, and initially drove only two pairs of millstones.

A review of some 70 building dates of watermills in western England shows that the period 1780-95 was the most popular for new mills to be built, or old ones to be rebuilt. This was due to pressures of an exploding population and the shortages of meal and flour created by the demands of the Napoleonic wars.

This is the point to introduce the late Mrs Gwladys Jones (1902-1992), who was a daughter of the last full-time miller of Felin Lyn, and who was born in the mill house. In her eighties, she enthusiastically collaborated with the author and supplied many intimate details of life at the Mill as she knew it. Her many quotes are interspersed throughout the book and her name has the identifier (FL) attached to it. Her first quote is germane to the topic of a building date and gives a tantalising peep into the past.

Mrs. Jones said; *"As a child, I used often to go up to the Mill attic and in there were at least two big ledgers. I used to examine them and was intrigued to find that all the letters 's' were written as 'f'. My father told me they were very old and went back to the 1700s."* (Note 1.3)

The use of the long 'f ' in place of 's' was still in vogue

in parts of Wales well into the nineteenth century; indeed the Tithe Commission map of 1839 showing Felin Lyn has the word 'Township' written with an 's' or an 'f' indiscriminately across the parchment. This suggests the draughtsman used 'f' through habit but knew the new style was with an 's'.

The Reason Why

Without the evidence the reason why Felin Lyn was built must remain a matter of conjecture. The population of England and Wales increased by about a quarter in the seventeenth century and by a half in the eighteenth century, being about six million in 1700 and nearly nine million in 1800. Why this surge took place, which started in earnest by about 1750, is still being debated by historians. (Note 1.4)

This must have put great pressure on everyone – consumers and growers alike – to clear more land and make farming more productive. This was because virtually all foods had to be grown locally, probably within a radius of ten miles or less, because transportation was difficult and expensive. The concept of importing food from other regions of Britain or from other countries to any specific locality in Britain was unthinkable, the only exceptions being where waterways, such as coastal areas and large rivers, provided a convenient and cheap 'highway'.

This pressure must have been felt in the Ceiriog, like anywhere else in the country. Two of the ways to make agriculture more productive was to enclose tilled land into hedged fields and do away with the cumbersome method of strip farming, and to enclose 'waste' land and put it to better use. This was achieved by private enclosure Acts initiated by large landowners. Between 1760 and 1820, it is estimated that over four million acres of arable common land and two million acres of waste land were enclosed in England and Wales.

Altogether some 5,700 enclosure Acts were passed in a period of less than one hundred years. As in World Wars I and II, the British Government stimulated farming during the Napoleonic Wars of 1793-1815. One of its measures was a streamlining Act of 1801 which made it simpler and quicker to pass Enclosure Acts through Parliament. (Note 1.5)

There was no intent to defraud the small man who eked out a marginal existence on the land, using the commons for grazing, foraging, and small animal hunting. But the outcome was that he became a wandering landless labourer and much poverty was created. On the other hand, British agriculture could not have produced the volume of food required by the ballooning population and the demands of war unless enclosures had been resorted to.

An Enclosure of Lands Act of 1777 affected parts of north-west Shropshire and the parish of Selattyn which lies four miles south-east of Felin Lyn. Forcible enclosures came late to Dyffryn Ceiriog with an enclosure Award of 1848 (under an 1839 Act) permitting some open lands of the Lordship of Chirk in the parishes of Llangollen and Llansantffraid Glynceiriog to be fenced. This would have been on the hilltop land. It also came too late to be one of the determining factors in the decision to build Felin Lyn.

The author is of the opinion that it was the bottom lands of the Ceiriog that were cleared for agriculture sometime in the late eighteenth century. Up until then these were the least desirable of the local lands, being woody, marshy and untamed; a kind of no man's land. Clearing would have been done by felling trees, cutting brush, draining land and forcing the Afon Ceiriog into a definite and fixed channel.

It is significant that all the pre-nineteenth century hamlets in the Ceiriog – for none were yet large enough to be called villages – were sited on higher ground, examples being Glynceiriog, Graig, Garth-obry, Nantyr, and Pentre Cilgwyn. The original hamlet of Glynceiriog is a prime example of this siting policy and can be examined today, for it is now the uppermost part of the village of the same name. It lies beside the church, 300 feet above the centre of the modern village, and is approached by a lane that steepens to 1 in 4. The Graig is less than half a mile away from Felin Lyn and if you stand there today, you can instantly sense its historic position up on the hillside.

This bottom land clearing operation would have created the present-day field pattern at Dolywern, Llwynmawr and Pontfadog, and would have added over a square mile (600-800 acres) to existing farm lands. A possible confirmatory clue lies in the place-name 'Llwynmawr', which means 'great grove or bushland' and it could well be that prior to clearance it was just that. Dolywern means 'meadow/marshland of the alder trees' and since alders always favour river banks and low-lying moist lands, here is another suggestion of 'waste' land.

The creation of this additional farming acreage meant that some of it would be put to cereal crops, which, in turn, would have to be ground. This would put pressure on the existing mill of the area and if that mill was of small capacity, or had antiquated machinery, the logical outcome would be the building of a new mill. It is fairly certain that this is how the Felin Lyn of this book came into existence.

The final Felin Lyn was built on the site of a medieval mill, which by comparison would have been primitive and low-powered. The earlier gristmill was probably driven by the waters of Nant Gwryd only. The 'new' Felin Lyn, being a more powerful mill, needed a larger and more constant water supply and this meant it had to be taken from the Afon Ceiriog. Designing a new millrace that merged with Nant Gwryd and gave sufficient head of water, dictated a weir at least a half mile upstream of the intended new mill. The site selected for the weir was in fact two-thirds of a mile away, which created a lengthy millrace.

A fortuitous clue suggests that a weir and mill had existed at the site chosen for the weir of Felin Lyn, at some date prior to 1800. The written recollections of a native of Dolywern (nearest hamlet upstream from Felin Lyn), born in 1802, refers to a mill at Dolywern as Felin Uchaf or 'Upper Mill'. This implies a Felin Isaf or 'Lower Mill' but none is mentioned so possibly it was derelict or demolished. The suffixes 'ucha' and 'isaf' are much used in the place-names of Wales and a survey of their usage in the Ceiriog shows that the two places, usually farms of the same name, can be 150-800 yards apart but that the average is 400 yards. Four hundred yards downstream from Felin Uchaf at Dolywern brings us to the site of the weir of Felin Lyn, suggesting that an existing or dilapidated weir was taken over and strengthened or rebuilt. (Note 1.6)

Since in the 1700s there was only one landlord for most of the Ceiriog, there would be no legal difficulties in assembling land parcels and constructing the route of the millrace. Sometimes these requisites posed problems in other parts of Britain when the interests of two or more landlords clashed. An examination of a large scale map shows that Felin Lyn's millrace acts as a field boundary throughout its length except for the field adjacent to the Mill. This neatness suggests that land clearance, millrace construction and field making all took place at the same time.

Data From Maps and Illustrations

Our earliest detailed knowledge of the Mill comes from the activities resulting from the passing of the Tithe Commutation Act of 1836. Tithes were a form of church tax which went to defray the day-to-day expenses of the Church of England, the state religion of Britain. Needless to say in Wales in the late 1700s, in the fervour of a Non-Conformist Christian revolution, it was an unpopular tax! The tax was based on the notion that one-tenth of the produce of land, stock, or other wealth should be donated to the Church.

Because a cash, rather than a barter, economy had come to most parts of Britain by 1835, the payment of tithes in kind was becoming an anomaly and the Act rectified this by converting kind into money. As a result, thousands of rural parishes throughout the land were surveyed and mapped in detail for the first time. This was particularly true of Wales because the Doomsday Book of 1086 covered little of Wales, as it was not then a part of the Norman realm.

The Parish of Llangollen, in which Felin Lyn stood in 1836, was duly surveyed and inventoried in 1839 to allow the commissioners to assess the new cash tithes. A detailed plan or map was drawn for each parish and the one for Llangollen Parish is now held by Clwyd Record Office. The details of the survey included names of owners, names of tenants, names of farms, names of all fields, the acreage of every separate piece of land and the use to which each such piece of land was put. (Note 1.7)

The 1839 Tithe map, which has a scale of about $13^1/_2$ inches to the mile, shows the Mill to be in Llangollen Parish and in Nantgwryd Issa Township, but the boundary of Croggen Iddon Township is immediately adjacent and runs down the course of the earlier sited tailrace on the edge of the Mill's riverside meadow.

The map itself shows two distinct and separate buildings on the mill site and like many other buildings on the map neither is named – which is not helpful to the modern researcher!

Three parcels of land relate to Felin Lyn; they are:

Parcel 347: *'House, flourmill, and garden. Garden, homestead'*. Totalling 1 rood & 36 perches. (This comprised the mill yard and garden beside the Llwynmawr road as it existed in this century, plus a small wedge of garden between the millrace and the upper side of the lane to the Graig.)

Parcel 346: *'Mill meadow'* totalling 2 acres, 3 roods, 36 perches. (Identical to the present-day meadow.)

Parcel 561: *'Patch by the Mill'* at 27 perches. (Delightful description; is approximately where the barn stood till 1981.)

For those of us who never knew or who have forgotten our school tables, a perch or pole is $30^1/_4$ square yards, and 40 perches/poles make one rood, which is a quarter acre.

The description 'flourmill' is telling. In such a context it had the same connotation as 'steam' in steam laundry of the last century or 'computer' in computer draughting of today. It implied progressiveness and modernity. In the early part of the nineteenth century a 'flourmill' specifically meant a mill which ground wheat and had machinery to dress or bolt it into flour. Older type mills that ground grain but did not refine it in any way were called 'cornmills' and in earlier centuries 'gristmills'. So this entry tells us that the equipment found in Felin Lyn in the twentieth century was already installed in 1839.

This Tithe Survey is quite invaluable because here was a public record of acreages, ownerships, and plans showing field shapes and sizes. By modern standards, the plans look somewhat amateurish but this history would have been the poorer without them.

Turning to *published* maps, the first to appear within this book's terms of reference was in 1793. It was a 'Map of the Six Counties of North Wales' published on nine sheets by John Evans and engraved by Robert Baugh. Sheet 6 'Oswestry' shows the Ceiriog and is to the scale 0.8 inches to 1 mile; it is reasonably detailed for the period. The map shows Pont Fadog and Llwynmawr and in the vicinity of 'Pont Fadog' three watermills are depicted with waterwheel symbols. The most easterly is known about and is mentioned later in the book; the middle one shown just downstream of the bridge is an unknown; the westerly one is shown at the site of Felin Lyn but the symbol itself is ill-defined.

The next map to appear was one of Shropshire published by Robert Baugh in 1808 to the scale of 0.95 inches to 1 mile. It is a beautiful piece of draughting and engraving and shows a mill (using the same waterwheel symbol) halfway between 'Pont Vadog' and Llwynmawr. Curiously, it is the only mill shown on the Afon Ceiriog between Chirk and a point half-a-mile upstream of Llansantffraid Glynceiriog.

The next mapmaker on the scene was the Ordnance Survey. This institution was founded in 1791 under the Board of Ordnance for military purposes but soon found a civil use. It was asked to map the whole of England and Wales to a scale of 1 inch to the mile. Maps of Kent and of Essex were published in 1801 and 1805 and the task was completed by 1874.

Dyffryn Ceiriog was field surveyed in 1830-31 at a preliminary scale of two inches to the mile. The draughting showed the millrace as it existed in the nineteenth century and the building is marked 'Glyn Mill'. All this work was in preparation for Sheet 74 'Llangollen', the first ordnance Survey map of the region, published in 1837-38 at a scale of 1 inch to 1 mile. When published, the Mill had its name changed to 'Melin Glyn' because the Ordnance Survey was sensitive to the needs of Welsh orthography and had invited a Rev. Davies of Bangor to check all Welsh placenames.

This Ordnance map is more accurate and detailed than Baugh's map of 1808 but seems more cluttered.This is because it indicates height by detailed hachuring whereas Baugh gave indications only. The 1837 Ordnance map shows three watermills on the Afon Ceiriog between Tregeiriog and its confluence with the Dee; they are 'Pandy Melin Deirw', 'Melin Glyn' (Felin Lyn) and 'Castle Mill'. The omission of the mill at Chirk is a strange one as this was the largest mill on the river.

In 1854 the Ordnance Survey decided to map all the urban and cultivated areas of Great Britain at a scale of 25 inches to the mile. This was a gigantic task as it involved measuring every building, field and wood lot, and was not completed until 1896.

As part of this project an Ordnance Survey party arrived in the Ceiriog in 1872 to undertake a very thorough mapping job and spent two years in the district. The results concerning Felin Lyn are shown on a large scale map of 25 inches to 1 mile, published 1899 of impeccable draughtsmanship and much detail, which to this day remains the only large scale map (plus a later revision) of the Mill property. It is now an obsolete publication and cannot be purchased except as an historic photo reprint.

This Ordnance Survey map shows few basic differences from the 1839 Tithe map except for the shortening of the tailrace to its twentieth century position and the existence of a toll road in the valley bottom. Alongside this road ran a narrow-gauge tramway or light railway. The mill is lettered 'Glyn Mill (Flour)'.

The last map to be issued affecting the history of the Mill was a 1914 issue by Ordnance Survey at a scale 6 inches to 1 mile. The only difference shown was the conversion of the ford to a bridge crossing to the Mill. (Note 1.8)

Perhaps it should be noted that maps are excellent source material for local histories but are not infallible. The 2½ inch to 1 mile Ordnance Survey edition of 1957 covering the lower part of the Ceiriog (Sheet SJ 23 Chirk) shows Felin Lyn as 'disused', whilst there is a working mill shown at Castlemill which has not been in operation for at least 100 years – possibly for 200 years!

Photographs, sketches and paintings can also play a part in helping to fill out historical perspectives and they have done just this with Felin Lyn. Nowadays we take photography so much for granted that we assume it will come to our aid in almost any historical investigation covering this century, but this does not necessarily follow.

Photography in Dyffryn Ceiriog seems to be divided into two phases. The earliest known photo of the area that survives is dated between 1873 and 1887; its quality is the equal of any printed today. Between then and the end of World War I, almost all photographs of the Ceiriog would be taken by visiting professionals using tripod cameras and glass negatives. One such professional, Burns, settled at

Glynceiriog in about 1910 and his work included publishing picture postcards. The second phase started in the early 1920s when mass-produced hand-held cameras, using the now familiar rolls of film, came on the market. This made the art and hobby of photography potentially accessible to all. The son of the last miller at Felin Lyn possessed such a camera in the late 1920s when in his teens. In the 1930s there was a 'dispensing & photographic' chemist at Glynceiriog who developed and printed films, so within 50 years making images of the Ceiriog moved from a distant possibility to a local reality. While the number of photographic prints produced in the second phase far exceeded those made in the first, their quality was markedly inferior in most instances.

It is usually possible to embellish the history of almost any locality in Britain with at least one photo taken over 75 years ago, but when the target of the camera is one particular and very ordinary private building, the task suddenly becomes formidable. Since no one person is consciously assembling a photographic record of such a building, the taking, survival and present whereabouts of one or more such photos is in the lap of the gods. Prior to 1980 there had been no conscious effort by anyone to preserve the history of Felin Lyn, so for three photos of the Mill (1908, 1927, 1942) and one of the weir (c. 1910) to have surfaced since then from different sources, can only be regarded as remarkable, nay, a miracle.

The earliest photograph of the Mill was taken by a professional in 1908 and its existence is due to Mrs. Margaret Lloyd-George, whose husband was then Chancellor of the Exchequer and was later the first Welshman to be a Prime Minister of Britain. The owner of Felin Lyn, and his wife, were friends of the Lloyd-Georges and on this occasion they had invited Mrs Lloyd-George to stay at 'Brynhyfryd', their home just up the lane from Felin Lyn. From a surviving photo album, it appears they asked Lettsome & Sons (1889 – c. 1920s) of Llangollen to take several group shots and also some local views. One of the views taken from 'Brynhyfryd' looks up valley and it so happens Felin Lyn lies conveniently in the foreground; that is how good fortune has given us a 90 year-old view of the Mill.

Capping this photographic luck comes an unlooked-for bonus. There is in existence a watercolour of Felin Lyn painted in the mid 1950s by a Megan Glyn Jones – now Mrs Dawson – who by happy association is the grand-daughter of the last miller to work the Mill. Mrs Dawson says: *"I was 19 at the time, with my home in Derbyshire, and attending Durham University. The sketch was a small 'thank you' to the Jeffreys, tenants of the smallholding and former mill, for allowing me to use the llofft wellt (hay barn) as a studio one long hot summer vacation. It was warm and sunny, I remember, and much of the time was spent lying in the straw, reading. The subject of the sketch, Felin Lyn, was a natural choice because this was where my mother was born and brought up."*

Energy Source

In an age when we are all so conscious of the cost of fuel, it is an eye-opener to learn that water and wind mills availed themselves of free energy. Not only was it free but non-polluting and could be used over and over again by other millers; indeed, a rare commodity. Another minor advantage, caused by the turbulence created by the water-wheels, was the aeration of the water which was beneficial to fish life.

The energy source for Felin Lyn was the Afon (river) Ceiriog and one of its tributary streams, the Nant (brook) Gwryd. The Afon Ceiriog is 19 miles long and flows from west to east, from Wales to England. It rises in the Berwyn Mountains and after falling nearly 1,700ft, joins the river Dee two miles north-east of Chirk at 160 feet above sea level. At this junction the Afon Ceiriog is contributing about one-tenth of the flow of the larger river and is the Dee's second largest tributary.

The Dee itself is the 13th longest river in Britain, at 70 miles, and has a catchment area of some 850 square miles. After absorbing the Afon Ceiriog, the Dee turns north and becomes a sluggish and meandering river, reaching the Irish Sea beside the town of Flint on the North Wales coast. This compares with the longest river in the United Kingdom which is the Severn, at 220 miles and with a catchment area of 4,410 square miles.

The Afon Ceiriog finds birth in desolate mountain uplands at the 1,825 feet level and for the first four miles of its length drops precipitously to the first hamlet at the head of the Ceiriog valley, aptly named Pentrebach (*little village*). Here the elevation is 1,000 feet and thereafter the river falls at a more even and sedate pace, averaging a descent to the Dee at some 50 feet in every mile.

In the vicinity of Felin Lyn the Afon Ceiriog is about 12 paces wide, with a rock strewn bed and has a depth amongst these rocks of 6-18 inches in normal flow periods. However, seasonal or weather abnormalities can change this to swirling floods or an almost dry water bed. Between Dolywern and Pontfadog the river falls variously at 50-60 feet per mile, which translates into a gradient of between 1 in 90-105.

As to rainfall in the area, the only recent weather

records have been maintained at Llanarmon. This village is at twice the elevation of Pontfadog at 875 feet above sea level, and over the last 38 years has averaged 48.4 inches per annum. It is estimated that at the source of the river at Ceiriog Ddu it is about 60 inches, and at Pontfadog about 42 inches, per annum. (Note 1.9)

The water catchment area available to Felin Lyn was 60 square miles of land but the water so collected was not the exclusive preserve of that Mill. Rather the other way around; the water was enjoyed by all the riverside farms and mills along the valley and none of them had legal title to it, being allowed only to abstract its moisture or energy before returning it to the river.

A wind-miller is always preoccupied with the wind, a tide-miller with the tides, and a water-miller with water, for these are their respective sources of power. There is a tendency to think that in Wales, a country of considerable rainfall, a water-miller had little to worry about when it came to his water supply. But this is not so, for there were both seasonal and sporadic changes which could deprive a miller of satisfactory water levels. It can be truthfully said that a miller of the Ceiriog was one of the few people in the community who continuously prayed for rain in the summer months.

An excess of water was not troublesome to the millers of Felin Lyn because a satisfactory overflow system had been engineered at the time the Mill was built. However, the millers had concern for their water supply in the summer months of at least half, and perhaps two-thirds, of the summers in a century. The most likely time water might be scarce was from the last week in June to the end of September, with critical periods from early July to mid-August and the latter half of September. These shortages sometimes occurred as early as late May and as late as mid-October, but these were almost always in isolation and were allied with improved flows in mid-summer.

The recording of water flows on the Afon Ceiriog did not commence until well after the Second World War and after Felin Lyn's wheel had ceased to turn. It is worth examining the meticulously recorded daily flow reports of the Afon Ceiriog, kindly supplied by the former Welsh Water Authority. A ten year period, 1970-1979, was selected and the river flows, month by month, are shown on the accompanying graph. It is presumed these flows are somewhat similar to those experienced in the two preceding centuries. (Note 1.10)

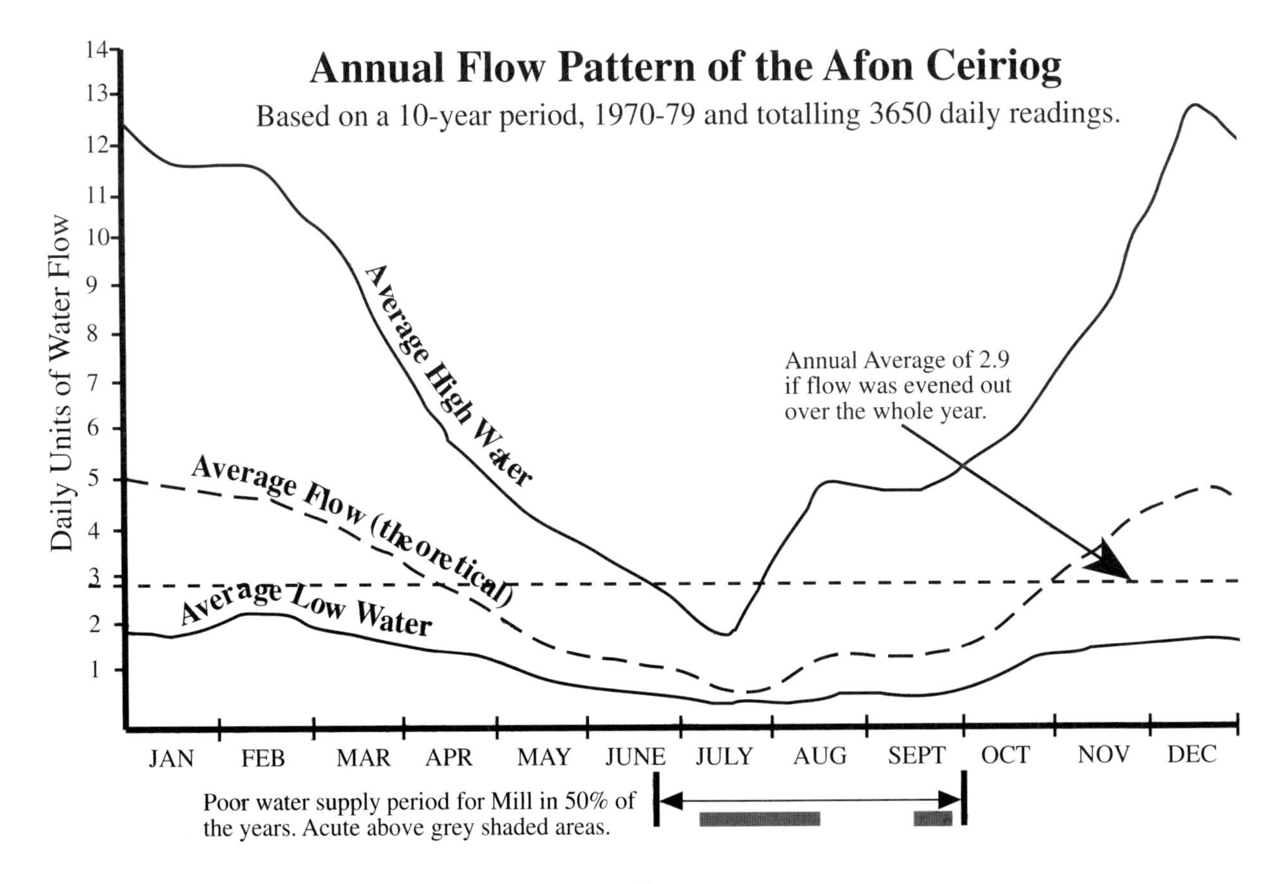

The dilemma of statistics is that they can simplify complex matters and present them in an easily understood form, but in the process differences frequently tend to get ironed out, and a blandness is introduced. This has happened here. By looking at the graph one gets the feeling of a restrained and predictable river, but this is not the situation at all. If there is one dominating characteristic of the Afon Ceiriog, it is its inconsistency. Apart from the obvious, that there is more rain in winter than in summer, there are contradictions at every turn. Use whatever adjective you like to describe the flow – *unpredictable, capricious, erratic, deviant* – and you will be correct.

The study of the data was rewarding. In the ten years analysed there was a flow difference of 150% between the seasons of winter and summer; in December the flow was 75% above the average annual flow and in July it was 75% below it. No two years showed the same pattern; 1975 was a year of drought and river flows were 33% below average, whilst 1977 was the wettest year in ten and had flows 21% above the average. Some other extremes are worth noting.

The average (theoretical) daily flow throughout the ten years was 2.9 units of water and the maximum flow was 30.0 units which lasted for one day on 27 December, 1979, whilst the minimum was 0.14 units registered for three days on 25, 26 and 27 August, 1976. The minimum recorded flow in the winter months was 1.0 units on 4 January 1971 and the maximum flow in the summer months was 15.8 units on 6 August, 1973.

The point being made, as the miller looked at the water falling on his wheel, was that water in the summer could never be taken for granted and that each and every day was different, and its rate of flow had to be taken philosophically.

The author has calculated that the head race was capable of taking 0.2 units of water, and if this is correct, then it is probable that Felin Lyn did not operate when river levels were below the 0.5 to 0.4 level. Land owners adjacent to the Afon Ceiriog had riparian rights which included the watering of livestock and fishing, and in extremely low water all water diversions – which included mill races – were not permitted and every drop of water had to run down the river bed. In the ten years, 1970-79, there were 314 days in which the flow was below 0.5 units of water per day, giving an average of one month per year of water supply problems. Needless to say this cosy average gives little hint of reality, for in two years the abnormal low flow had a continuous duration of three months in each year; in six years there were scattered and often discontinuous periods, and in three years the flow was always above 0.5 units.

George Borrow, author of the classic travelogue *Wild Wales*, visited the village of Glynceiriog in August 1854 and noticed the low water levels in the river. He wrote: *"...the water was very low, and that there was little but stones in the bed of the stream."* (Note 1.11)

No great harm was done to the miller when the water shortage occurred between mid-July and mid-September, since by then all the grain of the preceding harvest had been milled. However, a deficiency of water in late September and October (as happened in 1972 and 1973) would have been most unwelcome because the first grains of the new harvest were needed by the community to replenish their dwindling or non-existent stocks of wheat flour.

Floods were of minor consequence to the millers of

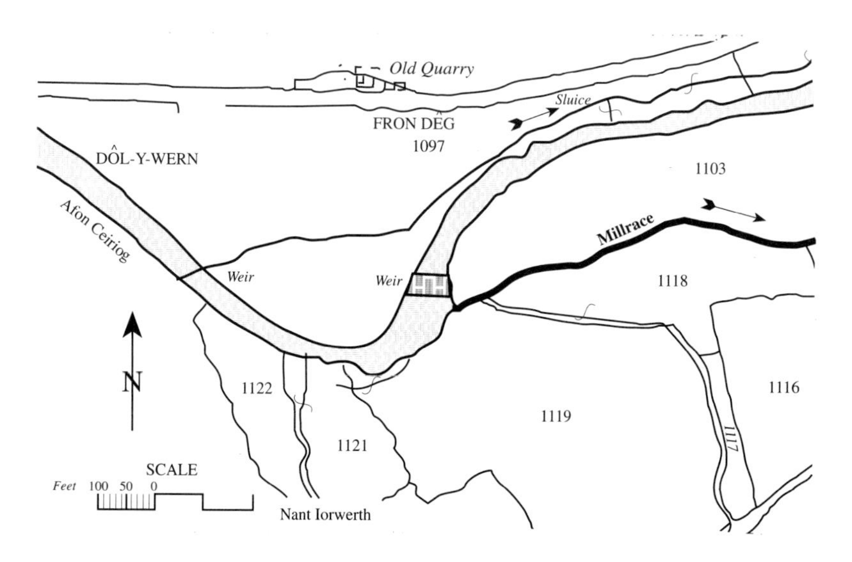

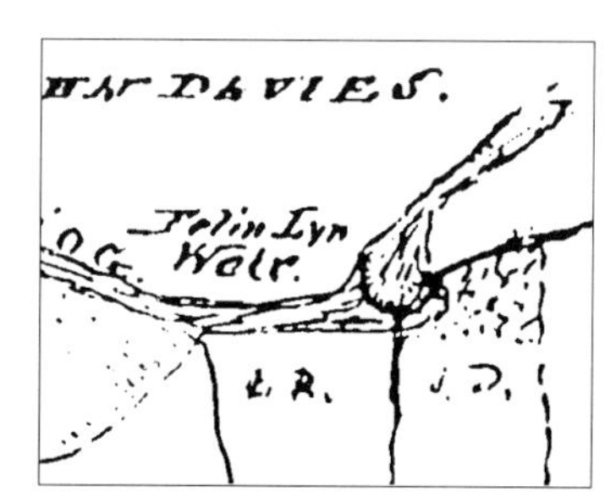

Weir details

Above: at early 19th Century.
Left: in 20th Century.

Felin Lyn because such waters could be deflected and the Mill itself did not stand on the river's edge. Such floods could cause inconvenience and damage as they came roaring down the valley, flooding the bottom lands and eroding the banks. An example of inconvenience would be the sometimes impassable ford that lay close to Felin Lyn (before being superseded by a bridge in 1894), whilst an example of damage was the 1901 severing of the main road and steam tramway just below Glynceiriog. In most recent years the worst flood took place on 3 January, 1982, when 48.6 units of water passed down, or twelve times the rate of average flow.

The Weir

There used to be a watermill at Dolywern and its history is related in the section 'Neighbouring Watermills' in Chapter 5. John Hughes (1802-1889), who was brought up as a child at this mill, has become a very useful source of localised history in the Dolywern-Llwynmawr area. This is because in the 1870s he compiled two thick notebooks, in good handwriting in Welsh and some English, about all manner of things. Hughes, who became a woollen manufacturer in Llangollen, was a man of great curiosity, had a good eye for detail and was an able sketcher. As a result his eclectic notebooks cover a wide range of topics – not just local history.

Comments made by him which have furthered this history are meagre but because they are the only ones so far discovered that refer to the first part of the last century, they are invaluable. John Hughes will be quoted subsequently in sundry places and his name will be suffixed with (Dol) as an identifier; this is necessary because there are other Hughes' in the story.

This introduction has been made because John Hughes is our only source as to what the weir of Felin Lyn looked like in the early and mid 1800s. The weir was sited two-thirds of a mile upstream on the Afon Ceiriog or about a $^1/_4$ mile below the hamlet of Dolywern; it lay 150 yards south of the existing house 'Frondeg'.

Whoever built the first weir, picked the site shrewdly. Looking downstream, the river makes a 90 degree turn to the left and the headrace was sited on the far side of the turn, so that it was natural for water to continue flowing headlong into the race. Beyond the turn was the weir and this meant the bank took the initial brunt of any floodwaters rather than the weir itself.

In one of Hughes' notebooks is a sketch map of Dolywern that he drew in 1875. It is intended to show the locality as it was in his father's and his own childhood's time. He says his scale is *"memory, eye and finger"*. The section of the sketch showing the weir is reproduced here and shows the weir in the shape of a semi-circle with the convex side upstream. Hughes appears accurate in his statements, drawings and sketches and it is not thought that he inserted a half circle merely as a conventional sign. The site of the weir appears to be in the same location as its successor. This is all we know about Felin Lyn's earlier weir and we would have been ignorant even of this but for the chance finding of the sketch.

Whether it was made of wood or stone is unknown, but quite possibly the former. Curving weirs were often favoured in the 1700s – early 1800s. An example, still in use, lies four miles north of Felin Lyn at the point where

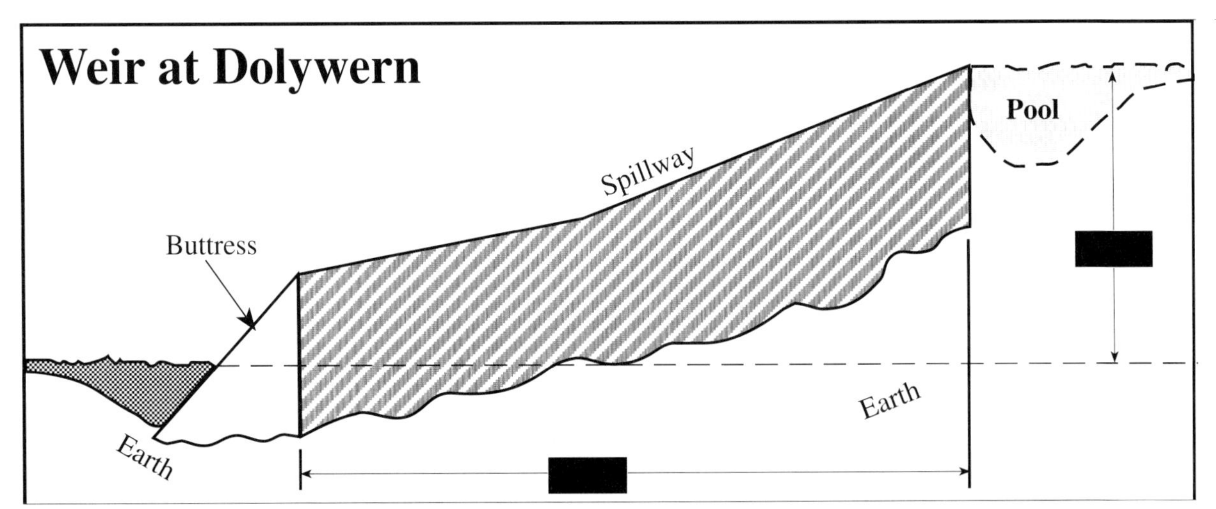

It is doubtful if a drawing was ever made of the weir of Felin Lyn. This conjectural sketch (elevation view) is based on local memory, one photograph, and some imagination and should be reasonably close to reality.

the Llangollen Canal takes its waters from the River Dee at Llantysilio. It is a large stone weir built by Telford in 1830, twenty-two years after the canal leat had been put into service.

This semi-circular weir was replaced with one of more conventional design before 1873. This is because the weir familiar to the author and many others appears on maps which resulted from survey field work carried out in 1872-3.

The author has a theory that the renovation and upgrading of Felin Lyn itself and the rebuilding of the weir was a single project and occurred when a national economic boom was taking place at the beginning of the 1870s. However there is no evidence with which to test the theory.

The large scale 25" Ordnance Survey map shows the weir to be of trapezoid shape, with the top and bottom sills parallel and the sides narrowing in at the bottom. Its dimensions appear to be about 70 feet wide at the top sill, narrowing to about 50 feet at the bottom sill, with an apron stretching some 35-40 feet between the sills.

A postcard view of the weir has recently come to light, owned by a lady who lives in Dolywern. It was published by F. Frith & Co. Ltd. of Reigate, Surrey, who issued postcards 1898-1970. The Company published some 90,000 views of the British Isles, three-quarters of them emanating from photographs taken prior to 1915; in its early years it was the largest photographic distributor in the world. Most of the cards carry a numbering system which permits dating to within one year, but this particular card of Felin Lyn's weir is a rogue and carries no number. It is thought to have been published between 1905 and 1914; a competitor, Valentines, was active in the area in 1907.

This find is fortunate because it is the only view of the weir in its active days; a second view does exist taken in 1939 but by this time Felin Lyn was only occasionally worked, if at all. These views suggest the weir was rectangular and this is also the author's vague childhood remembrance, so it is possible the weir was subject to improvements or alterations after 1875.

In its final form in the twentieth century, the spillway was in two roughly equal parts but of differing slopes, the upper half being about 20° from the horizontal whilst the lower half had a more gentle slope of perhaps 10° from the horizontal.

All weirs and dams suffer from the potential hazard of having their foundations undercut at the lower end, where the water falls from the structure back into the stream.

It is quite feasible that this is what happened to Felin Lyn's original weir, with possible undermining and scouring of the river bed which caused water levels below the weir to drop. The only defence was to extend the weir downstream so that its lower sill was brought closer to the surface of the water in the bottom pool. This would explain the jointed look of the structure in its final form, which was achieved some time prior to 1873 as evidenced by the Ordnance map.

A fragment of an undated letter written by a solicitor, possibly in the 1920s, says *"...one portion of the weir was renewed some years ago to replace a portion which had been washed away..."*. This suggests a major renovation in the possible period 1900-1925 and could have included the addition of three substantial buttresses to the lower end of the weir to restrain its mass at some time prior to the postcard view.

In its final form the whole of the weir was built of stone cemented into position, with the spillway given a smooth finish to provide an unimpeded water flow. Oak sills were fitted at the top and bottom lips of the structure. It is estimated that in the twentieth century there was a water level difference of at least 10 feet between the water impounded above the weir and the water in the pool immediately below it. Immediately upstream of the weir,

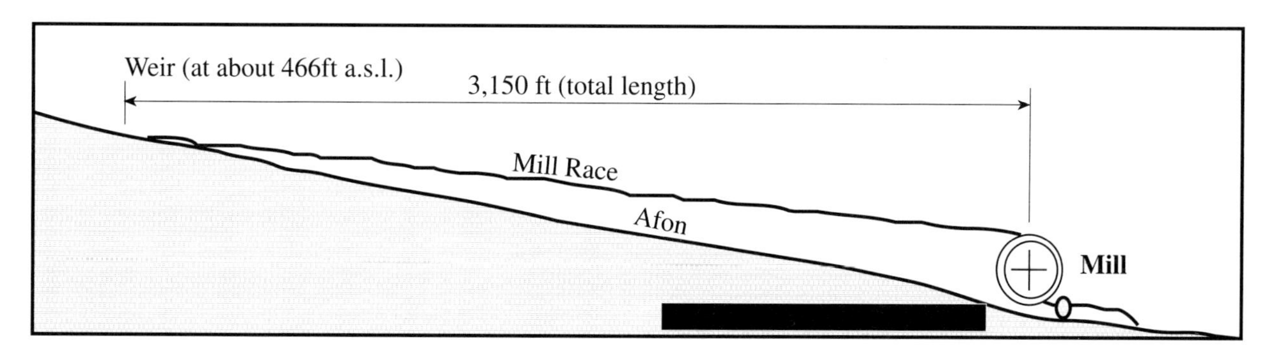

Elevation sketch of Felin Lyn's millrace, showing water gradients of it and Afon Ceiriog, with water wheel inserted between them.

on the south bank, was the sluice gate which gave access to the headrace of Felin Lyn. In this century this inlet gate was made of wrought iron and was raised and lowered by a long vertical threaded shaft which was turned by a key. This key was really a 3 foot long spanner which was normally kept by the miller but was sometimes lent to the farmer whose fields bordered the weir and race. It is likely this metal sluice gate was installed at the time the weir was rebuilt.

Close to this sluice gate a small pool had formed which was 4-7 feet deep, an unheard of depth for the Afon Ceiriog! As a result, it was used by the local farmers to carry out the washing of their sheep and by others in the summer as a swimming hole. The author can remember having picnics beside the weir as a child but the lower pool was used as it was safer, as he had not yet learned to swim.

On the west bank of the weir in its final years was a set of shallow stone steps with natural pools at each step. This allowed the trout and salmon to ascend and descend the river, and no doubt this fish-ladder facility was insisted upon by the authority that had jurisdiction over the river – the River Dee & Clwyd Catchment Board. The postcard view does not show this. In its place and parallel with the top sill of the weir is a primitive-looking stone wall with a 2-3 foot drop below it. This must have been the original and crude fish-ladder, which served also as a secondary escape route for flood waters.

As is well known, water has great destructive powers when it goes on the rampage and will very quickly discover any weaknesses in a natural or man-made barrier. Although this weir at Dolywern was maintained in good condition through the years, the miller and the landlord kept a vigilant eye on it during the winter months. Each summer at the time of low water in the months of July and August, the weir was thoroughly examined for any defects, however minor. Where necessary, the stonework was repointed and sometimes weakened sections were rebuilt; this was the landlord's responsibility and expense, for inattention could soon bring about a defective water supply to the Mill.

The weir was badly damaged in a flood in February 1941, a breach being created on its western side between it and the fish ladder. If Felin Lyn had still been an operating mill, the weir would have been given an immediate temporary patch and then repaired properly in the summer. It is quite possible the breach occurred because of the lack of inspection and maintenance in the immediate preceding years, when the Mill ceased to be run full-time after 1936.

Since the weir now had no economic value, nothing was done and the breach slowly widened. The River Dee & Clwyd Catchment Board would not tolerate this situation as the weir was now an obstruction to the free passage of water and fish, and so it had the weir dynamited and broken up in 1943. The dynamiting was probably undertaken by military sappers as a training exercise.

It was this destructive flood of February 1941, caused by exceptionally heavy snowfalls, which also broke up the weir of Chirk Mill. That weir and its race had been disused since 1928 but it was the intention of the Chirk millers to revert to water-turbine power (and discontinue oil-engine drive) after they took tenant possession of the mill in 1938. However the war put paid to their plans and the Dee Catchment Board served them notice to rebuild the damaged weir or forfeit the water rights. At the time the Chirk millers did not have the resources to rebuild the weir and so the possibility of using water power was relinquished for ever.

Headrace

This commenced at one side of the weir and was an artificial cut that ran parallel to, but at a field's distance away from, the river itself. Its length was 1180 yards or two-thirds of a mile.

The length of any headrace is determined by whether a mill is using an undershot or overshot wheel and by the contouring of the land in the vicinity. The shorter the headrace the better, because this reduced maintenance and water losses. A rough and ready survey of 30 watermills in the Welsh borderland showed the length of headraces to range between 50 yards and one mile, with the median at 400 yards and the mean at 690 yards. This puts Felin Lyn's headrace on the longish side.

The Mill had an overshot wheel of 12 foot diameter calling for about 15 feet head of water and this was easily achieved as the Afon Ceiriog falls at a much greater rate in the same distance. There was a difference of about 30 vertical feet between the weir and the river adjacent to Felin Lyn, which gives a water gradient of 1 in 120 between these two points.

The person who designed the water courses and gravity head, allocated a fall of 12 feet in the head race (gradient of 1 in 300), a gravity head of 14 feet (into which a 12-foot diameter waterwheel was inserted), and a final fall of 4 feet in the tailrace (most of this being fall from mill meadow into river bed). These elevations are shown in the accompanying sketch.

About two-thirds of the way along this headrace, a tributary of the Afon Ceiriog, Nant Gwryd, augmented its waters. This stream, which became a mere trickle in high summer, was about a mile in length and drained the small side valley of the Gwryd. A little further down the race, and not far from Felin Lyn, was an overflow sluice gate which allowed excess waters to escape to the Afon Ceiriog, some 75 yards distant at that point.

In the last decade of the Mill's life this floodgate was padlocked, as a security measure, into the required position and the key was kept by the miller. At this point the race and the sluice formed the edge of the Llwynmawr side-road and because of its position would suggest to any prankster how the Mill could be dramatically deprived of its power. In fact, Mr. Harry Roberts of Llwynmawr, now in his mid 70s, recalls lifting the sluice gate when on his way home from Pontfadog Primary School; no doubt other boys had the same urge!

In this vicinity the waterways looked like two crossed sticks. When viewed going down-flow, the left bottom part of the sticks was the millrace, the right bottom was Nant Gwryd. These two amalgamated for 150 yards and then once more separated. The top left stick was the overflow back to the river, whilst the top right stick was the headrace on its final run to the Mill.

The headrace itself was some 4 feet wide and had a nominal depth of fifteen inches, which was sometimes in places reduced to a six inch depth due to silting. It was designed to pass about 3,000 gallons of water per minute when river levels were better than average. However, in practice, this often fell to 1,000 gallons, or even as low as 500 gallons per minute in times of drought.

This headrace was stopped and drained twice a year to allow it to be cleaned of the accumulation of silt, dead vegetation, sticks and the like. In the summer it was also cleared of water-weed, not by emptying, but by cutting with a long handled billhook.

The weed so cut eventually drifted down to the grating just upstream of the waterwheel and had to be removed to the bank. Watercress, rich in minerals and a blood purifier, was not touched in this operation and was allowed to grow in the race, being harvested by the locals including the miller's family.

Cleaning a millrace was important to any mill's efficiency and was undertaken at least once a year, if not twice. It also had communal and social implications throughout Wales. This derived from the days when the mill was important to everyone in the neighbourhood, not just to the miller. An account of a Felin Lyn millrace cleaning is given in the section "Welsh Remembrances" in Chapter 5. (Note 1.12)

Along the length of the headrace were three side-placed sluice gates fitted into the north or river-facing side of the channel to allow farmers to irrigate their fields. These gates were made of wood and were lifted by hand and then held in the required position by a wooden peg. There were also fords across the race to allow animals and carts to reach these same fields which bordered the Afon Ceiriog.

When first built, just as with canals, the race was lined with 'puddled clay' to make it reasonably watertight, otherwise a mere trickle of water would reach the mill in summer months, the rest being soaked up en route. This puddled clay was not a true clay but was locally available loamy soil mashed into a paste with water and then trodden into position by labourers using their boots or bare feet.

Half a century later, after Felin Lyn has ceased to function, a short section of this head-race still survives and carries water. It is the 150 yards of the 'crossed sticks' analogy described above and is now a permanent section of Nant Gwryd. It contains a ford and a sluice through which all Gwryd waters now flow. The excess floodwaters sluice had a wooden gate – long since removed – 30 inches square which fitted into stone side pieces and a stone lintel straddling the aperture to allow someone to manipulate the gate. The stone pieces were still *in situ* in 1994. The crudeness of design of this sluice (but still most effective) is in marked contrast to the iron inlet sluice beside the weir and suggests it was built when the millrace was first constructed.

A reading was taken at this sluice at the end of September 1987, so as to roughly assess the water volume being passed. There was a depth of four inches of water above the sill and this after a wet summer and a dry September. The velocity of the water, which is an important component in calculating flows, was not measured but it was thought the Nant Gwryd was producing about 500-600 gallons a minute. This would have turned the wheel at Felin Lyn but would have been at the bottom limits of its requirements.

The construction of the weir and the headrace raises the question of who was the designer. Was it the millwright or some other specialist who was part surveyor? Because of the length of Felin Lyn's head race, the siting of the weir was quite critical and had to be accurate to the nearest vertical foot in fall of water. If the weir was sited too low down the river course, the wheel diameter would have to be decreased to accommodate the shortened head with consequent permanent inefficiencies. If the weir was sited too high up the river, the water in the head race would flow with excessive velocity and might set up a scouring action along the course.

The author has only ever seen one reference to the

subject and that a fleeting one. An American writer was decrying the eclipse of the country blacksmith and said the blacksmith was following the long road into oblivion tramped by others such as the flint chipper, fletcher, lute player and *weir-maker*. Another clue may lie with the surnames 'Ware' and 'Wear' which could have originally carried the meaning 'weir or dam', but whether these people designed and built dams or merely lived beside them is another matter; the Scottish 'Weir' has an entirely different derivation. The word itself comes from the German 'wehr' which has the same meaning; *Wehrmacht* (armed forces) originally meant soldiers who were a barrier or dam against invaders.

The author is inclined to the view that there was a specialist who laid out weirs and water courses with surveying skills. Whether he used instruments or had an intuitive sense honed by years of experience and judgment is difficult to say. There is no doubt, however, that his contribution to the creation of a watermill was very significant and in the case of Felin Lyn his water catching and delivery system was evidently first-rate. (Note 1.13)

Complex of Buildings

The mill buildings formed a cluster which can be divided into four parts for purposes of description. Three of these buildings (*a, b,* and *c* below) were physically joined to each other but were not interconnected. All of the buildings were roofed with slate, which had come from quarries less than three miles away, when the Mill was first built. The mill itself and the mill house – which formed one building – are thought to date from the end of the eighteenth century, and remained essentially unchanged throughout their life. All the other buildings were later additions though this cannot be proved by documentation.

It appears that only once was Felin Lyn given a facelift. No documents survive to tell us when this happened but the most likely period is the 1870s. This matter is more fully discussed in Chapter 4. Until at least World War II, all the buildings of Felin Lyn were well maintained and kept in good repair by the joint efforts of landlord and tenant. The front of the mill building and the cowhouse were always whitewashed, and the effect created was one of care and neatness.

Perhaps this is the point in the narrative to remark that Felin Lyn, to the casual passer-by, did not readily disclose itself as a watermill. Some mills proclaim their function immediately with sight of watercourse and wheel, but Felin Lyn was coy in this matter. A stranger walking along the Llwynmawr side-road might assume the place was a reasonably prosperous 'bottom' farm of 50-75 acres. This was because the headrace was nowhere to be seen, the waterwheel was tucked away at the back of the building, and the tailrace ran in a culvert beneath the farmyard. It needed an inquisitive person to walk up the lane behind the Mill to discover what the place really was. Even then, he had to get to the spot where the millrace was carried under the lane and look to his left and see the wheel just below him before realising what it was.

The buildings comprised:

(a) Mill Building. This consisted of the mill itself and the miller's house, and is described in detail in Chapter 4.

(b) 'Glandwr' Cottage. This cottage or house is well named, for 'glan' means '*bank or shore*' and 'dwr' is '*water*', hence '*waterbank*'. The bank carried the millrace and 'Glandwr' squatted under its lee.

The 1839 Tithe Map and Schedule shows a dwelling at this location but it must have fallen into decay by the turn of this century, for the miller-of-the-day was using the spot as pigsties. It is believed that this was the site of the medieval mill and had been a single-storeyed building roofed with thatch.

However, between 1906 and 1911, the landlord built on the old site a new cottage or small house consisting of six rooms on two floors. The cottage had nothing to do with the Mill and was let separately, but there was a joint boundary wall. Shortly after the cottage was built, the common landlord of both properties took one bedroom of the Mill which lay in an annex and gave it to the cottage. This odd arrangement produced slight legal problems in the future, for it is rare to have an upstairs room of one dwelling protruding into another.

Tenants of the cottage used to complain of dampness on the ground floor when waters in the millrace were excessive or the leat itself needed cleaning. Perhaps these waters were percolating through the filled-in medieval watercourse which led straight to Glandwr. This house remains to this day but has somehow changed its name to 'Glyndwr' (after Welsh Prince Owain Glyndwr, c1359-1415) in the last 60 years. It was a separate legal entity and so was untouched physically by the Mill's demolition in 1981.

(c) Cowhouse and Pigsty. These were contained in narrow end-on buildings that jutted out from the complex and were built of yellow brick and stone in unusual fashion, in that the wall facing the road was of brick whilst other walls were of stone. The yellow bricks could suggest these buildings were a part of the general improvements of the 1870s. The cowhouse was next to the Mill and held four stalls and beyond was the sty which had two pens with 4 foot high internal partitions and an access passage. Pigs were very much a part of a country mill and it would have been most unusual if they had been absent at Felin Lyn. Cows were kept if sufficient land was available.

(d) Combined Hay Barn and Stable. This was a two-storey building of stone, nearly 40 feet long and about 15 feet wide. It was built into the hillside, in this particular instance at right angles to the bank. The top floor had large double doors at both ends and its south or bank end led directly on to the Graig lane, which at this point was at the same level. Its prime purpose was to hold hay, though turnips and the like were also chopped here. The lower floor was the stable and was level with and had access to the stockyard. It housed the miller's one horse and also feed, horse tack, tools and implements. (Note 1.14)

Today, out of buildings (a), (c) and (d), only the cowhouse and pigsty remain. The former shows it to be a modern building in terms of finish and fixtures. This seems to be something of an oddity until it is realised that cowhouses were subject to more rules and regulations than any other farm structure – and for good reason.

Tuberculosis, its earlier name was consumption, was first identified medically in 1882 and it was soon found that half of the cows in Britain were infected with it and were constantly passing the disease onto humans. The remedy was to pasteurise milk and to kill the infected cattle. The British Government passed a series of Acts from 1890 to 1909 to combat tubercule-contaminated milk and to improve the hygiene of milk handling, and this effort was essentially successful. Felin Lyn's cowhouse stands as testimony to this policy and the enforcement of the various Acts.

On any farm, the principal building used to be the barn, for here were stored the sheaves of corn after harvesting and here also the hand-threshing took place. Since mills grew no corn, it follows that they had no need for such a building. In Welsh the word for '(corn) barn' is 'ysgubor' and its Welsh evolution as a word is plain to see since 'ysgub' means a 'sheaf of corn'.

Tailrace

The Tithe map of 1839 shows that original course of the tailrace ran along the southern edge of the flat meadow or approximately where the dividing fence between fields 778 and 799 (see 25" map) now stands; it was about 225 yards long. It is not without significance that this earlier tailrace acted as the boundary between the Townships of Nantgwryd and Crogen Iddon at this point, suggesting an early landmark useful for boundary making.

Sometime between 1852 and 1873 the tailrace was shortened by two-thirds. In this century it commenced at the base of the waterwheel with a 60 foot long culvert which took it under the stockyard. It then ran diagonally across the meadow in a 3 foot wide and 18 inch deep ditch, which was lined with low stone sides to prevent grazing animals breaking down the edges. This newer tailrace was about 85 yards long and discharged into the Afon Ceiriog some 70 yards below the low iron bridge which in 1894 replaced the ford. When first built, the bottom of this tailrace was completely floored with stone slabs, some of them still surviving into the 1980s.

In late spring the waters of the tailrace were diverted by stop-boards into shallow grass covered channels, so as to irrigate the miller's only meadow which provided part of his hay crop. Such an operation would fascinate any young child and the author can clearly remember this being done in the mid 1930s.

The medieval definition of a meadow is land that borders water which is used to produce hay and is grazed, so it seems the meadow of Felin Lyn well fitted such a description.

Smallholding

Like all country dwellers, the miller and his family needed some livestock, poultry, and a vegetable garden to sustain themselves, so the Mill was also operated as a smallholding. They also needed animal transport.

Apart from the buildings, yard, and garden, which amounted to quarter of an acre, the acreage of the smallholding fluctuated through the years. It ranged from three to six acres, and at one point was listed as twelve acres. This was because for a period in the middle of the last century, the miller was also renting seven acres at Nantgwryd, a farm one mile distant. It appears that at all times it consisted of the riverside meadow adjacent to the Mill, plus other fields rented by the miller on long term leases.

A rough and ready survey of some 40 mill properties in Britain, ranging from $^1/_4$ acre to thirteen acres, showed that three acres was the average size of land attached to a mill. Since for much of the time Felin Lyn's acreage stood at six acres, it shows it was well endowed with land when compared with other watermills. Prior to 1900, a quarter of all the farms and smallholdings in England and Wales were of less than five acres, so as an agricultural entity Felin Lyn was quite representative of an era.

At the turn of this century, the holding was of 6.5 acres. Apart from the cluster of buildings, it contained four fields.

There was the flat and lush riverside hay meadow (2.3 acres), a very steep and poor quality grazing field beside it (2.2 acres), and on the upper side of the Graig lane another two small fields. These were also steepish and inferior; they measured 0.99 acres and 0.93 acres, and were used for grazing and hay making. The more northerly of these two fields was called 'Erw', which is simply the Welsh word for 'acre'. They also grew good crops of primroses and cowslips. Sales particulars of 1852 show that these two small upper fields were not then part of the property and were probably added to the holding in the 1880s. Sometime between 1910 and 1930, the hedge dividing these two fields was broken down and they became one. As a result, the miller now had three fields, one a lush meadow and two steep inferior ones.

Finally, there was a kitchen garden of 75 feet by 30 feet which was situated beside the road and in front of the millhouse. It produced all the normal annual household plantings, plus rhubarb, gooseberries, currants, and herbs.

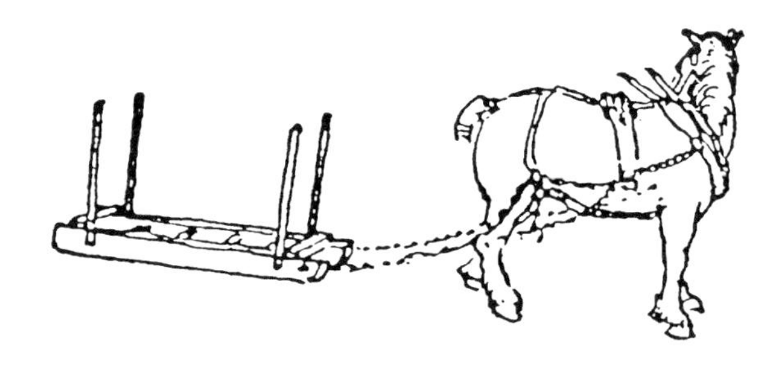

The last miller, Edward Evans II, kept one horse, three milk cows, many pigs, and some poultry. His farming equipment included a typical Welsh two-wheeled cart of 20cwt capacity, which could tip its load, and was made less than a mile away by a joiner-cum-wheelwright at Llwynmawr. Other items included a trap (light two-wheeled horse drawn passenger vehicle), horse-drawn grass mower for hay making, and a hay sledge (*car llusg*) which was used to remove hay from the two upper fields because of their steepness. The author can remember, as a boy of about four or five, asking for a ride on the loaded hay sled and being refused because of the danger of an upset; he suspects he remembers the incident because of the refusal!

In present day terms the miller's trap was his car, being used for quick trips to the market town and for social visits. By contrast his cart was his tractor and trailer and was equally at home in his meadow or delivering grain products or a pig to a distant customer.

The author has childhood memories of all of this equipment and the recall seems triggered by the senses of sound and smell, rather than sight. There was the crunch of the cartwheels on the macadam roads, the rattle of harness, the click of knives and the whirr of gearing on the grass mower, and the smell of hay-a-making.

The running of the smallholding revolved around the care of cows and pigs and, like any stock farm, the routine was rigid and unyielding. The three cows had to be milked twice a day – with never a single exception – in the early morning and late afternoon and each milking took about 30 minutes if done by one person; the related jobs of mucking out the stalls, cooling and panning the milk would total an hour's work. The milk found its way into the economy of the smallholding with the minor share appearing on the family's table as rich milk and butter, and the major portion going to feed the pigs in the form of skimmed milk – having had the cream removed.

It is probable the miller's cow in the 1800s was a Welsh Black. These were one of the most ancient breeds of British cattle and were raised primarily for beef but were also satisfactory milkers. In this century it is likely the miller opted for the Dairy Shorthorn, favoured in the district. This was a traditional British milker derived from eighteenth century breeding experiments and rarely seen nowadays.

It was common practice to raise pigs at a mill and this is what the millers at Felin Lyn did. We have no local quotes about the particular activity except the following. George Borrow, who toured Wales in 1854 and subsequently wrote a book about his experiences, visited the Ceiriog and happened upon Tregeiriog, a hamlet five miles upstream from Felin Lyn. He provides this word picture of a mill and its pigs: *"About a hundred yards distant was a small watermill, built over the rivulet, the wheel going slowly, slowly round; large quantities of pigs, the generality of them brindled, were either browsing on the banks or lying close to the sides half immersed in the water; one immense white hog, the monarch seemingly of the herd, was standing in the middle of the current. All was a scene of quiet rural life."*

Like humans, pigs are incapable of digesting fibre, such as hay or straw but thrive on grain. If well fed, they require little grazing land – a crucial factor on a smallholding. Pigs are one of the most easily raised of farm animals for they are unfussy eaters, though needing lots of water which is no problem at a watermill.

The pig is also a very 'efficient' animal from a farmer's point of view. For example, a pig retains, in body weight, three times the amount of food that cattle or sheep do.

When slaughtered, a sheep yields 50% of edible product by weight, a steer 60%, and a hog 80%.

Any miller was adept at raising pigs because these animals gain one pound (lb) of live weight for every 3-5lbs of grain (in various processed forms) fed to them. It needs 10-20lbs of potatoes or 25-40lbs of mangolds to achieve the same result, so the superiority of grain is plain to see.

Sows could be bred twice a year and usually produced litters of about ten piglets in March and September. During her gestation period a sow ate daily $1^1/_2$lb of barley and drank a gallon of water for every 100lb of her body weight. Hogs preferred ground grain as being easier to digest and always took barley as they found the oat husks troublesome.

Millers would keep or sell the litter in any combination that took their fancy or was profitable to them at the time. Sometimes they sold off some of the 'weaners', other times they kept them. Whatever they kept they fattened from the proceeds of milling and eventually sold them for slaughter except for one or two which they kept for home consumption.

Optimum slaughter weight was 200-225lbs and was achieved in about seven months; it yielded 135-155lbs of dressed meat. In the days prior to refrigeration, the rule was *'Only slaughter a pig when there is an* R *in the month'*; this excluded the months of May to August. (Note 1.16)

The animal was always slaughtered at the mill where it had been grown and was to be eaten. Most localities had a farmer who was also a part-time butcher and the 1891 Census shows that such a man lived at Pandy Bach; this was the nearest farm (22 acres) to Felin Lyn and lay only 300 yds away. The butcher would arrive one day, kill the pig and, with male help, would wash the body in hot water and scrape the hide to get rid of the bristles. He would then remove the viscera and cut the animal in two, allowing it to hang overnight to cool and drain away all the blood. Next day he would return and cut up the carcass into hams, bacon flitches and other assorted eatables. Very little was wasted or thought of as inedible.

At this point the miller's wife and helpers took over and would be busy for the next ten days or so. Much of the meat was salted, flitches were cured and smoked, chitterlings (small intestines) were stuffed with groats to make hog's pudding, and the inner fat of the animal was scraped and melted to make lard. About a dozen large pork pies were made from the meat scraps; this was a tedious process but the results were eagerly awaited by any family. Early editions of Mrs. Beeton's cookery book show recipes now out of fashion, which included boiled pork and pease pudding, brawn, pigs' feet and ears in jelly, faggots, and boiled pig's head.

The miller always had a ready market for his pigs because until a century ago pork was the only flesh that ordinary people could afford to eat as part of their normal diet. An 1863 report about Welsh eating habits said North Walians ate 9oz of bacon per adult weekly. This translates into a minimum of one hog per family per annum, and two for more affluent households, which would have included Felin Lyn since millers always ate well.

All this is not to suggest millers had some kind of hold on the pork market; far from it. The pig was a very popular animal and was kept by most countrymen who had even the smallest piece of land and almost always by farm labourers. The miller's advantage was that he had ready and constant access to highly nutritive pig-feed which came into his hands at very little cost.

Pork remains to this day a popular food in Britain, with 40lb of it being eaten by each adult a year in one form or another.

Poultry reared at Felin Lyn certainly included fowls and ducks and possibly geese. This aspect was always the wife's domain and was often delegated to the children. Hens appear to lay their eggs indiscriminately around a farmyard but very soon children could see a pattern and became adept egg hunters. Ducks like grain and water, both in easy supply at a mill, and were best and cheapest for eating in September-October, providing a 3lb roast. Their down was also welcomed to fill pillows and bed covers.

Geese have always been associated with milling. Good quills were used by the stone-dresser or miller for marking out the furrows on a millstone with red raddle or tiver, and to this day a quill is considered the best aid to checking the verticality of a stone spindle. Wing feathers were also made into hand brushes for sweeping grain and meal. Just as importantly, a 15-20lb goose could provide a rare table treat in autumn and early winter. Goose grease had many applications, being used as the base for ointments for man and his beasts, to soften leather work, and as an anti-rust covering on metal surfaces. It was too thin to be used as a lubricant. Rheumatism and severe colds were often alleviated with goose grease and red flannel. But having itemised all these benefits, one wonders if they were appropriate birds to have at a mill and smallholding. Geese have little fear of man and are very territorial and this makes them the best of sentinels; the wings of an attacking gander can quite badly bruise a person. Since watermills were visited daily by all manner of people, there was the potential risk of an unfriendly welcome to a customer. A more compelling disadvantage was the fact that geese are herbage – not grain – eaters and need to run free on grasslands. Here they would compete with the miller's other animals on the meadow and would have to be excluded from it for about three months prior to haying.

Finally there was the vegetable garden that all country dwellers had. This was located immediately in front of the Mill between the road and millyard. The late Mrs. Gwladys Jones (FL), who was brought up at Felin Lyn prior to World War I, says her father dug and planted the vegetables and then her mother took over. Plants specifically remembered were *"potatoes, peas, broad and runner beans, kidney beans, onions, roots, and rhubarb"*.

Returning to the subject of this smallholding, it is important to record that whilst Felin Lyn was worked on a full-time basis the mill and the attached smallholding were self-supporting and profitable. After 1936 this was not so, for all subsequent tenants had to seek some outside work to make ends meet.

Property Values, Rents, and Rates

There is a difficulty in composing this section because no factual data survives about the worth of Felin Lyn as a property and consequently how much rent was paid by the tenant miller.

However, property value and rent are such fundamental aspects of the history of a parcel of land that they cannot be ignored, and the author feels obliged to make some comment, even if it turns out to be well-intentioned but inaccurate or even mistaken.

Felin Lyn and its attached smallholding was sold only three times in its life time: first in 1852, secondly in 1905, and finally in 1962 when it was no longer a mill. The prices of the first two sales are unknown and the third was for £1,600.

For rent amounts there is also a complete blank until the period when Felin Lyn was no longer a mill but simply a smallholding. In 1950 the rent for the ex-mill and smallholding was £1-0-0d a week, and for Glandwr cottage (beside it) was 2/6d a week, with the tenants being responsible for paying the rates. Even these rent amounts are unreliable as indicators, since they were controlled by government legislation dating from World War II and were not at a free economic level. (Note 1.17)

Where does one start in an inquiry of this sort? It seemed perhaps easier to ascertain a likely rent in a particular period and from this deduce a property worth. The author found a great paucity of information about mill rents throughout Britain. After several years he accumulated 33 rent details in Wales and Scotland, randomly obtained. In almost all cases the data was superficial, consisting only of date and place. Capacity, age and condition of the watermills were unknown, making comparisons of the apple and orange kind. When the data was plotted on a graph, the result was analogous to a shotgun firing rent pellets in a widening cone, where distance is measured in decades, the firing point is 1700 AD, and the point of aim is the 20th century. In 1750 the rents ranged between £7 and £25; in 1800 it widened to between £10 and £45; in 1850 it continued to widen and lay between £10 and £70; by 1900 thc cone affect had ceased, the range being between £15 and £75. It should be noted that the lower level of rents for any age were a flat line constant, suggesting that monetary inflation was not a factor. The ever widening range of rents is partly explained by the fact that prior to 1750-1800, all country mills were primitive grist mills with one, possibly two, pairs of millstones. After that period such mills were upgraded or new ones were built (Felin Lyn being an example), with improved gearing, an ability to grind wheat, and bigger and better floor and storage areas. Naturally, these improvements called for higher rents. (Note 1.18)

Based upon this very crudely constructed survey and taking a middle ground position, one would surmise that Felin Lyn had rents of about: £30 in 1800; £30-£35 in 1850; £40 in 1900. Can these approximations be tested in any way? Fortunately the answer is 'yes', allowing them to be modified and finer-tuned.

In 1867 local government listed Felin Lyn as having a 'gross estimated rental' of £31-15-0d and a rateable value of £27-4-1d. Such valuations can be on the conservative side and be out of date, so it is possible to infer that the rent actually paid in 1867 by the miller could have been closer to £35. Confirmatory clues come from another source. Clwyd County Record Office kindly supplied a list of watermill rents in Denbighshire and Flintshire in the third quarter of last century when farming was profitable and rents were correspondingly high. The list had eight entries and covered mainly village and country mills, some perhaps similar to Felin Lyn. The range in years was from 1851 to 1876 and in annual rents from £26 to £70: the rent median was £40 and the median year was 1866 which carried an entry of £40 rent. This suggests in the middle of the last century in N.E.Wales an average rent for a water-mill was about £40 per annum. (Note 1.19)

With these kind of cross-checks, the author puts forward the following suggested rents for Felin Lyn, with 1867 being the anchor point.

1800: £30 Mill was new, so high rent to match.
1850: £30. Little or no change; depressed agriculture 1815-40.
1867: £32 to £35. Local government valuation.
1875: £40. Mill recently upgraded/improvements.
1900: £40. After 1875/80 small country watermill went into slow economic decline, so difficult for landlords to make rent increases.

Now comes the equally important task of trying to determine how much it cost to build Felin Lyn and what was its worth over the years. If rent detail is marked by paucity of data, it can be said that property value information is almost non-existent.

In Wales, the author could only find four watermill sale prices and all but one relate to this century. They are: Coedpoeth Mill, three miles west of Wrexham, built for £1000 in 1832 on or beside the site of an earlier mill; King's Mill on the south-eastern outskirts of Wrexham, was sold by the long term owner to a farmers' co-operative for £1250 in 1920 and resold to the owner for £400 in 1932; Felin Newydd, Crugybar, near Llandovery, two-pair millstones, sold for £725 in 1918; Howey Mill, two miles south of Llandrindod Wells, was out of repair by 1932 and was sold for £375 with 6.1 acres of land in 1933 to Radnorshire County Council for use as a road repair depot.

These prices being unhelpful to the inquiry, some other way of determining property values has to be found. At the beginning of the nineteenth century, a rich man with money in a bank could earn interest at $3^1/_2$-4%. If he was going to invest this money in a new watermill, he would need to set an annual rental that returned him his investment over a set number of years plus his lost bank interest. It is thought the 'return of investment period' was about 15-20 years for poorer quality buildings, 20-25 years for better class buildings and 30-33 years for land. On this basis, Felin Lyn, as a better class building at year 1800, would have cost £30 annual rent times 25 years, equalling about £750.

At the time of Felin Lyn's supposed construction, tradesmen were being paid about 1/- (or 1s 0d) per day. Assuming it took a mason and two helpers three months to put up a three-storey stone building, comprising mill and millhouse, then construction costs would amount to about £250. Add another £500 for all the machinery and its installation and a total cost of about £750 is arrived at. The machinery allowance of £500 is based on an 1870 valuation of machinery inside an English watermill at £466. (Note 1.20)

These computations seem quite in line when compared with the costs of building the last windmill in Britain. This was at Patcham, near Brighton, Sussex, in 1884 the brick tower cost £300 and all else £1,100.

All these figures about rents and building costs are speculations at best, but they do provide a dimension where none existed before. They also illustrate the mechanics of construction finance.

Finally, a reference to property levies. Valuations of the property for the purposes of levying local taxes or 'rates' have survived for the years 1838, 1867 and 1916. This information is of value but does not lend itself to prose, and so has been placed in Appendix VIII.

Landlord and Tenant Responsibilities

Virtually none of the mills in Britain were owner-operated and Felin Lyn was no exception to this rule. The Mill was always owned by a landlord who lived locally or had local affiliations and there never arose the problems and neglect that frequently come with absentee landlords. In fact, co-operation between landlord or his agent and miller-tenant always seems to have been satisfactory during the life span of Felin Lyn, with both parties discharging their responsibilities fairly and conscientiously.

When Felin Lyn was downgraded to a smallholding it was leased for another twenty-five years in five-year terms; three tenants had occupancy for the years 1937-47, 1947-52, and 1952-62, respectively.

No lease agreements relating to Felin Lyn between landlord and miller have survived, but with clues scattered here and there it may be possible to infer what was expected of each party.

In the last century leases for agricultural property normally ran for a five or seven year period, but frequently in practice a family held a tenancy for one or several generations. This would be left undisturbed by the landlord (and by his heirs and successors in turn) providing the

property was being properly cared for and the rent paid when due. It would appear this was the situation at Felin Lyn for the second half of the nineteenth century and the first third of the twentieth century. There is an indication that rental agreements for Felin Lyn ran for seven-year terms. Edward Evans I (1841-1912) was miller from 1872 to 1900, which is a twenty-eight year span of four seven-year terms; his son is believed to have continued this arrangement.

It would also have been interesting to know at what frequency and on what dates the mill rent was paid. If half yearly, it could have been on 6th April and 11th October, otherwise it would have been on the traditional Quarter days, which were 25th March (Lady Day), 24th June (Midsummer Day), 29th September (Michaelmas) and Christmas Day.

In the case of a mill property there were really two lease agreements rolled into one. One was a standard lease which would apply to any kind of country property and the other was a specialised one covering the machinery of the mill and possibly water-courses.

Dealing with the 'standard' type first, we are fortunate in having a specimen created by a one-time landlord of Felin Lyn. A Government Land Report on Wales of 1896 quotes a typical lease agreement of Chirk Castle Estates. It runs: *"...the tenant to do all repairs, upon being allowed timber in the rough and other materials; and to paint the internal woodwork of house and cottages once in every 7 years and the external woodwork of all buildings, gates, etc., once in every 5 years, landlord supplying paint. In case of default the landlord may execute the repairs himself and charge the expense thereof on the tenant."*

Such terms could have been general in England and Wales, for an East Anglian printed lease of the 1850s says much the same thing; *"The landlord shall find rough timber, brick, tiles and lime for repairs of buildings and will pay one-half of workmen's wages employed on such repairs, but the tenant is responsible for carting such material and for paying his half share of labour costs plus beer money."* This lease also states it is the tenant's obligation to keep ditches, drains and water-courses in good repair.

As to the terms of the specialised lease relating to the mill machinery, it may well be that the landlord provided all the fixed basic machinery and its long term replacement, and the miller was responsible for maintenance and all else. For example, a millstone worn thin over the years would be replaced by the landlord but one shattered by faulty setting-up would have to be replaced by the tenant miller; likewise a fractured cast iron transmission wheel would be the landlord's duty to replace, but broken or stripped wooden cogs, or broken belts, would be replaced by the miller.

Another variation of responsibilities might be that the tenant miller was responsible for the upkeep and replacement of all machinery and at the end of a tenancy was credited with improvements and part of the renewals, and debited for wear and tear.

Fortunately details of a few isolated instances of repairs carried out at Felin Lyn have survived the years, and from them a certain pattern of landlord/tenant responsibility emerges. All the quotes below, excepting the first, come from an account book kept by Jonah Phillips (1858-1929), joiner and wheelwright at Glynceiriog, covering the period 1913-20 and all in Welsh. (Note 1.21)

Landlord charges *(Mr/Sir Alfred Davies)*

(a) *Renewal of timbers to waterwheel, using heart of larch obtained from Coward & Co. sawmills at Llangollen; date c1920. (Charges unknown)*

(b) *19 Dec 1913. Gas-tarring the gates at Felin Lyn...1/3d. (In 1914 another customer was charged 19/- for two gates and 4/6d for supplying and setting the posts)*

Tenant charges *(Mr Edward Evans, Felin Lyn)*

Items (c) and (d) do not advance the distinction but are included for general interest.

(c) *21 Mehefin (June) 1916. Rypario y drol (repairs to cart): byrddau (boards) at 6d, hoelion (nails) at ld, gwaith (the work) at 5/-; also pen cribyn (hayrake head) at 1/4, troed bwyell (axe shaft) at 6d. Total: 7/5d. (In 1914 another customer was charged*

£2-1-11 for the body of a 2-wheeled farm cart and £2-1-6 for its wheels & axle; total £4-3-5. Seems a bargain)

(d) *30 Tachwedd (Nov) 1917. Gwaith. (the work – but no details and no materials used) at £1-15-0. Also dyled (debt) at 1/-.*

(e) *24 Ionawr (Jan) 1919.*

Gwydro ffenestr (repairing windows)	*1/9d*
Am weithio yn y felin (working in the mill)	*2/9d*
Ail roi troed bwyll (redoing shaft of axe)	*2d*
Gwydr i lamp (glass for the lamp)	*2d*
Diwrnod efo saer melinau (working with the millwright)	*5/6d*
Hoelion (nails)	*8d*
Hogi llif (saw sharpening)	*6d*
Cynio bowc (chiselling the baulk?)	*6d*
Tario caint y ddwy olwyn (tarring the rim of two wheels, presumably means 2 rims of waterwheel)	*8d*
Gwaith ar y drol (work on the cart)	*4/6d*
Hoelion (nails)	*2d*
Croes bren cratch (cross piece of animal feed rack)	*9d*
Bwrdd gwaelod (bottom board)	*9d*
Ffon seafft (shaft stick) 1/-	
Total	*18s 10d*
*Am flawd i Edward Evans sef blawd mochyn * <credit >*	*<15/10>*
Net billing:	*3s 0d*

*The literal translation is *'For flour to Edward Evans that is pig meal.'* This does not make sense in milling terms, and it is thought Jonah Phillips either gave the miller barley and had 15/- of grinding time to convert it to meal, or that Edward Evans gave him 15/- worth of barley meal; probably the latter. This is also a fascinating example of barter at a late date.

Apart from the initial reason for recording these repair details, they have an intrinsic interest. For example, it shows a specialised millwright did work at Felin Lyn though Phillips himself was a competent and versatile joiner. The account book also showed Phillips to have the Celtic artistic temperament, for scattered through the pages are snatches of verse created by him. There was even one about the iron bridge close to Felin Lyn which had supplanted the ford a quarter century before; his trait passed to his son who was inducted at the Welsh National Eisteddford in 1934.

These entries tend to reinforce the earlier supposition that the landlord was responsible for provision of machinery and renewal thereof, and all else was the tenant's responsibility. Specifically, in the case of the waterwheel, the landlord renewed the timbers whilst the tenant kept it well preserved by having it tarred.

Decline and Demise

The last miller continued to work the Mill till his death in 1936. His daughter wrote, *"My mother was allowed to sublet the mill and she moved out. A man from Oswestry took it; he was in charge of the animal market there. Felin Lyn became a smallholding only, as all milling and selling of foodstuffs ceased, and all future tenants had to seek outside work."*

After 1936 the Mill appears to have been worked occasionally, but certainly not on a regular basis, nor run by an experienced miller. After a short while the new tenant moved out and was replaced by a smallholder who also had some milling experience. He was a Hugh Davies from Flintshire and rented Felin Lyn for five to six years. He is remembered as being a very strict Methodist and a member of Llwynmawr Chapel. Mrs. Lewis, formerly of Crogen Wladys farm, recalls her husband taking two bags of corn to the Mill and being told by the part-time miller that he did not work on Saturdays as he was preparing for the Sabbath! It is probable that during Davies' tenancy the Mill's machinery and/or water supply failed – for ever.

In February 1941 the weir was breached and made useless in a flood and this meant that if the machinery was still operable, the waterwheel would have had to be driven by the waters of Nant Gwryd alone.

In 1942 the late George Heald (1922-91, who lived at Llangollen for much of his life) was asked by his father to inspect Felin Lyn. His father was the miller of Foelas Mill, Pentrefoelas, Denbighshire, from 1920-1949 and so as a child and youth Heald had much experience of water-milling. As it happens Foelas Mill was the last surviving commercial watermill in former Denbighshire, working until 1982. Its future as a working watermill was in jeopardy but is now secure, being a part of the Pentrefoelas Heritage Village.

The inspection was done for the benefit of the Denbighshire War Agricultural Executive Committee who wished to re-activate all dormant cornmills as part of the war effort. George Heald said: *"I soon discovered that it was not possible to get Felin Lyn working again, and if I remember rightly, this was due to the pit wheel, or one of the other cast iron wheels, being fractured."*

These circumstances are confirmed by the amateur mill historian, E. Mitford Abraham (1883-1959), who one year later, in 1943, noted *"...waterwheel in bad condition and teeth in one pinion wheel broken"*. This implies a cast iron wheel with integral cast teeth and not an iron wheel with inserted wooden cogs; the latter type being easily repaired.

It was in the same year of 1943 that the river authority, responsible for the management of the Afon Ceiriog, blew up and dismantled the broken weir at Dolywern because it was considered an obstruction to water and fish flows.

This made Felin Lyn the last water-powered cornmill to work in the Ceiriog, though it should be made clear the qualifiers 'water-powered corn' are essential. A waterwheel worked at a farm at Tregeiriog until 1952, driving farm machinery which included the bruising of grain. At Chirk the cornmill survived until 1951 grinding animal feed but it had used a diesel engine as a power source since its re-opening in 1938.

By the 1950s the landlord was reconciled to the obvious, that the machinery would never be used again, and so in 1956 he permitted a scrap metal merchant to gut the Mill of all metal components. The visible signs that Felin Lyn had been a watermill were now gone.

Mr Stan Jeffreys, a Welshman, Welsh speaking, and now of northern Alberta, Canada, is a member of the last family to live in the ex-mill and he provides an interesting glimpse of Felin Lyn in its final years. *"We lived there as tenants for 10 years from 1952 to 1962. My father was a stone mason and builder and he used the ex-mill as a home and a smallholding. We kept four head of cattle – milking cows – and would winter about 20 sheep, which were put on other pasture during summer; we also kept pigs and chickens. The meadow beside the river was used for hay, as had always been the custom. I recollect an old metal stencil plate, lettered 'E. Evans, Felin Lyn' which Ned y Felin must have used years ago to mark sacks. My childhood was spent here and they were some of the happiest years of my life."*

In 1962, the landlord, who was now seventy years old and whose father had purchased the property in 1905, sold Felin Lyn and the attached smallholding to a Wrexham man who did not take up residence or work the land. By this time, once proud Felin Lyn now consisted only of three fields, some farm buildings in poor repair and a small house without any modern amenities. This new owner disappeared in the mid 1960s and has not been located to this day. As a result, the buildings slowly fell into disrepair and then became dangerous.

The author last visited and examined the interior of Felin Lyn in May 1981. At this time all the rooms of the Mill were still essentially intact and accessible but much care had to be taken because of the instability of floors and roof. For a wary adult, it was a place of hazard and for a child it could have been a death trap. Surviving mill machinery at this date consisted of the three bed stones sitting in their proper places, and a five foot length of the 17 inch diameter vertical main shaft lying forlorn on the ground floor.

Apart from the threat to life and limb, the owner of 'Glyndwr' was also much concerned. The Mill was physically attached to the cottage and in its unoccupied and neglected state, it was causing damp and structural problems to the latter building. The adjacent barn was also disintegrating.

After much local concern, Glyndwr District Council (head office in Ruthin) invoked powers under the Public Health Act 1961 and had the Mill and all its outbuildings, except one, demolished on 21st September, 1981. This was a prudent decision.

The author feels compelled to add an emotional postscript. *"I visited the Ceiriog in 1987 for the first time since Felin Lyn was demolished in 1981, though in between these years I had lived mentally with the Mill on an almost monthly basis. I thought I knew what to expect when visiting the site but on arrival was suddenly shaken by what I did not see. Where the buildings had stood, there was nothing, only the lie of the land that had existed before they were ever built. My subconscious expectation must have been to see low ruined walls with a mass of debris inside to remind me of the past. Instead it was plain to see that after demolition all the rubble had been removed and the land meticulously tidied.*

I stood looking and felt lost, robbed of history. An acute observer of the twenty-first century will not have the slightest idea that a needed local business, a way of life, once existed here. The weir has been totally destroyed, the mill has been totally destroyed, and the connecting ribbon of the millrace has already been passively changed or actively obliterated.

Looking at this reverted landscape, a counter emotion slowly took over. The tedious research, continuous correspondence, draft writing and endless hours of consumed leisure time suddenly seemed very worthwhile. All the physical aspects of Felin Lyn had disappeared but its story was safe for future generations."

Having recorded the 'death' of Felin Lyn as a full-time cornmill in 1936, where does it fit into the chronology of watermill closures in Wales, or Britain, in this century?

The answer cannot be found objectively because one would need to know the cessation date for every mill in a given area and this is almost impossible. Watermills, in the twilight of their lives, faltered and then quietly expired and it is only in a small minority of cases that a closure year survives in archives or literature.

The author has come across an unidentified source stating that Breconshire had 100 watermills in 1900, 64 in 1905, and 20 in 1926. It is not known if this listing is accurate or typical of Wales but it does suggest a high mortality in a quarter century.

The reasons for the closures of rural mills are fairly obvious: cheap imported wheat after 1875; railway network that brought a new style of (food) marketing to the countryside; farmers switching after c. 1880 from previous profitable grain growing to the only alternative – livestock and dairying.

Thirty mill closure dates, commencing 1900, have been examined for Radnorshire and its related Marcher lands. Not too much can be read into such data because post-1930s dates have been remembered more easily, whereas 1900-30 dates are sparse. The list perhaps suggests that mills still at work between World Wars I and II were plucky survivors and probably reflected a miller's determination and business acumen.

If a mill was still operable in 1940, it was recruited into the war effort (1939-45) and given a further lease of life. Most such mills closed by about 1947 when need and profit were evaporating. Any mill that continued to work after 1950 was a rarity.

After 1930 it seems that a mill was abandoned for one of three main reasons. Firstly, the massive national depression of the 1930s snuffed out what local corn trade still existed: secondly, when an elderly miller retired or died, there was no one willing to take his place in what was obviously a dying trade. Thirdly, when a major mechanical defect appeared, there was no money or motive left to fix it.

Having looked at these various facets, it seems reasonable to conclude that Felin Lyn was a battling survivor, and if managed more timidly could have succumbed somewhere between 1900 and 1930.

Notes

1.1 **Book:** *The First Farmers*, Leonard, J. N., Timelife Books, 1973, 160pp. Reference is to J. R. Harlan, then Professor of Agronomy at University of Oklahoma, U.S.A.; see pp. 22-3.

1.2 **Book:** *Chirkland and Chirk Castle*. Mahler, Margaret. London, G. Bell & Sons, 1912, 232pp. Covers period 1300s to 1600s, with references to medieval watermills in the Ceiriog.

1.3 **Mrs Gwladys Jones (1902-1992)**. Daughter of Edward (miller) and Jane Jones, Felin Lyn, Ceiriog. Became a school teacher and lived much of her married life in Yorkshire, but maintained property in Glynceiriog. Corresponded with the author 1981-85.

1.4 **Population Statistics:** from encyclopaedias & *Whitaker's Almanack*. England only and estimated: 6,045,000 in 1700; 6,517,000 in 1750; England & Wales by census: 8,893,000 in 1801; 17,928.000 in 1851; 32,528.000 in 1901.

1.5 **Book:** *English Local History*. K. Tiller, Allan Sutton Pub, Stroud. 1992, 247pp. See p. 131-5 on 'Enclosure'. One sentence in the book is worth mentioning; *"Doing local history is like tackling a very large jigsaw puzzle, where all the pieces are not kept in the same box and some may ultimately turn out to be missing."* Very well said!

1.6 **John Hughes (1802-1889)**. Was born nearby and brought up at former grist mill at Dolywern. For biographical details see beginning of section "The Weir" in this chapter. Dewi Jones of Llwynmawr is to be thanked for drawing the author's attention to this and other relevant passages and for translating them.

1.7 **Tithe Map & Apportionment, 1839, Llangollen Parish**. Townships of Hafodgynfor, Nantgwryd, & Talygarth. Specifically, parcels 346, 347, & 561. Valuer was Edward Tench, Junior, of Plas Newydd, Ruabon. Parish copy held by Clwyd Record Office, Ruthin.

1.8 **Ordnance Survey Maps**: 25 inch/mile, Denbighshire, Sheet XXXIX-12, 1899 & 1912; 6 inch/mile, Denb. Sheet XXXIX-S.E, 1880, 1900 & 1914; 2.5 inch/mile, Sheet SJ23, Chirk, 1957. First two sets of maps give good detail, last map provides hill contour profiles.

1.9 **Weather Records:** Data kindly supplied by Mr G.J. Edwards, Llanarmon Dyffryn Ceiriog, October 1994.

1.10 **Water Flow Data, Afon Ceiriog, 1970-79**: Welsh Water Authority, Northern Division, Bangor, Gwynedd. Flows began to be monitored at Chirk in 1952 in cubic meters per second. All quoted data relates to Chirk but in practice for Dolywern deduct about 15%.

1.11 **Book** *Wild Wales* by George Borrow, first published 1862; see Chapter 17.

1.12 **Millrace Maintenance:** See p.17 of *'Melin 10'* (1994), annual Journal of Cymdeithas Melinau Cymru/Welsh Mills Society, as it relates to leat cleaning of Hundred House Mill, Radnorshire, in 1932; over 50 men involved, 2 photos.

1.13 **Water Supply: Ditches & Flumes.** In preparing this book only one reference to the construction of water courses was found and occurs in booklet "*Placer Mining: Handbook for Klondike Miners*", published in 1897 in USA. The Klondike gold fields are in Yukon, Canada, and much water was needed to wash the gold bearing gravels and power the then primitive equipment. Following is quote worthy. "*Before any work is commenced, an assessment must be made of anticipated volumes at all seasons of the year and probable en-route losses caused by leakage, absorption and evaporation. In surveying, stations should be created every 50-100 feet apart, numbered and staked, with pegs driven to grade. Trapezoidal forms should be adopted for ditches with half a regular hexagon being the most common. Water resistance due to friction is smallest when ditch width is twice the height. Ditches with grades of 16-20 feet per mile (1 in 300/264) are quite common. Banks should be 3 feet wide at their tops.*"

1.14 **Book:** *Traditional Farm Buildings in North-East Wales, 1550-1900.* E. Wiliam, Cardiff, Welsh Folk Museum, 1982, 344pp. Thoroughly researched and well-presented subject. See p. 122. Survey covered 363 farms and of these four lay in the 'territory' of Felin Lyn – see Nos. 339, 347, 349, & 361 on p. 287. Other relevant topics: Barns, Barn Machinery; Brewhouses; Estates; Granaries; Pigsties; Rickyards.

1.15 **Book** *Wild Wales* by George Borrow. Chap (64) LXIV.

1.16 **Book:** *The Pig - Breeding, Rearing & Marketing*, Spence & Sanders, London, Pearson Ltd, 1919, 184pp.

1.17 **Newspaper cutting**: Oswestry Advertiser, 29 Aug 1951. Landlord, T. L. Davies, wished to evict an unsatisfactory tenant from Felin Lyn smallholding but had to take the matter to Denbighshire Agricultural Executive Committee at Ruthin in May, because of wartime regulations which gave protection to tenants. Landlord said tenant was grossly overgrazing the land and neglecting the property. Tenant had 6 cows, 1 calf, 1 sow, 4 small pigs and half a-dozen hens. Landlord lost his case and was now appealing the decision at the Agricultural Land Tribunal at Llangollen. Tribunal deferred its decision until it had visited Felin Lyn. Tenancy was for 5 years commencing 1947, so had only a year or less to run.

1.18 **Rent Record of one Welsh Mill**: Felin Hen, nr Llanbadarn Fawr, about 4 miles E. of Aberystwyth, Cardiganshire. Abstracted from article by Jill Barter (p.26-38) in *'Melin 8'* (1992), Annual Journal of Welsh Mills Society". Probably a small grist mill of one pair millstones to which was added a pair of burr stones to grind wheat in 1825 at installation cost of £89-16-1.

1733 - £10-5-0	1746 - £11-0-0	1796 - £21-0-0
1740 – £ 9-5-0	1769 - £12-12-0(b)	1825 - £26-0-0(c)
1743 – £10-l0-0(a)	1775 - £13-13-0	1867 - £36-18-8(d)

Notes:
(a) £7-10-0 for mill, £3-0-0 for farm.
(b) Plus 2/- for item previously rendered in kind.
(c) £5 rent increase for installation of wheat stones.
(d) Had ceased working by 1884.

1.19 **Annual Rents of Watermills in N.E.Wales in 19th century**: Supplied by Clwyd County Record Office, Ruthin, Clwyd. Random list: 1851, Harwarden mill-£50; 1851, Minera mill- £70; 1851 House & mill in Gwersyllt/Llay- £40; 1866, Little Mill, Mold-£40; 1870, Corn mill & brewery, Holywell-£60; 1871, Coed-y-cra mill, Northrop-£28; 1871, Middle Mill, Northop-£26; 1876, Treddyn mill-£30.

1.20 **Valuation of Mills at Tamworth, Staffordshire, 1870**. Newsletter No.25, Midlands Mill Group, England, August 1986, pp. 8 & 9. Valuations for larger mill; Waterwheel & shaft-£175; gearing & stone furniture-£97; two pairs of stones-£60; flour machine-£40; bolter-£24; smutter-£15; banding-£30; sack tackles-£25; Total: £466.
In the smaller mill, values were: waterwheel & shaft-£60; gearing & stone furniture-£50; hursting & job posts-£15; two pairs of stones-£17.

1.21 **Account Book of Jonah Phillips (1858-1929)**: Joiner & wheelwright at Glynceiriog, Denbighshire. Handwritten in Welsh and covering period 1913-20; approx. 120 pages. Four references to work done at Felin Lyn. Held privately in Ceiriog.

Chapter 2

*d*oing *b*usiness

Waterwheels also drove other types of machinery in Dyffryn Ceirog. In the last two hundred years they ran the spinning and weaving operations in woollen manufacture; operated the bellows and tilt hammers of an iron forge; ground ingredients for making gunpowder; squared slates with a guillotine cutter; powered fixed pieces of farm machinery and churned butter. Earlier they fulled cloth and more recently produced electricity.

However, it was the cornmill that first used water-power in the valley, used it continuously, and outlived all the other types of users.

Man's Diet and Daily Food Intake

Because man's physiology, and especially the size of his stomach, has not materially altered for the last 5,000 years or more, it is reasonable to assume his total daily intake of food measured by weight has remained a constant. The structure of his diet, if he lived in Britain, may have varied because of geography, culture, and status, but there was a sameness about it through the millennia and only in the last 100 years have there been radical changes in diet patterns. Notwithstanding these recent diet changes, it is thought that man is continuing to cat the same amount of food bulk as before, or perhaps a little less.

How much do we eat each day in the temperate climate of Britain, measured in pounds' weight? Such a basic question proved difficult to answer in spite of the fact that each one of us participates in the activity at least twice a day. Statistics were equally elusive.

A nationwide survey in Canada in the early 1970s showed the daily food intake per person averaged between 2.6 and 4.0lbs. The lower figure applied to older women and the higher to youngish men; it may come as a surprise – except to mothers – to learn that children aged 5-11 inclusive ate 3.8lb. In nutritional terms, food consists of carbohydrates, fats, proteins, minerals and vitamins. Carbohydrates and fats give us energy, proteins build and repair our body tissues, whilst trace minerals and vitamins 'oil' the system.

Carbohydrates provide the bulk of our daily food, simply because carbohydrates comprise three-quarters of all plant life in the world. It has always been so in the past, is now, and probably will be in the foreseeable future. Ever since man became a farmer 7,000-10,000 years ago, and before that time when he was a gatherer and hunter, he has lived mainly on vegetable foods derived from grass seeds, legumes, roots and tubers. In temperate zones he concentrated on growing grass seeds because they gave him an all-seasons food due to their twin attributes of being nutritious and storing well over long periods. These grass seeds have remained man's prime foodstuff and have never been seriously challenged, except perhaps rather ineffectively by the potato which Europeans started growing on a wide scale in the 1700s.

Bread is the principal end-product of these domesticated grass seeds and in Europe has been the dominant food for countless centuries. The question now to be asked is, 'what proportion did bread form of the total daily food intake of the average person in the last and preceding centuries?' Details about the present century have been purposely avoided because of the very considerable changes in the national diet.

With our affluent diets of recent years provided by world-wide marketing and universal commercial and household refrigeration, it is all too easy to forget the recent past. It has to be remembered that, less than 100 years ago in rural and urban Wales, food was monotonous, especially in winter. At all times of the day, and in all seasons, bread was the cornerstone of the average diet and was eaten at virtually every meal. This was especially true in the dead of winter when fresh vegetables and fresh fruit were non-existent, and fresh meat or fowl were rarely seen on the table.

The bread was nutritionally satisfactory but frequently had a dense unappetising texture, especially when it started to turn stale after standing beyond one full day. This bread was spread with all manner of things to make it more palatable, such as butter, thick cream, jam, honey, dripping, goose fat and other renderings. Such spreads were also nutritionally sensible because they gave extra energy. (Note 2.1)

The meagre references in literature suggest that in the nineteenth and earlier centuries bread provided between a quarter and a half the weight of the total food eaten daily by the Welsh. Based upon a total daily food intake of between $2^1/_2$ and 4lbs, this provides a theoretical range of between about $^3/_4$ and 2lb of bread eaten by an individual daily. These references also pointed out that wealthy people were able to buy a wider range of foodstuffs and tended to eat less bread, whilst poor people were forced to exist on large quantities of bread as no cheap nourishing alternatives were available.

Evidence from miscellaneous sources suggest that in the nineteenth century and earlier, everyone ate at least a pound (1lb) of bread a day. In the 1760s London bakers had a rule of thumb that said an individual consumed one Quarter (8 bushels) of wheat per annum. At the time this amounted to about 450-480lbs, which works out to about

$1^{1}/_{4}$lbs per person per day. In Nelson's navy a seaman was issued a weekly ration which included 7lbs of bread and 3 pints of oatmeal. A 1927 reference said that a family of four needed 24 bushels of wheat per annum to keep from starvation and this works out at 1lb per day. In Asia it was said that a family of seven needed 60 bushels of rice/wheat per annum, which is the equivalent of 1.4lbs per person per day.

This daily minimum of 1lb of bread is also borne out by British institutional diets of the time for such people as soldiers and inmates of prisons, asylums and workhouses. One local example is that of Ruthin Gaol – 15 miles north of Felin Lyn – where prisoners were fed the following monotonous and deficient daily diet in 1851: Breakfast and supper – 1 pint of gruel containing $1^{1}/_{2}$ozs of oatmeal; Dinner-$1^{1}/_{2}$lbs of bread and 1lb of boiled potatoes, to which on three days a week a little diced meat was added. (Note 2.2)

For this study of Felin Lyn, the convenient figure of 1lb of bread per person per day will be taken as a 'benchmark' measure for all calculations in this book. It may be a trifle conservative, since so much of man's and woman's work was so intensely physical in those days.

As well as bread, other cereals were also eaten in relatively generous amounts in such forms as porridge, gruel, soups and various forms of sweetened breads. It is entirely possible that in winter, at least half the food intake of a Welsh person was in grain in one form or another. In this century, things have radically altered, for British bread consumption in 1940 was $^{1}/_{2}$lb per person per day and since has fallen to $^{1}/_{4}$lb.

Now we are in a position confidently to say that the primary function of Felin Lyn in much of the last century was to grind a minimum of 1lb of wheaten flour per day for each person who lived in the neighbourhood. Its second function, and almost as important, was to provide grist for animal feeding.

Locally Grown Grains

The preceding discussion about bread in human diets may have unintentionally focused attention on wheat, the best bread flour, but it must be made clear at the start that wheat has never been the prime cereal in Wales or any part of the uplands of Britain. One Welsh nineteenth century farmer characterised the problem of growing wheat by saying; *"It has long been grown in small amounts on the most favourable hillsides, but with an unpredictable yield from season to season"*. In the Ceiriog, oat was king and barley and wheat shared second place equally.

Until this century oats were the principal cereal crop of Wales or, for that matter, all the 'uplands' of Britain. This was determined by geography and climate. The oat is a hardy plant that thrives on shallow, but not poor, soils in a cool damp climate and will tolerate more soil acidity than wheat or barley. It used to be seen growing on the Welsh uplands to about the 1,200 feet level, but nowadays is totally eclipsed by barley which is usually not grown above the 600 feet level. Oats lost its pre-eminence in Wales when the horse gave way to the motorised vehicle between the two World Wars, for the bulk of the crop was destined as horse feed. (Note 2.3)

Though barley was likely to have been the first cereal grown in Britain, oats have always been associated with the uplands and more barren parts of the British Isles. It would appear from phrases in the English language that the oat was a staple grain in a considerable part of Britain in earlier times. For instance, we do not say 'To sow one's wild barley' or 'To feel one's barley'. An army haversack used to hold field rations and originally must have held oatmeal because in old German 'haber, hafer, haver' meant oats. Incidentally, the oat is not mentioned in the Bible simply because it is a crop quite unsuited to a Mediterranean climate.

Oats, with the exception of wheat for bread making, is considered one of the best all round cereals for man or beast in the northern hemisphere. In older times it was the principal or staple part of an 'uplander's' diet in the form of porridge, addition to stews, oatcakes, and some desserts. As for animals, both the straw and the grain were eaten by horses, cattle and sheep, but not pigs. The other cereals grown in Wales were, and are, barley and wheat. This last sentence should be qualified because some rye was grown in Denbighshire prior to the eighteenth century. It was grown as a bread-making grain and for its thatching straw in the days when most buildings were thatched, prior to the introduction of cheap slating. When technology gave upland mills the capability of milling both soft and hard grains, it was superseded entirely by wheat, which is a superior bread-maker and an equal as a thatch. Elsewhere in Britain in the 1700s, rye provided one-seventh of the population with its bread grain.

Barley was used as stock feed for dairy cows and pigs and for making beer. Barley grain was always fed to the miller's animal, the pig, because that animal cannot handle the high husk content of oats. Wheat, a valuable human bread food, was never given to animals except for the low grade by-products of milling which were indigestible to man. Wheat achieved its eminence as a bread flour because of its gluten content which assists a loaf to rise and is markedly superior to barley and oats in that regard.

Wheat is a deep rooted plant that likes rich loams or clays and needs a mean summer temperature of at least 55°F for three to four months to ripen. It requires plenty of sunshine. It is generally ill-suited to Wales, though the Vale of Clwyd in the north-east of the Principality is one of the exceptions.

Virtually all of Wales has at least 30 inches of rain per year and most of it suffers also from having at least nine inches of it in the months of June, July, and August. This does not favour wheat growth. Compare this with the eighteenth and nineteenth century bread basket of England, in East Anglia where the annual rainfall averaged 22-30 inches and there were minimal summer rains.

Notwithstanding the less than favourable soil and climate conditions, wheat was being grown at Chirk over 700 years ago; and in the last century in the vicinity of Felin Lyn there was as much wheat grown as barley.

A brief reference should be made to the botanical aspect of these three grasses which man has learned to cultivate over the last 3,000 to 6,000 years. A quick look at the accompanying drawings of these plants shows that barley and wheat have some similarities but that oats are quite different. This difference caused problems for a miller and the housewife who had to bake the daily bread, and earlier still for the prehistoric hut-wife before there were watermills.

Oats bear the grain in a tuft or crest, in contrast to barley and wheat which are carried in ears, and women have always experienced the greatest of difficulty in separating the hull of the oat from its kernel. Prehistoric woman very early on discovered that the application of heat was the most effective method and the system is in use to this day. The use of heat was at first primitive and drastic, but by the time Felin Lyn was built the method had become sophisticated and is described in a later chapter.

Reverting to the subject of cereal growing in the Ceiriog, oats and barley, and later wheat, were grown in previous centuries mainly on the hilltops at an average elevation of 1,200 feet, which is virtually the maximum growing altitude in Britain for these crops. This situation had been forced upon the farmers because the valley bottom of the Ceiriog is narrow and was used to produce hay crops and for pasture. The steep lower slopes were quite unsuited to tillage and this left the treeless and flattish hilltops as the only places suitable for cultivation. Almost every generalisation has its exceptions and in the case of the Parish of Glyn Traian there was an area south of Llwynmawr where the hill flanks had more gentle gradients and it was quite feasible in places to grow arable crops.

The Mill's Function

In order to understand how Felin Lyn was worked as a commercial venture, it is worth placing it in historical perspective within Dyffryn Ceiriog and surrounding districts.

In this history we are not concerned with periods earlier than 1775 but a small digression to earlier times is pertinent. In Britain and Europe early mills were built and owned by the local feudal lord, and this lord insisted that all his tenants, or serfs, take their corn to his mill for grinding. In the process the miller, a superior kind of tenant, took a measured portion of the corn which was a three part payment. The parts consisted of a service fee to the miller, a contribution to the maintenance of the mill, and a legitimate tax and/or an unjustified 'rake-off' to the

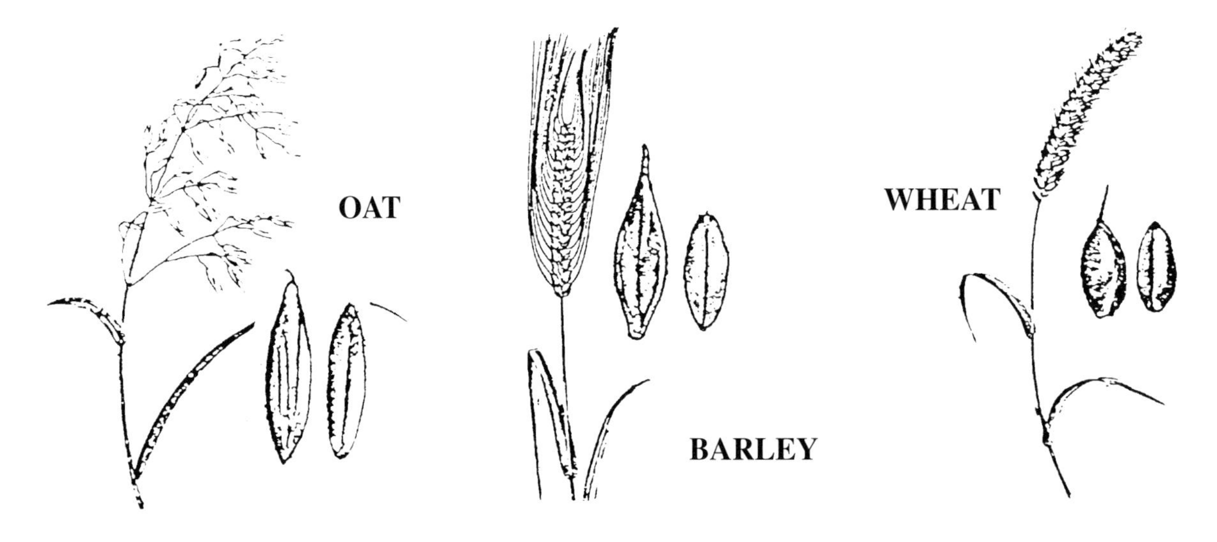

lord. The arrangement resulted in centuries of bad feelings between tenants, millers and their feudal lords.

This system existed in the Ceiriog after Chirk Castle was built, for the Castle records of 1331-32 (20 years after it was built) state that free tenants had to pay 'treth melin' (mill tax) in lieu of being forced to go to the lord's mill. (See Appendix X)

As the centuries progressed the power of the local lord slowly diminished and that of his tenants correspondingly increased, so that by about the 1600s the system was becoming one of private enterprise rather than feudal domination. Felin Lyn was built by a landowner (who happened to be the owner of the Lordship of Chirk) as a form of business investment, letting it out at a healthy rent to a miller tenant. The miller in turn made his living by charging a fee in grain or money for grinding corn. This method of operation was called Toll milling. At the very end of watermilling was a phase called Trading milling, which is a kind of postscript to the history of grinding local corn at a country mill.

Until the fourth quarter of the nineteenth century the cornmill was an essential part in the highly localised food chain of any community in Britain. Man has eaten crushed grain for at least 5,000 years and some type of milling is essential to his digestion, whether the process is done by hand-operated quern, mortar and pestle, stone mill, or present day rollers. The processing of cereals was very much a local matter and up to about 125 years ago the cornmill dominated the process; it was the converter at the half-way mark in the food chain.

The farmer grew his grain, harvested and stored it, and at frequent intervals brought it to the local mill to have it processed. Prior to the nineteenth century, the miller retained a small portion of the grain, ranging from a sixteenth up to an eighth, as recompense for his services and the remainder went back to the farmer. In fact, the practice continued into this century in places. Most times the miller purchased excess wheat from the farmers, ground it to flour, and sold it to those inhabitants who did not grow corn or who possessed little or no land.

The process was an uncomplicated one in which the farmer visited the mill between ten and twenty-five times a year with his batch of grain and received back his meal and flour.

Because the local inhabitants could not survive long without their local mill, it assumed an importance not readily apparent in today's supermarket world. Many in the community had occasion to visit it several times a year, and so it became a focal point where people met, much as the country store and the railway station became in later years. It was here that information, gossip, and deals were traded. The mill also had a certain mechanical kudos in the vicinity as it was the only example of a machine or 'engine' in that locality.

But all this, with centuries of tradition behind it, suddenly changed. North America, with its vast newly cultivated lands and minuscule labour force, perfected the mechanical harvesting of grain before anyone else in the world. At the same time safe and reliable transportation across the North Atlantic, in the form of steam driven iron ships, became a fact. The result was that North American wheat, superior in bread-making characteristics and cheaper than British wheat, arrived in great quantities in the British Isles in the last quarter of the nineteenth century.

The localised cereal food chain took only some twenty years to be destroyed and corn grinding mills were left with but three alternatives. They could close down and this was usually the fate of mills that were mechanically obsolescent, poorly maintained or ineptly run; a second possibility was to make the waterwheel drive some other equipment or process, like the turning of wooden bobbins for the cotton trade or generating electricity; or thirdly, the mill could continue to grind corn but would be managed in an entirely different way; this was to be known as *Trading* milling.

A Trading miller was a businessman in his own right. He purchased grain from a limited number of sources, frequently a Corn Exchange, and ground it into animal food which he sold to a limited number of customers, some of them not local.

In the Ceiriog, Felin Lyn successfully made the transition from Toll to Trading mill, as did Chirk Mill. The cornmill at Glynceiriog gave up the struggle altogether and its structure was absorbed into the next-door woollen mill, whilst the one at Tregeiriog continued to work but in what mode is not known. These two phases of Toll and Trading will now be examined in detail. The history of Felin Lyn as a Tolling mill is arrived at circumstantially because no documents of any kind survive, but as a Trading mill it is based on personal recollections and recently discovered tramway invoices.

Territory and Tolling

Any mill anywhere could only operate if it had an economically satisfactory *territory* from which it obtained its grain supplies. The size of this territory was determined quite simply. Its top limit was equal to the maximum capacity of the mill and its bottom limit was the area required to give a miller an adequate livelihood. The delineation of a mill's 'territory' is crucial to understanding what amounts of grain a mill processed in a year. Curiously, scant attention has been paid to this matter in modern milling literature.

It would appear that the average size of a Tolling mill's *territory* ranged between four and eight square miles. The *Domesday Book* of 1086 lists 5,264 mills and shows that there existed a mill for about every five square miles across a wide range of counties from Dorset to Norfolk and that each mill served some 50 households. The Tithe maps for Cheshire in the period 1839-40 showed some 250 cornmills in use, or about one mill for every four square miles. (Note 2.4)

No research work has been published on the density of mills in Denbighshire, but it is likely that there would have been fewer mills per square mile than in Cheshire because of a smaller population. Their distribution would have been uneven because of the terrain – proportionately more in the Vale of Clwyd than the uplands, for example.

All the foregoing has been mentioned because we have to guess the size and extent of the land that Felin Lyn serviced, or its milling territory. The ledgers mentioned in Chapter 1 would have provided clues but today we do not have any direct evidence.

In feudal times, farms were allocated to a particular mill by the local lord but by the time Felin Lyn was built in the late 1700s there was no compulsion or direction. Custom and convenience probably decided that a farmer used the mill nearest to him, and only if he disliked the miller's methods or manners might he go elsewhere.

There is an example of a farm in the Parish of Glyn Traian that used another watermill because of access problems. This was Plas-onn, which is a mountain top farm at the 1,000 feet level lying to the south of Pontfadog and close to a road system that led eastwards to the village of Weston Rhyn in Shropshire. It was easier for the farmer of Plas-onn to take his grain $2^1/_2$ miles down a fairly evenly graded road to Selattyn mill, than to go only $1^1/_2$ miles to Felin Lyn down a sharply descending lane. Whether going up or down hill, he would be carrying a heavy load.

A rare view of Felin Lyn taken in 1908. looking south-west and up-valley. The building nearest the camera is the barn. The millrace ran under the lane at the left of the photograph and passed between the barn and the mill; it fed the waterwheel obscured by the left end of the barn and directly in line with the roof apex. The tailrace exited from a culvert at the edge of the yard and becomes a thin line parallelling the bottom edge of the photograph. The former oat kiln is the nearest left-sided part of the main building and is fitted with a prominent ventilator. Notice also the 'sentry box' privy at the edge of the yard.
The Afon Ceiriog is identified by the line of trees and the 1894 steel bridge in the mid-section of the view. The lane at to the right leads to the valley main road and in the opposite direction proceeds to Llwynmawr. The farm in the centre middle distance is Pandy Bach, which was purchased by the last full-time miller of Felin Lyn in the 1920s.
Author's grandfather.

A mill's territory was not something committed to paper or drawn with boundaries on a map, but a miller would know in his head the area he served. If we wish to understand the mechanics of how Felin Lyn was operated, it is necessary to estimate the extent of this Mill's territory. We may not deduce the precise limits but we shall have a good enough picture.

Any territory is partly determined by the siting of neighbouring mills. In the case of Felin Lyn, the north and south boundaries were determined by the mountain tops, for beyond these were more valleys with their own watermills. To the west the boundary would be somewhere between Felin Lyn and the next upstream mill which was at Dolywern. However this mill was inoperable for much of the life of Felin Lyn and so an arbitrary decision has been taken to make the boundary halfway between Felin Lyn and the next upstream mill above Dolywern. To the east and downstream there had been a small mill at the hamlet of Castlemill but by 1800 it was closed or was about to be. This left the large Chirk Mill, the nearest mill to the east, being two miles downstream from Castlemill. It seems reasonable to conclude that the eastern boundary was at Offa's Dyke, near Castlemill. This makes for a rough rectangle of three miles by two miles, giving a minimal area of six square miles; other arguments could probably stretch it to eight square miles.

This supposed territory of Felin Lyn happens to sit within the boundaries of the Parish of Glyn Traian, though it predates this newish Parish by several centuries. It is interesting to see that on two sides the boundaries of the Parish and the territory are identical.

We are now in a position to make a guess as to the acreage of this 'territory'. The Parish of Glyn Traian contains 7,830 acres or $11^{1}/_{2}$ square miles. There are 640 acres to a square mile. Making an arbitrary decision that the territory of Felin Lyn contained seven square miles, then it covered 4,480 acres. This represents 57% of the area of the Parish, but to make the mathematics easier and also to deny that the figures have that amount of precision, let us suppose that the territory was six-tenths the size of the Parish or 4,700 acres.

Corn Harvest

Having estimated the approximate size of Felin Lyn's territory, it is now necessary to estimate the amount of corn grown on it annually in the last century. By a piece of good fortune, this proved easier than anticipated and has a fair degree of accuracy.

The first modern British farming statistics were collected in 1853 as a pilot project covering the counties of Hampshire and Norfolk, and the Board of Trade decided that eleven selected counties should be covered the following year. The two counties selected in Wales were Denbighshire and Brecknockshire.

There being no adequate rural civil service, the survey task was given to the Poor Law Inspectors with the result that they grouped their returns by Poor Law Unions (districts). The Ceiriog lay in the Llanfyllin Poor Law Union and the following statistics are derived from that Union or district.

The table below indicates the acreage under corn as a percentage of farmland in the mid-nineteenth century and provides three comparisons. First is a national figure of 1866, followed by Denbighshire as a whole in 1854, and then a localised area inclusive of the Ceiriog derived from the same survey. (Note 2.5)

Table 1

Acreage under corn as a percentage of farmland

Locality	*Oats*	*Barley*	*Wheat*	*Total*
Great Britain, 1866	9.6%	7.8%	11.7%	29.1%
Denbighshire, 1854	7.0%	5.3%	5.7%	18.0%
Llanfylin Poor Law Union, 1854	2.8%	2.9%	2.4%	8.1%

It is believed that farms at Chirk had a productivity similar to Denbighshire as a whole and that Pontfadog – because of its close proximity to Chirk – could not have suffered so sharp a decline in cereal cropping as indicated by the Llanfyllin figures. As a consequence, a 'guestimate' has been made for the farming area around Pontfadog which is about halfway between the Llanfyllin and Denbighshire returns.

Grain Type: Territory of Felin Lyn

Types of grain	Oats	Barley	Wheat	Total
Acreage put to grain:	5.0%	3.75%	3.5%	12.25%

Using these percentages of corn crops, it is now possible to calculate the corn acreage within the Mill's territory, which in the preceding Section was estimated to be 4,700 acres.

Grain Acreages: Territory of Felin Lyn

Oats:	5.00%	of 4,700 acres	= 235 acres
Barley:	3.75%	of 4,700 acres	= 175 acres
Wheat:	3.50%	of 4,700 acres	= 165 acres
Totals:	12.25%	of 4,700 acres	= 575acres (corn)

There are no statistics relating to harvest yields of cereals in and about Pontfadog, but from a variety of sources an approximation can be formed. The 1849 figures for South Wales come from an entry in the Journal of the Royal

Agricultural Society of England; the 'Wales 1896-1905' entry comes from Government returns; the world wide statistics provided by United Nations include the undeveloped countries of the Third World and are given here for comparison.

Table 2
Cereal yields in bushels per acre

Cereal	*South Wales 1849*		*Wales 1896 to 1905*	*World 1959 to 1961*
	Superior land	*Inferior land*		
Oats	32 bu	24 bu	33.4 bu	37 bu
Barley	36	28	30.6	26
Wheat	24	15	25.5	18

An 1839 source gives the average yield of wheat for England as 26 bushels per acre. Since a bushel is a measure of volume, and not of weight, it is necessary to convert bushels to pounds (lbs) and this has been done by using the nineteenth century weights quoted immediately below. Present day rates are also quoted to provide comparisons.

Period	Oats	Barley	Wheat
For 19th century	32lbs/bu	48lbs/bu.	60 lbs/bu.
(Present day rates)	(42lb/bu)	(56lb/bu)	(63lb/bu)

[For those readers unfamiliar with the volume unit 'bushel', please refer to Appendix II; where abbreviated it will appear as 'bu'.]

Another factor to be considered in these calculations is the uncertainty of any harvest. There are a few despairingly bad years counterbalanced by exceptionally good years, but for the most part the swing of the corn crop is in the order of 5-7% on either side of the average. (Total swing or range: oats, 10%; barley, 11%; wheat, 14%).

We are now in a position to estimate the likely corn harvest in the territory of Felin Lyn for any fairly ordinary year in the 19th century.

First, from the table 'Cereal yields in bushels per acre', an arbitrary, but reasonable, average yield has been established. It is: oats at 32 bushels/acre; barley at 29 bushels/acre; wheat at 24 bushels/acre.

Table 3 below shows likely yields for three types of harvest: poor, average, good. The 'poor' and 'good' harvests represent the maximum swings about the average.

The mathematical exactitude illustrated in the table above must give way to common sense. In the first place, all the factors in the equation have been estimated, or guessed at with care. Alter any one of the factors and obviously the results are going to differ. In the second place, in any given harvest not all three grains will perform consistently poorly or well; for example, oats could be 'good' and wheat 'average'.

As a result, the table needs to be rounded off. One can come to the conclusion that the lands of Felin Lyn's territory produced in an average harvest about 320 tons of grain. A poor harvest would give about 10% less and a good harvest 10% more.

A startling aspect of the table is that the tonnage produced for each type of grain is identical, though one started out with different acreages, differing conversion factors from bushels to lbs, and differing yields per acre. (Note 2.6)

Miller's Compensation

Whilst Felin Lyn was worked as a Toll mill, the miller took a proportion (called *multure* in earlier days) of processed meal or flour as his milling due, or he charged a cash fee based upon the number of bushels of grain he handled. The former system came down from medieval days and varied in Britain by custom and locality. The portion was usually between a sixteenth (6.25%) and an eighth (12.5%). (Note 2.7)

In 1796 an Act of Parliament made it obligatory for a miller to charge cash for his services unless both parties agreed to payment by the traditional portion or 'toll'. The timing of the Act is significant as this was the time of the Napoleonic wars. The Government of the day was anxious to maximise farming productivity and the use of the 'toll' by a devious miller could result in a farmer getting short-

Table 3
Grain harvests from Felin Lyn's territory at 4,700 acres

GRAINS			*POOR*			*AVERAGE*			*GOOD*		
Type of cereal	*Acres of grain*	*lb per bu.*	*bu. per acre*	*Total bu.*	*Long tons*	*bu. per acre*	*Total bu.*	*Long tons*	*bu. per acre*	*Total bu.*	*Long tons*
Oats	235	32	28.8	6768	96	32	7520	107	35.2	8272	118
Barley	175	48	26.1	4568	98	29	5075	109	31.9	5582	120
Wheat	165	60	21.6	3564	95	24	3960	106	26.4	4356	117
Totals	**575**	—	—	**14,900**	**288**	—	**16,555**	**322**	—	**18,210**	**355**

changed. Making the miller accept cash for his services made it that much more difficult for a dishonest miller to extract grain during processing, and at the same time removed a legitimate grievance held by many farmers throughout Britain.

The feeling that millers cheated on their customers was widespread and was certainly held by Welsh farmers. This is confirmed in a lyrical way by the poet, John Ceiriog Hughes (1832-87), whose bardic name was 'Ceiriog'. He wrote a poem, or else recorded another's work, called *Ymgom-y-Felin* or 'The Mill Chat'. It is about a conversation between a young observant farmer and a wily old miller, with the farmer making certain that he is not double-tolled. At one point the miller soliloquises and this is what he has to say.

Pe bai pob cwsmer fel efe?	What if all my customers were like him ?
Chawn i ddim siwgwr yn fy nhe;	I'd have no sugar in my tea
Na bara bwff, na theisen fraith	Nor buff bread, nor bara brith
Na menyn efo'n nhatws chwaith	Nor butter spread upon my potatoes
Roedd nhad a nhaid a nheidiau	My father, grandad and forebears
Yn dwbwl dolli'r yd	Double-tolled the corn
Heb fawr o feddwl deuai'r	Without ever thinking such a change
Fath newid ar y byd, –	Would come to our lives
Ymhell bo'r bobol 'raian,	Far are the people now that weigh
Sy'n pwyso'r yd a'r blawd;	The corn and the flour
Yn wir; mae'r byd yn galed	Really, times are very hard
I hen felinydd tlawd.	For a poor miller.

The Ceiriog was turning to a cash economy by the beginning of the nineteenth century, and it is probable that for the whole of that century the service charge at Felin Lyn was a mixture of toll or cash, each customer being accommodated by the miller.

On many occasions bartering was also resorted to and the miller would grind so much grain in return for such things as medicine, horse-shoeing or family boots. This was evidenced by a credit given by a Glynceiriog joiner in 1919 when making repairs to the Mill as quoted in Chapter 1.

The miller would use the cash to buy food and necessities at local markets such as Oswestry, and to pay taxes, mill running expenses and so on. With what cash residue he had, he purchased more from his farmer customers. To this he added the toll grain he had already acquired and would produce wheaten flour, oatmeal, and maybe malt. This was then sold to about three-quarters, or more, of the population within the mill territory, for these people worked smallholdings too small to produce cereals of their own, or lived in cottages with no more than a garden.

A secondary income came from the sale of pigs. The grinding and bolting (sieving) of grain produces 'dregs' which are unfit for human consumption but make good animal feed. This was a valuable perk for the miller which he fed to his pigs and poultry.

Regrettably there are no details of tolls or charges at Felin Lyn until the last decade of its existence. Several recollections show, perhaps surprisingly, that though now ostensibly a Trading mill, it still tolled to the very end. (Note 2.8)

The late J.W. Davies of Glynceiriog was the first person to compile a history of all the watermills of the Ceiriog. He did this in the 1930s but his work was not published till 1941 when it appeared as a series of articles in an Oswestry newspaper. In one of the articles Davies says the charge at Felin Lyn was 5d per 100lbs of grain or a toll of 10lbs for every 100lbs of grain.

At first glance this charge seems to be a trifle on the low side but $5^{1}/_{2}$d per cwt. (112lbs) stands comparison with a Yorkshire country mill of the same period which was charging 6d per cwt. At the same time, Pentre Mill, near Mold, Flintshire, charged $1^{1}/_{2}$d for a small parcel of 20lbs. This works out at $8^{1}/_{2}$d per hundredweight.

Mr Dewi Jones of Llwynmawr, who has cheerfully acted as the local investigator for this history, says: *"I also recall going, as a boy, with an uncle of mine with corn to grind at Felin Lyn and would agree with J.W. Davies that the charge was about 10lbs of corn per hundredweight. My uncle would take oats and barley every three to four weeks but wheat only twice a year and totalling about three to four hundredweight."*

Mrs Margaret Lewis, aged 91 in 1995, has a different recollection of milling charges. She spent her married life at Crogen Wladys, a farm almost two miles to the east of Felin Lyn. She says; *"From 1927 on my husband took one hundredweight of oats and one hundredweight of barley to the Mill about every fortnight and was charged l/6d in total or 9d per hundredweight. I remember the charge because my husband used to take loose change from the jug on the dresser. On the farm we had about 20 cows which in winter were fed on hay, chopped straw and pulped turnips or swedes and perhaps a little grain feed".*

Another tolling recollection, but of a different kind, comes from Mr. Stan Jeffreys, who lived in the ex-mill as a boy from 1952 to 1962. His comments draw attention to an aspect which is rarely, if ever, mentioned. He writes: *"As I understand it, Ned Evans, the last miller, was seldom paid cash for milling but would take a percentage of the corn. He kept a large number of pigs and would feed them with his miller's share. However, a problem arose whenever there was a poor corn crop, for the miller had to keep his pigs fed and so his toll percentage went up and this led to wrangles with his customers."*

And finally a memory of an unhappy customer. The late Mrs Elizabeth Humphreys of Pontfadog, who died in 1983, said: *"My father, William Thomas, farmed Caecoed, a hill farm not a mile from Felin Lyn. He used to take wheat to the mill but didn't like the levy or grinding charge and moved his custom to Selattyn Mill, which was inconveniently placed being some three or four miles away. This would have been round about the First World War."*

The most recent reference to tolling in the Ceiriog, but unrelated to Felin Lyn, comes in a 1985 letter from the Reverend Alex Davies who, in partnership with his brother, worked Chirk Mill (see Appendix V) from 1938 to 1964. He wrote: *"We were never flourmillers but provender millers grinding and mixing our own feeds. During the war years (1939-45) we were also a toll mill. If memory serves me right, we took 7lb out of every 112lbs ground, or one-sixteenth."*

In reviewing these comments one is struck that there is no mention of bushels, everything is weighed, not volume measured. It may be instructive to imagine two scenes at Felin Lyn separated by 100 years.

It is 1809 and Hugh Edwards has brought two sacks of wheat to the Mill. At the farm he has carefully measured six bushels into the sacks with his own bushel measure, so that he knew exactly what he was taking. This does not imply that Edwards automatically mistrusts the miller but he is a prudent farmer and it has cost him much in toil to plough, plant, weed, harvest, thresh and winnow his grain.

On arrival at the Mill, there is no weighing device because since time immemorial corn has always been measured by volume, with the bushel as the accepted unit. The miller also measures the farmer's parcel by scooping out the wheat with his bushel measure and then emptying it into the hopper above the stones (before the advent of a cleaner). He also finds the parcel to have a volume of six bushels.

The miller takes his toll fee by dipping his toll dish into the wheat. The volume of the dish will be a divisor of a bushel, so an eighth will be one gallon and a sixteenth will be a $^1/_2$ gallon or two quarts. His dish is of $^1/_2$ gallon capacity and since his toll for wheat is an eighth, the miller extracts 16 dishfulls of corn each levelled to the rim. He does this in the presence of Edwards, the owner of the grain. The bran and thirds are also returned to the farmer, less remnants caught in the machinery, troughs and bins. (Some wily millers fixed tiny ledges to their equipment to catch milling products and shook off what was caught before the next customer was processed.)

It is now 1909 and Owain Parry has brought three sacks of barley to Felin Lyn. Parry does not have a scale or bushel measure at his farm and he makes no attempt to weigh or measure the sack contents before he leaves the farm. The miller weighs the sacks on a platform scale in front of Parry and both agree on a weight of 483lbs. The miller's toll is 10% of each cwt. (112lbs), so out comes a pencil and an old envelope; 483 divided by 112 is 4.31, and the miller removes 43lbs of barley with Parry watching the abstraction. The residual 440lbs is bruised by the miller and all of it is returned to Parry, except what is trapped as 'dregs' in the equipment.

Why this change in procedure? It was simply the outcome of industrialisation, commercialism, and the railways. In the last half of the nineteenth century, vast numbers of sacks containing all kinds of commodities were moving across the country by railway or were being held somewhere in temporary storage. A corn factor or a railway agent needed to know the contents by volume or weight for charging purposes but to do this by volume was hopelessly outmoded.

Industrialisation had produced accurate and relatively cheap weighing scales, so measuring by volume was abandoned at the practical level and all was weighed. As to why millers did not charge 10% toll on 100 lbs so as to make the maths easy, one can only say that the British had never thought in metric terms and were quite accustomed to more complex reckoning when dealing with money, weights or measures.

In earlier decades there would have been a tolling dish at Felin Lyn, made of wood or latterly metal. This would have carried an approved government mark as required by the Weights and Measures Acts of 1835 and 1878. Needless to say, the Mill's dish has long since disappeared. (Note 2.9)

Just as the previous chapter attempted to calculate rents and property worth in the absence of direct evidence, so it would be interesting to produce an Income & Expenditure account for any given year in the life of Felin Lyn. What kind of a living did a miller make in any given decade? Again, there is no evidence of any kind but an attempt will be made at a reconstruction in the next Section, when Felin Lyn was operating as a Trading mill.

Trading Era

Because of external-to-Britain marketing forces, all rural cornmills after about 1875-80 faced a new role. Whereas previously they were central to their communities, now they were to become subordinate or even redundant.

A brief look at world trade in grain in the last quarter of the last century will help to explain the silent revolution that descended on all British country mills. In 1880 the six leading grain growing nations in the world (in units of millions of bushels) were: United States (480), France (320), British India (228), Russia (216), Austria-Hungary (168), Italy (120). In 1887 the United Kingdom needed 205 million bushels of wheat to feed its ever-increasing population, but grew only 76 million bushels.

Of the six countries growing large quantities of wheat, Britain imported from three of them – USA, Russia and British India – with two thirds of the total imports coming from the United States. Things changed quickly in this volatile international market; twenty years earlier Russia had been the major exporter and thirty years later it would be Canada, once her prairies had been settled and cultivated.

From 1873 British grain prices took a prolonged and severe descent, except for two wartime periods, and have never regained their former strengths.

Exports soon ousted the localised product and completely altered the links in the food chain – undisturbed for centuries – to the great detriment of British farmers and country cornmills.

The imported American grain was off-loaded at major ports, stored and milled there in steam-driven factories using high speed metal rollers. From these ports the flour was distributed by the newly developed railway system to the then emerging grocery shop or country general store.

It was also soon discovered by bakers, home or commercial, that the North American hard wheat had more gluten in it than the native plants, and so made such wheat preferable as bread flours. Slowly but surely, British wheat was relegated to the making of biscuits, cakes, pastry, and the like, where gluten content is less important. It has been estimated that by 1900 only 20% of all bread eaten in Britain contained British flours, and that most bakers added North American flour to increase the gluten content.

For at least the first hundred years of its life, Felin Lyn was a Toll mill, then at some date between 1875 and 1881 it made a rapid transition to a Trading mill. This can be said with great certainty because of a dramatic local revelation made within the last five years.

During the renovation of a building at Glynceiriog a big ledger was discovered tucked away in the roof space. This ledger contained pasted-in copies of all traffic invoices issued on the Glyn Valley Tramway between September 1881 and April 1883. This tramway ran alongside the 1860s built valley-bottom road and passed within 200 yards of Felin Lyn. It had a unique gauge of exactly half the British standard gauge and the wagons, of two ton capacity, were drawn by horses. It was opened in 1873.

Suddenly the whole of the lower Ceiriog was accessible to all types of merchandise, which could be delivered in one day at reasonable prices. Examination of the invoices

GLYN VALLEY TRAMWAY,

No. ___ Date ___ 188__ From ___ (Station)

INVOICE ARRIVED, 188__ __.m. GOODS ARRIVED,

Reference to Delivery Book	Waggon: Owner	Waggon: No.	No. of Consignment Note	Consignor	Consignee and Residence	No. of Articles	Description

Invoice issued by Glyn Valley Tramway (horse) Company of 19th September 1882. Typical of many transactions. Consignor is E. Evans of Felin Lyn who is sending 7 sacks of meal and corn (probably all maize) to two customers at Glynceiriog, two miles distant.

show the wide range of goods being carried into the Ceiriog, for example: books, chairs, coal, drapery, glass, hay knives, herrings, lead, matches, oranges, saw bench, tank of oil, turnip drill, windows. This influx definitely altered the style of life in the Ceiriog and this included Felin Lyn.

The precious ledger contains nearly 2,000 invoices covering the 18 month period and 135 of them refer to Felin Lyn or to be precise "E. Evans, Glyn Mill, Pontfadog". Some of the Mill invoices were 'incoming' (67) from England and others were 'outgoing' (68) with destinations further up the Ceiriog valley. (Note 2.10)

The inbound deliveries to the Mill were placed on the tramway at Pontfaen. The lower canal-side terminus of the Tramway was at Gledrid so the 'Pontfaen' entry tells us that the shipments had come from the standard gauge railway (G.W.R.) at Chirk and had then been carted for $^3/_4$ mile to the transfer point at Pontfaen. It is thought the shipments originated with a corn factor in Liverpool or Birkenhead. Felin Lyn was the only cornmill in the Ceiriog to use the Tramway.

The delivery point on all 'incoming' invoices is listed as Pontfadog, and not Dolywern the next 'station'. However a slight clue suggests they were dropped off about halfway between these two places at Pandy-bach farm which lay beside the Tramway and 200 yards from Felin Lyn. This would have been an unofficial arrangement but made sense as neither Pontfadog nor Dolywern had freight sheds; what would have happened whenever it rained – as it did frequently?

These invoices are invaluable evidence for they show us what was happening at Felin Lyn in 1881-83; not the whole picture by any means but one of considerable detail. An analysis has been made of all 'in' and 'out' grain movements at the Mill, covered by 83 invoices for the 12 months of 1882.

Edward Evans, the then miller, received 39 deliveries in the year, all of which were in sacks. The largest delivery was 115 sacks on 23 January and the smallest was 20 sacks which happened on eleven occasions. The frequency of delivery varied considerably, from one a month for February and July to the maximum of seven in October, with five in January, June and August. This could suggest a canny miller who was buying when the commodity price hit a low spot. In all, the miller purchased 131 tons of grain in the year which arrived in 1,386 sacks.

The table below gives precise details of the purchases. Seventy percent of the purchases by weight were listed by the generic term 'corn' by the Tramway employees and a suggestion as to what this corn might be is deferred until the outgoing shipments have been examined. This corn always arrived in sacks of 240lbs which is a curious weight as it is not a component of hundredweights (112lbs) or of stones (14lbs). It is however half a Quarter of wheat at 480 lbs (at 60 lbs per bushel). There is also another explanation. The author has come across an old school textbook of the late nineteenth century which included a table with a progression of: three Bushels = one Sack (240lbs); twelve sacks = one Chaldron (2,880lbs).

Table 4
G.V.T invoices in 1882, INCOMING to mill.

Category	*Types*	*No. of sacks*	*Sack weights*	*Long Tons*
Maize	Corn*	863	240lbs	92.5
	Indian corn	130	240lbs	13.9
	Total maize	993	240lbs	106.4
Other grains	Bran	167	100lbs **	7.5
	Smalls	108	112lbs **	5.4
	Wheat	73	250lbs	8.1
	Sharps	30	170lbs **	2.3
	Gurgeons	15	170lbs **	1.0
TOTALS		**1,386**	—	**130.7**

* Listed as such on invoices but deduced to be maize.
** Deduced approximations; all other weights are exact.

The word 'gurgeons' is of interest as it is now an archaic term and suggests French ancestry, going back to the 1400s. It meant a coarse meal, or coarse refuse from flour, or pollard. Pollard in turn means *'bran sifted from flour, finer grade of bran containing some flour, or flour or meal containing finer bran.'* In the context of 1882 it was animal food.

The invoices for the 'outward' shipments from the Mill are equally revealing. They show 26 tons going up-valley to Glynceiriog, Pandy, Tregeiriog, and Llanarmon D.C. All were shipped in sacks weighing 2cwt. (224lbs). These would go on the tramway to its terminus at Glynceiriog and there would be locally delivered in the village or be sent by carrier further up-valley. What is pertinent is that on these shipments the invoices list the grain specifically as 'Indian Meal' (23 tons ground) or 'Indian Corn' (3 tons unprocessed), implying animal feed. There are no deliveries for local grains such as oats, barley or wheat.

So in one year the miller received 131 tons of grain and out of it he shipped 26 tons up-valley consisting solely of maize, processed as meal or still as kernels. It is presumed the residual 105 tons was disposed of within Felin Lyn's territory and the table above suggests it was made up of 80 tons of maize and 25 tons of other products. It seems certain the invoice-listed 'corn' was in fact maize.

Maize is a grain not so far mentioned as it is foreign to the Ceiriog. For human consumption in Britain it is probably only remembered through items such as corn flakes and popcorn but elsewhere in the world it is a staple food. It is the world's second largest cereal crop, outranked only by wheat and for the United States it is its most important crop.

Its other names are corn-on-the-cob and Indian corn, and this produces trans-Atlantic misunderstandings. In Britain, 'corn' denotes the dominant cereal or cereals in a region, whereas in North America this would be termed 'grain', the American word 'corn' being used exclusively for maize; in southern Africa it is called mealies.

Maize is the noblest looking of the cereal grasses and is therefore a grain, even though its fruit suggests otherwise. It was found only in the Americas until Columbus brought some back to Spain and then spread rapidly to the rest of the world. The plant prefers deep, rich, warm soils in climates that must have above 60°F night temperatures, so tends to be grown nearer the Equator providing there is adequate moisture. As a food for humans, it is inferior to most other grains, but is the cereal eaten by much of today's world population. By contrast, it is an excellent food for animals being high in energy, low in crude fibre, and is highly digestible; it is good for livestock fattening and is fed to cattle, pigs, horses and poultry. Bushel weights for maize were rated as: on the cob at 70 lbs; shelled at 56 lbs; meal at 50 lbs.

Maize gained an import foothold in Liverpool as a result of the Irish potato famine of 1845-7. It was allowed in duty free for a year to alleviate the famine which resulted in landings of a million Quarters of maize and 430,000 bushels of its meal. Afterwards the duty of a 1/- per Quarter was re-imposed but it was the beginning of a very large trade. By 1870 maize imports were 50% of wheat imports and wheat was Liverpool's prime import. In 1900 the ratio had moved to 75%, with wheat at 3.8 million Quarters and maize at 2.8 million Quarters. In this century maize became the mainstay of country mills and this included Felin Lyn. It can be regarded as the cereal that prolonged their working lives and should be so acknowledged.

Indian Corn

Returning to the analysis of outgoing shipments up-valley, the table below provides the salient facts.

Table 5

G.V.T invoices in 1882, OUTGOING shipments

Destination	*Road miles**	*No. of sacks (all 224lbs)*			*Long Tons***	*No. of customers*
		Ind. Meal	*Ind. Corn*	*Tot. sacks*		
Glynceiriog	2	140	15	155	15.5	4 +
Pandy	3.5	39	nil	39	3.9	1
Tregeiriog	5.5	28	8	36	3.6	2
Llanarmon D.C.	7	26	5	31	3.1	4
TOTALS (sacks)		**233**	**28**	**261**	—	**11 +**
TOTALS (Tons)**		**23.3**	**2.8**	**26.1**	**26.1**	

* As the horse plods, not as the crow flies. ** @ 2,240lbs.
Sacks of 224 lbs = 16 stones = $^1/_{10}$th of Long Ton.

These up-valley shipments averaged about two to four a month and there was a loose correlation with the grain deliveries made to Felin Lyn; the best example of this being October when the highest number of monthly shipments was made – seven. But there were also gaps in deliveries, the longest being 3-27 June, perhaps due to a lack of water at the Mill. The largest single shipment was one of 21 sacks on 24th November (1882) destined for Glynceiriog, Pandy and Tregeiriog, whilst there were seven instances of one-sack shipments.

A shipment could be entered on an invoice by groupings of sacks, suggesting they were going to different customers. For example, an invoice of 31st July for Glyn lists *"3 sacks Indian Meal, 2 sacks ditto, 1 sack ditto"*. From this listing format it can be deduced that the miller had four or more customers in Glynceiriog, one in Pandy, two in Tregeiriog and four in Llanarmon, or about a dozen all told beyond his territory.

In Chapter 3 it will be theoretically established that Felin Lyn in its Toll era was processing about 250 tons of grain a year. During the conversion to a Trading mill, we see that in 1882 some 130 tons were imported from outside the Mill's territory. So how did the Toll and Trading tonnage integrate? In the absence of another miraculous historical find, it is only possible to speculate.

It is probable the annual tonnage stayed about the same or climbed to close to 300 tons but not much more. Equipment and manpower stayed the same at Felin Lyn, so there were definite upper tonnage limits as to what could be processed.

The most likely grain to be reduced was wheat since housewives must have soon discovered that North American wheat had stronger gluten and so made a better risen loaf. This new style bread would have been seized upon as a different and enjoyable food experience, much as fish and chips, ice cream and pizza were regarded in years to come. A clue that imported flour was usurping local flour is provided by another GVT invoice that is displayed in the Ceiriog Memorial Institute at Glynceiriog. It is dated September 1881 and is for 1 ton 4 cwt. of wheat flour, off-loaded from a canal narrow-boat near Chirk and carried to Glyn by the 'tram'; probably it had been milled on the Mersey estuary.

It has been calculated that Felin Lyn was processing about 90 tons of local wheat into flour when it was a Tolling mill. It is quite possible that this dropped to about 10 tons in a very short time because farmers were growing less wheat and because the miller found sales resistance to his locally-ground flour. His former customers were deserting him for the newly opening grocery shops at Pontfadog, Llwynmawr and Glynceiriog. These offered 'gluten plus' flour at possibly lower prices. The practice of bringing wheat to Felin Lyn did not die out completely for we have evidence of it still happening in the early 1930s.

In 1882 it is conceivable that the mix of processed grains at the Mill was as follows: imports, 130 tons; barley, 90 tons; oats, 60 tons; wheat, 10 tons; total 290 tons. It is however no more than an imperfect guess.

As the years advanced from about 1875 to 1935, so did the ratios alter, with less and less grain coming from the territory and more and more being imported from Liverpool. However a dwindling handful of farmers continued to use Felin Lyn as a Toll mill until it ceased full-time working in 1936.

We are indebted to the late Mrs. Jones (FL) for the following account of Trading milling at Felin Lyn during the final twenty years of the Mill's operation. *"My father ground farmers' grain up to World War I but afterwards he branched out grinding Indian Corn (maize), though continuing to grind for a few local farmers. Up to 1934 he used to go to Liverpool Corn Exchange once a week to order Indian Corn, bran and thirds; these products are all used for animal and poultry feed. These goods were brought to Chirk, first by the Shropshire Union Canal to the early 1920s, and then by the Great Western Railway. I have postcards sent by the G.W.R. announcing the arrival of orders, and my father used to fetch the order from Chirk with his two-wheeled cart.*

Latterly, say after 1930, the orders were brought by lorry, hired from Gobowen, which on its return journey used to deliver Indian meal, bran and thirds, to farms in Rhiwlas on the Llanarmon-Oswestry road and to other places. My father made a brisk trade in these animal feeds selling to farmers and local shops, but by now there was not a good living in grinding farmers' grain as many farmers had their own oil engines for grinding oat/barley animal foods. At this period the only wheat flour he sold was flour already milled that he had purchased in Liverpool or from Peates Mill at Maesbury, south of Oswestry."

A partial list of post World War I customers of Felin Lyn was supplied by Mrs. Jones (FL) and is given in Appendix VI. The 'thirds' mentioned by Mrs Jones was the third product resulting from wheat milling, the first and second being flour and bran. It was the residue of the operation and farmers would mix it with other feed as a cheap substitute for maize – Indian meal.

The late Tom Roberts (1906-1987), who worked the 100-acre Bonc Farm, a quarter of a mile south of Llwynmawr, after World War I, made these comments in 1985 about the effect oil engines had on corn watermills: *"We all took our corn to be ground at Felin Lyn until about the mid-1930s when we and other neighbours purchased oil engines to crush our own grain"*. This crushed grain was livestock feed which meant it was barley and oats.

These references to oil engines are of interest because they show that the tottering rural cornmills of the 1920s and 1930s were given the coup-de-grace by this mechanical upstart. An 'oil engine' is a small stationary internal combustion engine using paraffin oil as its fuel and was first produced about 1900. Typical models ranged from 1-5hp and became popular and affordable between the World Wars. Many were purchased by farmers to do a variety of chores, including the coarse grinding of animal feeds, and so became the first 'on-site' source of mechanical power on a great many British farms. In the Ceiriog these oil engines were outmoded only by the advent of tractors – first seen in Glyn Traian in 1942 – and by post-war rural electrification.

An attempt will now be made to construct a hypothetical Income and Expense Account for Felin Lyn for year 1912. This is being done, not so much as to try and find the monetary truth, but rather to look at the mechanics of how the miller sought a profit each year.

The year 1912 was selected because the author came across a study of wheat flour milling costs which covered a period commencing in 1911. The study examined the costs of 30 large milling companies in Britain, so its scope was national. (Note 2.11)

The study showed $3^1/_2$cwt. (392lb) of wheat (5 parts Canadian and 1 part English) produced one sack of flour of regulation 280lbs at a 72% extraction rate. This term 'extraction rate' means that out of 100% grain, 72% of it became fine flour and the residual 28% was classified as 'offal'. This offal contained the bran, germ, and other parts of the grain berry that defied fine grinding and nutritionally was the better part of the whole. It conveniently weighed exactly 1cwt.(112lbs).

For the period 1911-13 the mean price of $3^1/_2$ cwt of wheat was £1-9-2d, the mean price of a sack of flour was £1-10-3d and the mean price of 1 cwt. of offal was 5/10d. This meant a factory mill purchased £1-9-2d in wheat and recouped £1-16-1d in flour and offal sales, giving a margin or gross profit of 6/11d. Out of this margin had to be paid steam power, coal, wages, fabric and machinery maintenance, product distribution, taxes, and so on.

The study refrained from publishing confidential data about operating expenses and profits. However, another source of 1910 quoted direct costs of 2/3d per sack of 280lbs and total costs of 3/1d per sack. For want of anything better these expenses will be integrated with the study. If total costs of 3/1d are subtracted from gross profits of 6/11d a net profit of 3/10d is obtained from what started out as 392lbs of wheat. This gives a net profit of 11.7 pence (call it 1/-) per cwt. (112lbs). It is worth itemising these prices and profits for the period just prior to World War I.

Per Hundredweight (112 lbs) of Raw Materials	
Raw wheat (usually milled at a port)	8/4d
Bleached Wheat flour	8/8d
Offal (left-overs from milling)	1/8d
Net/clear profit (questionable zone)	1/-

A country watermiller would have none of the economies of scale of 'big brother', nor would his expectations of profit be the same. All that these national figures do is to give us a perception, an upper limit, of what profits might be made at a country mill.

At this time toll charges appeared to be about 10% of the value of the product before grinding. In 1910 the average national prices for home grown oats and barley were 6/3d and 6/6d per cwt., respectively. This gives a Toll charge of $7^1/_2$d per cwt.of 112lbs.

This charge would have been applied in the circumstances of where the farmer owned the grain and both delivered and collected it from the mill. Presumably this Toll was set to cover the miller's operating costs and provide him with a wage. When the miller became a *Trader,* finances altered appreciably. He was now taking a risk, he had to find money to pay for bulk purchases, he had to pay freight costs to get grain to his mill, he had to absorb delivery costs, and finally he had to make a profit. If he was receiving $7^1/_2$d per cwt. as a toller, what did he need to charge as a trader? For this exercise it is assumed to be twice as much, at ls 3d per cwt., and even that may be on the low side.

Putting all this together and using a heavy dash of imagination produces the following set of accounts. The cost of the purchased grain has been omitted from both sides of the ledger.

Hypothetical Income and Expense Account, Felin Lyn, 1912

INCOME	
Sale @ 1/3d *mark-up* per cwt. on 200 tons of Trade (imported) grain	£312
Receipt @ $7^1/_2$d *Toll* per cwt. of 50 tons of local grain	£31
Subsidiary income (offal sales, etc.)	£50
Sale of Pigs*	£50
Total	**£443**

EXPENSES	
Freight charges re Mersey grain and local delivery expenses	£135
Mill maintenance and repairs	£50
Rent and local taxes	£40
Smallholding expenses/purchase livestock	£30
Purchased food	£30
Clothing, other essentials, coal	£70
All else: chapel, train trips, sickness	£50
Total	**£405**

Annual profit = £38

(*Sale of pigs. Millers always had this secondary income. There were usually two litters a year, each of nine piglets. In 1911-13 the dead meat pork price was 7d per lb and so would have produced an income of about £50 in the year.)

In all likelihood the miller acted like anyone of us today in that he lived up, or down to, his income and managed to save very little.

If nothing else, this somewhat risky exercise of looking at a miller's finances has been included to stimulate other mill enthusiasts and social researchers to further investigation of such an important topic. Individuals and businesses have always been pre-occupied with the generation of income so it seems essential to deal with this aspect, as it related to Felin Lyn, even if the above scenario and deductions are lightweight.

Transportation to and from Felin Lyn

Prior to 1800 virtually all transportation of goods within the uplands of Wales was done by pack-horse, mule or donkey. These animals were fitted with balancing side panniers of wicker, or wooden freight saddles, and carried a wide variety of goods including wool, cloth, coal, mineral ores, slates and corn. This method was in use in the Ceiriog until the 1860s, and the most downstream of all bridges over the Afon Ceiriog (below Chirk) bears testimony to this day to this style of transport as it is a narrow pack-horse bridge.

The 'road' pattern in the district consisted of ancient tracks which followed the spines of the open mountain tops on either side of Dyffryn Ceiriog; these ran in an east-west direction. There were connectors at right angles which ran down one valley side and up the other to meet the next 'spine' track. Naturally this network did not have the symmetry suggested by this description, and at Pontfadog the cross valley lanes had to accommodate themselves to the hilly terrain which involved descents of about 600 feet from the mountain tops to Felin Lyn on the valley floor.

Most of these trackways are still in use today, though tarred and used by motor traffic, and some have gradients as steep as 1 in 4. One casualty was a medieval lane that ran from the back of Felin Lyn, past Minafon and along the side of the hill slope, into the side valley of Gwryd. Presumably it fell into disuse when the flat bottom lands were cleared and cultivated in the late 1700s and a new bottom lane was made. This had been an important link for it connected the township farm of Nantgwryd with its mill and in recent times has been designated a public footpath.

Local access to the Mill from the north side of Afon Ceiriog was by means of a cart ford, the causeway being lined with flat stones. This lay less than 50yds from the millyard. In and before 1875 there was a footbridge beside the ford which was a necessity in winter and at other periods when the river was in spate.

The typical load of a pack horse or mule was 200 to 300lb, but probably 250lb was the norm. This load equates to about 8 bushels of oats, 5 bushels of barley, or 4 bushels of wheat. Because sacks have to be of common size,

A 1908 view looking down-valley (eastwards) in vicinity of Felin Lyn. The mill roof can just be made out, obscured by trees, at centre right and at 4 o'clock to Brynhyfryd on the hillside; Graig hamlet in the distance. The two fields marked with an 'X' were part of the Mill smallholding. The course of the Afon Ceiriog, spanned by the iron bridge, is tree-lined. In the foreground is Pandy Bach farm and the valley main road, edged by the Glyn Valley Tramway.

irrespective of their grain content, sacks were developed to carry 3 or more bushels, and the pack animal carried one sack in each pannier or side-saddle, each of equal weight. This suggests that a typical parcel of corn delivered to a mill by a pack animal held about 250lb of wheat or about 180lb of oats.

Three recollections at-or-before the turn of the century give specific load weights. One was for a donkey load of two sacks of wheat, each holding 6 pecks or $1^1/_2$ bushels, or about 90lbs each side. The other was a pony load of wool consisting of four sacks; there was an 80lb sack on each side, a 90lb sack straddling them and then finally a 50lb sack placed lengthwise, the whole totalling 300lbs. The third recollection simply said that $2^1/_2$ bushels were carried on each side; if this was wheat it would total 300lbs.

Commercial pack-train haulers in previous centuries had to be licensed by county Justices of the Peace and their rates were set annually or periodically. In the early 1800s typical rates would have been $^1/_2$d per cwt. per mile in summer and $^3/_4$d in winter.

Another traditional form of transportation was the carrying of one sack of grain across the back of a horse from farm to mill and returning with a bag of flour. A forebear of the author describes one such journey. (Note 2.12)

Two-wheeled carts probably appeared in the Ceiriog in the early part of the last century, but their cost and the poor condition of the 'road' system would have delayed their acceptance and general use.

In 1863 a toll road was built along the Ceiriog valley bottom as far west as Glynceiriog. At first it was little used because of poor construction, poor maintenance, and the tolls imposed. However it radically altered the focus of living and travel because for the first time dwellings were built in the valley bottom and movement in and out of the district was also along the valley bottom, instead of the age-old movement along the hillsides or mountain tops.

Ten years later, in 1873, a narrow-gauge horse-drawn tramway was built from the Shropshire Union canal at Gledrid, one mile south of Chirk, to Glynceiriog, much of it running along the edge of the toll-road. A refinement came to this railway in 1888 when steam traction was introduced and a more convenient lower terminus was built adjacent to Chirk Station of the Great Western Railway. At the same time all road tolls were removed in Denbighshire. There is no reference or recollection whatsoever as to the part the Glyn Valley Tramway played in delivering maize and other grains to Felin Lyn, in its steam-traction period 1888-1935. It is felt it continued the horse-days practice of carrying grain to Pandy Bach farm from Chirk (GWR or canal trans-shipment) from 1888 to sometime after World War I. The daughter of Edward Evans II said that at times he would collect some of his Mersey grain at Chirk GWR station himself; it is thought this was a post-1920 practice. His two-wheeled cart could carry one ton and the eight-mile round trip would have taken half a day. (Note 2.13)

Suddenly within a space of 25 years, Felin Lyn found itself within 200 yards of a modern transportation system instead of being in a rural backwater. This brought no comfort to Felin Lyn, for the penetration of such a previously isolated community and the simultaneous introduction of cheap grains from North America swiftly eroded the local importance of Felin Lyn and eventually led to its demise.

In the immediate vicinity of the Mill, the last improvement in the transport system was the building of an iron girder bridge, of 32 feet length, to span the Afon Ceiriog. This was done in 1894 and replaced the old ford; an extant plate records that the upgrading was performed by the Llangollen Road Improvement Board.

From 1920 onwards the last miller of Felin Lyn took full advantage of these transport facilities when he made his weekly purchasing journey to Liverpool. On his trip day he would leave the Mill just after 8a.m. and walk a field's length to the valley main road where he would take the steam tram. In twenty five minutes he would be at the joint stations of the Glyn Valley Tramway and the G.W.R. at Chirk, and would promptly join a standard gauge train which took him to Chester. By 11a.m. he had been deposited in the centre of Liverpool. A convenient returning train gave him just over five hours to conduct his business in the city, and by 7 p.m. he was back with his family at Felin Lyn.

The Llwynmawr side-road that passed the Mill was tarred and covered with granite chippings after World War I but the lane behind the Mill that leads to the Graig was never tarmacked whilst the Mill was operating.

Prior to World War II, as no farmer owned a tractor in Felin Lyn's territory and possibly in the whole of the Ceiriog, it can be said that all local carrying to and from the Mill was done by horsepower. This would take the earlier forms of pack-horse and later of two-wheeled cart. The only exception was the motor lorry, mentioned earlier by Mrs Jones (FL), which was used in the last decade of the Mill's life.

Four-wheeled horse-drawn wagons were to be seen in the area but none called at Felin Lyn. They were used on the mountain tops for harvesting, or for distribution of goods from Chirk along the valley main road. Such wagons kept to their own levels and never descended or ascended the hills. A remembered favourite was a covered wagon drawn by three horses that distributed flour and other grain products up-valley from Chirk Mill until about 1910-14.

This local memory fits the specification of a 'miller's wagon' which was a distinctive type of wagon used throughout much of Britain. It was a sturdy four-wheeled affair with a flat deck and spindle sides, fitted with hoops and canvas (called a *tilt*) to make a roof within which a man could stand. It was pulled by two horses abreast, with sometimes a third ahead, and was capable of carrying a two-to-three-ton load. Such wagons were traditionally painted yellow and were still being made up to the beginning of this century.

Sometime between 1908 and 1913 road steam wagons also entered the Ceiriog carrying flour and related products. They came in non-overlapping periods from mills at Wrexham, Llangollen, and Maesbury (south of Oswestry in Shropshire) and made deliveries to stores at Pontfadog, Llwynmawr, Glynceiriog, Pandy and Llanarmon. They never came to Felin Lyn because they were competitors. On the return trip, they frequently took the Oswestry road from Llanarmon, so making a loop journey. These steamers were a considerable improvement over the horse drawn wagon as they carried between three and five tons and had a much larger daily radius of delivery, but were in turn superseded by motor lorries c.1925-30.

Within a National Context

Rural communities all over Britain in the eighteenth and nineteenth centuries were very much self-contained and self-sufficient, and the folk living round about Felin Lyn were no exception. However there was an invisible and subtle link between the economic health of the nation as a whole and any one village or piece of countryside. If Britain was prosperous, so probably was the village; and the reverse also held true.

Historians have been able to reconstruct the financial fluctuations in Britain between boom and bust over the last 200 years with fair accuracy and have found that there used to be cycles of about 10-year periods. The 'busts' are thought to have started in the following years: 1763, 1773, 1784, 1793, 1803, 1810, 1815, 1825, 1836, 1847, 1866, 1873, 1883, 1893, 1907, 1920, 1929, 1937. (Note 2.14)

We have no idea how the trade flowed and ebbed at Felin Lyn prior to 1882 but by looking at the national scene we can have an insight as to what might have happened at the Mill.

The eighteenth century saw a population explosion in the United Kingdom and no doubt Felin Lyn was built to cater for the increase in the local population. In the sixty-year reign of George III the population doubled from about eight and three-quarter million in 1760 to fifteen and a half million in 1820. Twice the amount of food grown in 1700 was needed by 1820 and this was raised by substantial improvements in productivity on existing farmlands, and by making new farmlands through reclamation and enclosure. It is believed that in the 18th century land under wheat increased by about a third and yield per acre was raised by a tenth.

If this population burden was not enough to bear, Britain and France were locked in the long fought Napoleonic wars which lasted from 1793 to 1815. Before this war Britain had been importing wheat to feed its burgeoning population and had to do so for every year of the war. Having no access to its normal markets, it was forced to switch to Polish wheat loaded in the Baltic. For each of the years 1800, 1801 and 1810, Britain imported over one million Quarters of wheat and in 1796, 1802, 1805, 1813, and 1814 imported over half a million Quarters per annum; one Quarter is 8 Bushels or about 4501bs of wheat for those times. These details have been included to stress the point that Britain needed to grow every acre of corn it could from mid-eighteenth century onwards. So desperate was the situation that even during the 21 year war the shortfall had to be made up by imports that the French were trying to sink. As a result, farming and milling were buoyant activities from 1750-60 to the end of the war in 1815.

The urgent demand for corn brought with it ideas of how the land might be better used. Theories and experiments surfaced in the second half of the 1700s and centred on increasing the area of cultivation, reducing fallow and improving crop rotation, introducing root crops, making the soil sweeter, and enlarging crop yields through seed selectivity. No author or diarist has conveniently left a record of how this was applied to the Ceiriog but there are enough clues lying about to give us an insight. Six examples are given and the sixth is Felin Lyn itself.

Land enclosure has already been discussed as the likely reason for the construction of the Mill of this study. The periods of greatest intensity of land enclosure in Britain were 1760-80 and 1793-1815, the latter period particularly so for Wales where nearly half a million acres were enclosed. It is presumed no Parliamentary Act was needed by Chirk Castle estates to enclose and improve the areas about Llwynmawr because it was already theirs, rough and untamed, and not even usable in the past as 'commons'.

Improving the soil itself was also given attention. Much of Welsh soil is acidic and lime has the effect of neutralising it somewhat, so making the land sweeter and more fertile. In 1770 Chirk Castle Estates built permanent limekilns below a limestone outcrop directly opposite the castle and across the Ceiriog valley, at Bron-y-garth. The kilns lay two miles east of Felin Lyn and their remnants exist to this day. John Hughes (Dol) mentions that as a child (c1810-15) his grandfather took him to get coal at Chirk or thereabouts for lime burning, for the *"farmers at Glyn burnt lime for themselves, on some terms that I do not know, in the kilns near Tai'n-y-myndd"*, this is a mountain-top farm, close to Offa's Dyke and 1½ miles south-east of Felin Lyn.

Another innovation was the growing of root crops – which lessened the killing-off of stock at the onset of winter – and the introduction of a four-year rotation of crops. Thus turnips might be grown the first year, oats or barley the second year, clover the third year, and wheat for the fourth year. Previously there had been a three-year rotation of wheat, oats or barley and fallow which had the disadvantage of producing only two harvests, on a given piece of land, every three years. The new system produced a harvest every year and for the first time ever created fodder crops other than hay. Unfortunately it is not known when these improvements reached the Ceiriog but it is most likely to have been in the last quarter of the eighteenth century. The first local mention of turnips was at Llwynmawr in the 1810s but this is not to suggest that this was their date of introduction.

A new practice of irrigating meadows was observed by Walter Davies, the author of *'General View of Agriculture and Domestic Economy of North Wales'*, which was published by the Board of Agriculture in 1810. He wrote (p.305) that *"the late Mr. Lovett, Chirk Castle factor or agent, claimed the merit of first having introduced systematic watering into North Wales. He hired professional irrigators from South Cerney in Glos'shire who floated 60 acres of his grassland with a stream from the R. Ceiriog. Since 1799 watering has become ten times more common."* An historian has said agricultural innovations in Britain prior to 1850 progressed across the countryside at the rate of about a mile or two per year. One farmer looked over the hedge at a successful neighbour and copied him the following year. This observation may be generally true but overlooks the 'jumps' created by wealthy and progressive estates and Chirk Castle Estates could be numbered among them. The irrigation of Felin Lyn's only meadow, as noted in Chapter l, undoubtedly stems from the initiative of Chirk Castle Estates

In the late 1700s the Ellesmere Canal (later to be known locally as the Shropshire Union or the 'Shroppie') was being pushed from the plains of Cheshire to reach the southern edge of an emerging Welsh industrial complex centred on Ruabon and Wrexham. By 1796 the canal had reached the southern slope of the Ceiriog valley at Chirk and was on the north side of the Dee valley by 1805. This waterway would certainly have stimulated trade, outwards and inwards, in the vicinity. Goods being traded might have included: cast-iron farm implements, cheeses, coal, grain, ironmongery, limestone, pottery, salt, slates, tanning bark, timber and wool. (Note 2.15)

The last example of agricultural improvements affected the handling of cereals. Grain milling is an offshoot of the art of agriculture and at this period improvements in milling marched hand in hand with improvements in agriculture. The former included better methods of cleaning grain prior to milling, more sophisticated forms of sieving (bolting) the products of the millstones, and an increase in productivity by the use of better layouts and handling facilities.

This meant many existing grist mills had to be upgraded and in many instances it was found impractical to tinker with existing structures and machinery. It was easier to start all over again and apply fresh concepts. It is reasonable to conclude that the 'new' Felin Lyn was the last link in improvements to the local food chain that had commenced with any one of the agricultural improvements described above. The objective, as everywhere else in Britain, was to provide enough food for a ballooning population.

After this exciting period of innovation, growth, war and agricultural prosperity there came a sudden crunch. Peace often brings its own problems and this happened in Britain in 1816 when the Napoleonic Wars had come to an end. There was a violent recession which was felt all over the land, and in Wales many farms came to have no tenants, so depressed was the economy. This depression lasted for some 20 years and was mitigated only by the onset of the industrialisation of Britain. Many landless and unemployed country people migrated to towns and mining areas to seek new style jobs, but at the same time they discovered they had lost a treasured piece of their heritage, for now they were without gardens, small game, and fuel. Bread, the staff of life, was most expensive to buy because wheat was kept at an artificially high price, and these new townspeople often lived on cheaper and less nourishing substitutes.

The relatively few large landowners of Britain

(estimated at about 3,000), with their immense wealth and power, reacted to protect their investment which was land and its produce. They introduced a law in 1815 which restricted grain imports. There was nothing new in the concept which had been practised for at least two centuries. What caused the subsequent 30-year anguish was that the Act stipulated that British corn must reach a price of 80/- per Quarter before foreign grain could enter the country without paying duty. Duty was charged on imports in an inverse ratio to the price of corn, becoming punitive when the price of wheat was, say, 55/- per Quarter. In 1815 the average domestic price of wheat was 65/7d per Quarter, and until the Act's repeal in 1846 the median annual price was 62/2d; only in the years 1817, 1818 and 1821 did it ever exceed 80/- per Quarter.

The Act was a blatant piece of class legislation and its effects were so deeply felt that any history book of Britain covering the last century deals with it under the heading 'Corn Laws'.

Beyond all these figures was the reality that there was deep unrest amongst the common people of Britain, caused by poverty, hopelessness and resentment. Between 1815 and 1846 there were sporadic but widespread acts of minor sabotage and rioting which destroyed ricks, barns, tollgates, workhouses, corn granarics and so on. The tool most often used was arson. The best known manifestation in Wales of this unrest was 'Rebecca' sabotage and intimidation in 1839-44. Rural Denbighshire, including Dyffryn Ceiriog, appears to have been a quiet area but the inhabitants must have felt the tenor of the times. In January 1831 a protest march of coal miners passed through Chirk and were stopped there at the Welsh-English border by the Shropshire Yeomanry, fortunately without any violence. The nearest known example of unrest was in the vicinity of Whitchurch, 20 miles to the east of Felin Lyn, which in 1830-31 was considered a hotbed of rural dissent. (Note 2.16)

The Governments of the day were most apprehensive about the possibility of revolution, which was breaking out in many parts of Europe; the prototype of the French revolution of 1792 being very much in mind. It is no coincidence that the very watered-down concessions to democracy contained in the Parliamentary Reform Act of 1832 followed a year of very widespread unrest. Likewise, it was no coincidence that the Corn Laws were repealed in 1846 after the Irish potato famine of 1845, which dislocated grain distributions within the United Kingdom.

This long overdue measure made 'our daily bread' accessible and cheap and many of the tensions of the previous 30 years melted away, to be replaced by a mood of national positiveness and cohesion – later to be known as the Victorian era.

The landowners had always said that if the Corn Laws were done away with British farming would collapse; a scare tactic maybe. It did not happen for the simple reason that the population of Britain continued to increase and the average person grew less poor and amongst other things, sought a better diet. The result was a healthy demand for grain which British farmers attempted to meet, with the balance of the requirements coming from the Balkans and southern Russia.

The countryside flourished from 1850 to about 1885 when cultivated areas in England and Wales were at their maximum at any time in the history of these lands. The peaks of the growing of wheat, barley and oats occurred in the years 1873, 1879, and 1895, respectively. This was the golden age of British farming, and milling, when the sun shone upon an ordered and contented Victorian countryside.

But it was not to last because there was a great price fall in the last quarter of the nineteenth century: however, this was of great benefit to the common man for his purchasing power and standard of living rose considerably.

The event which tolled the death knell of the cornmill, whether driven by water or wind, occurred in the 1870s. This was the importation of North American wheat, mentioned already.

Its arrival devastated the market for British wheat and the 'homegrown' price fell accordingly. In 1880 English wheat was selling at 10s. 4d. per hundredweight and by 1890 it was 7s. 5d., a fall of 28%. Nothing like this had ever been experienced in the British local grain markets.

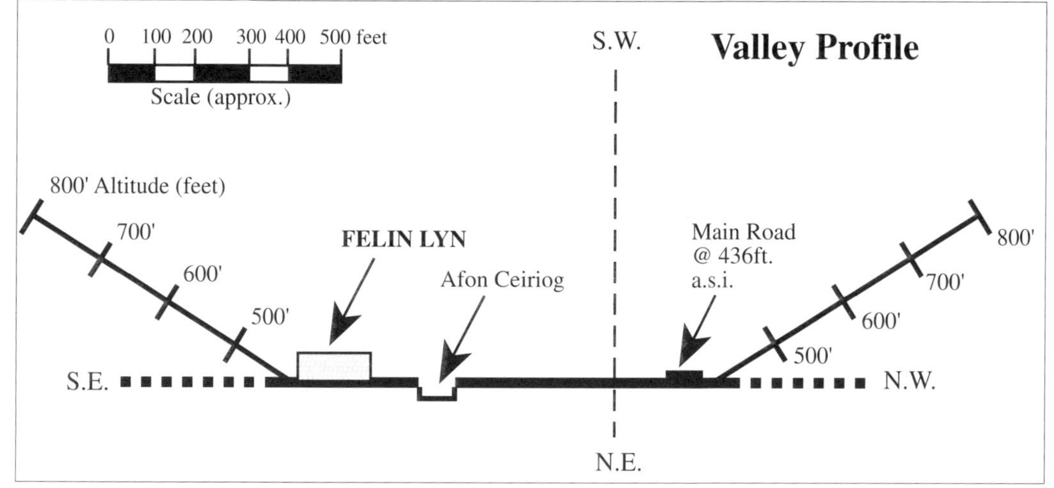

This drawing clearly indicates that the lower section of Dyffryn Ceiriog consists of a narrow ribbon of flat valley floor surrounded by steeply rising hillsides.

At this period the mechanisation of grain harvesting took hold in Britain which helped to cut costs. By the mid-1860s most lowland farms were using horse-drawn reapers. These machines cut the corn and piled it in neat bundles awaiting tying by human hands. The 1890s saw the arrival of the binder which took the reaper one stage further, for it both cut the grain and bound it into sheaves with string. But these machines never reached the land around Felin Lyn whilst it was in its prime.

Another improvement was the mechanical threshing of grain and it is understandable why the operation was mechanised, for it was the most arduous of all the harvesting work .

Fixed threshing machines, driven by horses or water, had appeared at the beginning of the nineteenth century. Much in advance of its time, the first recorded use of steam power in agriculture in the whole world refers to a threshing drum being powered by a primitive steam engine in 1798 on a farm close to Wrexham, Denbighshire. The owner was John Wilkinson, a very successful ironmaster and a business associate of James Watt of Birmingham. Wilkinson was also interested in agriculture and financed large scale land reclamation and afforestation; he used the thresher on his own estate adjacent to his iron furnaces.

These fixed threshing machines were not very common because of their cost and site inflexibility, though some were built in Wales. One surviving example, operable but unworked, is at the farm of Llwyn Diriad, seven miles east of Lampeter in Dyfed, where a waterwheel powers a thresher, winnower, saw, grindstone, and butter churn.

Some time after 1850 the threshing machine was made into a portable device and was powered by a portable steam engine. Both pieces of equipment were hauled from farm to farm by horses, making the hand flail redundant on most British farms.

Technology was very much the handmaiden of the last century and was assisting in every endeavour, including farming and milling, as we have seen. But technology is impartial when distributing her fruits and may create benefit or destruction. In the case of water and wind milling it brought eventual oblivion. In 1788 James Watt invented a system that made his steam engine produce rotative power. For the first time in the world the power of water and wind was being seriously challenged. With watermills the machine is located next to the power source, water, but Watt was able to reverse this by taking the fuel (coal) to the machine. Slowly, from that time on, industries large and small located themselves conveniently to their raw materials or their markets and were no longer tied to river systems. In 1833 a Swiss millwright called Sulzberger devised an alternative to the traditional millstones that had been used for a thousand years and more. It was a set of porcelain rollers – later steel – and is now in universal use throughout the industrial world.

The prime example of these developments in Denbighshire, as it affected the milling trade, was Cobden Mills in the centre of Wrexham. This had been a traditional watermill but in 1865 a new building equipped with all the latest machinery, and steam driven, was erected close to the old one. With forethought it had been built beside a main line railway and was provided with two sidings for incoming grain and coal and outgoing milled products. Soon this modern mill dominated the flour trade in eastern Denbighshire and in its heyday employed over a hundred workers; in turn it was overtaken by the regionalisation of the milling industry and closed its doors in 1929 after being purchased by Rank Flour Mills Ltd. *"Purchase and closure may at first sight appear odd, but was in fact the deliberate policy of a powerful British flour cartel in the late 1920s, that absorbed smaller competitors and closed obsolescent factory mills. It is believed that by World War II three firms controlled two-thirds of the industry; they were Ranks, Spillers, and the Co-operative Wholesale Society."*

The arrival of this century saw a complete alteration in the human cereal food chain, as already discussed, though animal foodstuffs were little affected. But the day of the country cornmill was almost finished.

Local markets for local corn stabilised at a low level for the first two decades of this century, except for the period 1915 to 1920 when prices doubled. This was due to the demands of World War I, in which both men and horse transport were great consumers of grain. For example, in this horseless age, it is difficult to grasp that the British army in France in World War I possessed over a million beasts of burden at any one time to move its ammunition, artillery, food and supplies. (Note 2.17)

The Corn Production Acts of that war ensured more land was put under the plough and by 1918 Denbighshire was harvesting a third more grain than in 1914. Naturally enough, Felin Lyn shared in this activity and profitability.

The financial collapse of the whole world in 1929-30 caused grain prices to fall to their lowest level in at least a hundred years, and it was only due to the initiative of the last miller of Felin Lyn that the mill continued to operate in the disastrous Thirties. He did this by grinding cheap imported maize and selling it as animal feed.

Making an attempt to summarise the periods in the life of Felyn Lyn, within a national context, suggests they fall into four recognisable segments.

(1)	1790-1815	Population boom and Napoleonic war, very profitable.
(2)	1815-1850	Postwar deflation, sluggish economy, national tensions, poorish profit.
(3)	1850-1875	Golden years of British agriculture, good investment and profits.
(4)	1875-1935	Arrival of cheap American wheat and roller milling at entry ports removes Mill from human food chain. Felin Lyn converts to Trading mill selling animal feed. Eventual decline and obsolescence.

NOTES

2.1 **Bread and Dripping**: The author was a recruit in the British Army in 1945, stationed at Cameron Barracks, Inverness, Scotland. Almost all the recruits came from Scotland and northern England and at tea/supper time the alternative to bread and jam was bread and dripping; a clear majority opted for the dripping, showing that a traditional bread covering was still in vogue.

2.2 **Per Capita Average Annual Grain Consumption in last 100 Years:** (covering bread, biscuits, porridge, etc.). Statistics for 1886 showed: Britain – 5.47 bushels (about 330lbs); USA – over 6 bushels; Canada – 5.77 bushels. Russian Government report of 1907 said that the average peasant needed 650lb of grain and anything below 550lb was subsistence level. The difference between 'western' and 'eastern' grain intakes was due to the fact that a primitive diet places great reliance on grains, whereas a sophisticated diet produces energy with other foods such as meats, fish, dairy products, vegetables and fruits.
In 1912 the French were the greatest consumers of wheat in the world, eating 8 bushels (480lb approx.) per head per annum or 1.3lbs per day. In 1925 the British average annual per capita consumption of grain had fallen to 227lb or 0.6lb per day; this was due to a greater diversity of diet.

2.3 **Oats.** Extract from Chap. IV (Agriculture) of *"Wales, An Economic Geography"*, Cundall & Landman, Routledge, London, 1925, 364pp. "By far the most important cereal crop in Wales is oats. In 1913, 200,000 acres or 29% of the whole arable area of the country was under this crop. By 1918, under the stimulus of the Corn Production Acts, the area so devoted had risen to nearly 40%. The crop is grown all over Wales at altitudes of up to 1200ft."

2.4 **Water Mills in Neighbouring Counties.** Cheshire has the best documentation about mills in counties that border Clwyd. See *"Water Powered Corn Mills of Cheshire"* by J. H.Norris, Lancashire & Cheshire Antiquarian Soc., Trans., Vols.75 & 76,1965-6, pp.33-71 lists 86 mills, of which 12 are described in some detail.

2.5 **Reports of Poor Law Inspectors on Agricultural Statistics, 1854.** Denbighshire, Llanfyllin Poor Law Union, House of Commons Sessional Papers, 1854-5, London.

2.6 **Grain Yields in the 'territory' of a mill.** The author has never seen this type of computation or even a hint as to how it might be obtained. He modestly presents these details as a piece of original research and hopes they will stand up to scrutiny.

2.7 **Tolling Grain, 19th century reference.** Extract from a novel "Jan of the Windmill" (1876), which first appeared in serial form as the *'Miller's Thumb'* (feeling the meal) in 1873, written by Mrs Juliana Ewing (1841-85) a prolific novelist.
The story is centred on a windmill, probably located in Wiltshire, with this pertinent dialogue on p. 186. 'Jan received grist from the grist bringers and took payment for the grinding in money or kind according to custom. The old women who toddled in with their

bags of gleaned (*) corn looked very kindly on him. Jan would say "Will ye pay or toll it ?". "Bless ye dear love, how should I pay", the old woman would reply. "I'll toll it, Jan, and thank ye kindly." On which Jan would dip the wooden bowl or tolling dish into the sack and the corn it brought up was the established rate of payment for grinding the rest." The description and conversation has an authentic ring about it and probably dates to the 1860s. **Gleanings:* Debris of grain harvesting left on a field; gleaners were poor women and children who were permitted to keep what they found without charge, but were not allowed on to a corn field until the last stook had been removed and a sign or signal given. The practice slowly died out in Britain in the latter part of the last century – this author's last known written reference is in central Scotland c1910.

2.8 **Some Examples of Tolling Charges.**

(a) Scotland, 1851: "When farmers get oats made into meal for family and servants, the miller retains $8^3/_4$lbs (Scotch peck) for every boll (140lbs) of meal produced." This works out to exactly one-sixteenth.

(b) Wales, undated: Toll-board at combined wind and water mill at Melin y Bont, Bryn Du, Anglesey. Current explanations in brackets:

"For 1 Quarter(8 bu.) of Oats to the kiln and dressing to oatmeal – One Bushel either in groats or flour (ratio is an eighth); For grinding 1 Quarter(8 bu. or 256 quarts) of Barley/Oats for pigs – 6 quarts (ratio is one 42nd); for grinding; 1 Quarter(256 quarts) of Wheat/Barley and dressing – 6 quarts."

(c) England, 1916: Wheat @ 9d/ cwt., barley and oats @ 6d cwt. (As wheat was selling for 7/4 a cwt. on the Welsh border, this equates to a milling fee of one-tenth of value of grain.)

2.9 **Tolling Dishes.** Museum of Welsh Life, Cardiff, holds three examples of tolling dishes, two of wood and one of tinned iron. The latter is of $^1/_2$-gallon capacity and is stamped 'VR' with crown and 'GNI'. A $^1/_2$-gallon is l/l6th of a bushel, so any division but one-sixteenth, one-eighth or one-quarter would have been cumbersome .

2.10 **Ledger-Invoices of Glyn Valley Tramway (horse).** Book of size 25 x 22 inches, 170pp, holding 1,960 pasted-in copy invoices. 135 invoices refer to 'Glyn Mill, Pontfadog'. Held privately by Ceiriog resident at 1994.

2.11 **Journal:** Royal Agricultural Society of England, Vol. 85, 1924, p. 109-21; Article "*Miller's Margin*" by A. W. Ashby. Study of prices of wheat, flour and offals in period 1913-23.

2.12 **Carrying sack of grain on horseback.** Because this was such a commonplace mode of transportation, it was rarely described on paper. However, one such description has survived and comes from the 'Cofiant' or memoirs of William Davies (1819-1904), great-grandfather of the author. At the time of the incident he would be about four or less and lived on his parents' farm at Pentre Saron, four miles south of Denbigh. His grandparents lived at a farm, Bodeiliog, closer to the town.

"On one occasion I recollect going with my grandmother to Felin Segroit with a sack of corn to be ground. The sack was tied upon the back of old 'Fanny', a very quiet old mare, and I was tied on top of the sack. On the return journey, Fanny stopped to have a drink at a roadside pond and somehow I slipped under the mare's belly. I remember well what a stew my grandmother was in as she began to throw stones at Fanny for her very life and shouting. However Fanny had her drink and after the ducking brought me once more safe on shore. The fact was the miller, in starting from the mill, had not tied me up very cleverly. I remember being more afraid of Nain (grandmother) hitting me with a stone than I was afraid of being drowned."

The correct name of the above mill is *Melin Segrwyd*, on the Afon Ystrad. It was a late survivor, working until 1960 and is still fully intact.

2.13 **Book:** "*Glyn Valley Tramway*", Milner, W.J., Dorset, Oxford Pub. 1984, 144pp. and booklet *Glyn Valley Tramway*, Davies, D.Ll. (same author as this book) Oxford, Oakwood Press, originally pub. 1962, repub. 1991, 96pp.

2.14 **Book:** *"Economic Depressions"*. An economic history of Europe. Heaten, H., New York, Harper & Row, 1936 and 1948.

2.15 **Book: "***Ellesmere and Llangollen Canal"*. Wilson, Edward. Chichester, Phillimore, 1975. 148pp. See Chap. 9 on 'Flour Milling'.

2.16 **Unrest in Whitchurch area 1830-31**. There were 16 acts of arson in the period. In 1830 Thomas Cook, 18 year old solicitor's clerk, wrote an anonymous note to a man who was assisting wealthy tenant farmers to put out arson fires. In it, he threatened to kill the man if he continued with this activity. It was typical of intimidation letters and there was no intent to murder. Cook was tracked down, tried, and sentenced to 14 years transportation to Australia. He survived the voyage and brutal penal life and remained forever in Australia. We know all this only because Cook was literate (rare in those days), a prison survivor, and that he wrote of his experiences under the title "*Exile's Lamentations*". These were edited and published in Sydney, Australia, in 1978. See also p.30-2 of *"Collieries of Denbighshire"* by G.G. Leary, Wynn Williams Publishers, Wrexham, 1968.

2.17 **Horses in World War I** (1914-18). 2,562,549 horses & mules were admitted to British veterinary hospitals in France during the four years of war. Most of them were suffering from exposure, not wounds, and 78% of them were returned to work. A quarter of a million horses died but only 58,000 were killed by enemy action. In four years these animals consumed 5.5 million tons of feedstuffs. ("*Horses in War*" by J. M. Bereton, David & Charles.)

The author explains: "Like the story of the windmill, what follows is not related to Felin Lyn but is worthy of inclusion. On one of my trips to the Ceiriog, I noticed some garden ornaments at a house situated in the former 'territory' of Felin Lyn. They were fashioned stones and were fitted with iron handles or eyes and are shown above.

Now, to this day, Britishers weigh themselves in 'Stones' and not in pounds or kilograms. This is a relic of recent times when a Stone weighed 14 lbs, and eight of them made a Hundredweight of 112 lbs. Going back 150 years ago there was a profusion of 'stone' weights and the variations were determined by the commodity being weighed and the traditions of the locality. Such were listed in detail in the Third Report of the Commissioners of Weights and Measures (covering England, Wales and Scotland), which was represented to the House of Commons in 1821.

All the 'Stones' listed covered one and a half pages and had the following range: 4, 5, 6, 7, 8, 11, 12, 13, 14, 15, 16, 17, 18, 20, 21, 22, 24, 26, and 32 lbs.

The three stones in the photograph were weighed on bathroom scales and were found to be (left to right): 21 lbs, 63 lbs, 84 lbs. This makes for a divisor of 21 and gives a ration of 1 : 3 : 4.

The only stones of 21 lbs listed in the 1821 report came from northern Scotland and weighed: butter & cheese; butter, cheese, flax, oatmeal; hay. It also said that a 21 lb weight was encountered in markets of South Wales but did not list the commodities.

An 1835 Weights and Measures Act outlawed all 'Stones' excepting those of 14 lbs, and so made the Stones above illegal. These particular stones have come from northern Denbighshire farms and had a use until after World War II. Corn ricks used to be secured with covering ropes and such stones were used as bottom-end weights. The question now to be asked is "What weights of Stones were used in Dyffryn Ceiriog and for what commodities?"

Chapter 3

*p*eople (& *a*nimals)

P*iecing* is the expression used when assembling a jigsaw puzzle and also can be applied to the process of finding out who were the millers of Felin Lyn in the last 150-200 years. Imagine a small cardboard box with no picture on the lid and a few pieces of puzzle inside. At intervals, add more pieces that were found on shelves and on the floor; this illustrates the process of what we now know. The jigsaw puzzle is still incomplete but we have enough of a picture to comprehend who operated Felin Lyn for a century and a half.

Millers

The research reveals that only two milling families, the HUGHES and the EVANS, worked the Mill from c1790 to 1936.

Our knowledge of the HUGHES millers comes from three sources; primarily from, and by kind permission of, Angela Downs of Paris who has been researching her ancestors; secondly from John Hughes (Dol); and finally from the older inhabitants of Llwynmawr for more recent times. For details of the EVANS millers, we are indebted to the late Mrs. Gladys Jones (FL), a daughter of the last full-time miller. (Note 3.1)

Before going into the personal history of each and every known miller of Felin Lyn, it may be useful to scan the tabulation overleaf to get a sense of the 'who and when'.

The oldest miller of the presumably 'new' Felin Lyn was Edward Hughes I (1760-1806). He was obviously not known with the suffix 'I' and this has been added here to assist with identification. On document entries he is variously described as 'miller', 'alehouse keeper', 'yeoman' and 'vintner'. Milling has always been closely associated with baking and brewing, so three of the job titles come as no surprise. The term 'vintner' is intriguing as this implied in Britain at that period that Hughes was a wine seller and the author has found no reference to wine in the Ceiriog.

We know he was miller for at least 18 years because there is an entry of 1788 listing him as 'miller' when he was 28. A similar entry was made in 1805. We do not know if his tenancy straddled the years of the old grist mill and the new Mill or that he was the first miller of the new Felin Lyn.

Edward Hughes I died in 1806, aged 46, presumably prematurely but we do not have the cause. He was buried in Glynceiriog churchyard. His tombstone, which was intact in 1979 but had disappeared by 1982, recorded him as "late of Felin Lyn" and the burial register records him as "miller of Township of Nantgwryd, Parish of Llangollen". (Note 3.2)

Who ran the mill between 1806 and 1824 has not been discovered and awaits another researcher. Reliable information about the population of Great Britain commenced with the national census of 1801 and since then a census has been taken every ten years with the exception of wartime 1941. No details of the families occupying Felin Lyn exist for the censuses of 1801 to 1841. This was because in those days the census was novel, poorly organised – and sometimes resisted – and was merely a head count at a dwelling.

We do know that a son of the 'first' miller returned to his childhood home as miller in 1824 when he was 30 and newly married. He was Edward Hughes II. John Hughes (Dol) has two comments about him: *"He was a handsome young man as I remember"* and *"Nedi Felin Lyn and two other men were noted for their tricks and practical jokes. They were blamed for all the wrongs in the area but they would never cause harm to anyone."*

Apropos of his behaviour, someone else wrote seventy-five years later, outside Wales, the following: *"It was quite a fad in those days to swap yarns about your friends and neighbours, and to play practical jokes on them. These people had a better sense of humour than nowadays. They said things and pulled off pranks that would land a man in trouble today, yet nothing ever happened but a good laugh all round."*

Sadly, like his father, Edward Hughes II died prematurely in 1841 aged 47 but this time the cause of death is known – typhus fever. This is one of the great epidemic diseases of history and often appears in cold weather. If unchecked, mortality rates can climb as high as 40%.

One hundred and fifty years later these middle age deaths cause us surprise but at the time this was the norm. The first tables of life expectancy in England were published by the Government in 1845. They showed that life was at great risk between birth and age four, 'normal' between 6 and 54, and with increasing risk thereafter. Over one in six of all babies died in their first year and 25% of all children never reached their fourth birthday. Half the population died before age 46, the next quarter lived to sometime between 46 and 69, and the final quarter died between 70 and 96 with age 82 as the upper limit for most. This will be expected for those readers who have researched their family trees back to the beginning of the last century, for there are countless cases of infant and young child mortality; mostly due to infantile diarrhoea. (Note 3.3)

By comparison, the most recently published life expectancy tables for England and Wales show that only 1% of babies under 12 months die and only 2% of people

Millers at Felin Lyn

Names in ***italics*** in the centre column are offspring who became successive millers. Details for the period 1806-1824 are unkmown.

Millers, in succession	Marriage year, wife & family	Details of active milling life
EDWARD HUGHES I, 1760-1806 Life: 46 years	1788 Jane Morris Jane b.1790 Margaret – ***Edward*** *b.1794* Thomas b.1796	Miller for at least 18 years, from or before 1788 (aged 28) to death in 1806.
Blank	No details	Period 1806 to 1824 not known.
EDWARD HUGHES II, 1794-1841 Life: 47 years	1824 Margaret Evans ***John*** *b.1825* Edward, Jane, Thomas, William b.1834	Miller for about 17 years from 1824 (aged 30) to 1841 when he died of typhus fever.
JOHN HUGHES, 1825-1893 Life: 68 years	c1845 Sarah Hughes 3 children	Did not live at Felin Lyn & was not its actual miller. Oversaw operations from c1845/50 to c1860/65. Lived in and worked pub at Llwynmawr.
EVAN EVANS, 1815-1880s Life: 70 years	c1840 Annie—?— ***Edward*** *b.1841* Godfrey, Mary, Ellis, Abraham b.1859	Was a farmer until aged 40 or more, then took to milling. Was living at Felin Lyn by 1867. Retired in 1872 (aged 59).
EDWARD EVANS I, 1841-1912 Life: 71 years	1870 Jane Jones ***Edward*** *b.1872* Richard, Sarah b1881	Miller for 28 years from 1872 (aged 31) to 1900 (aged 59). Retired to smallholding.
EDWARD EVANS II, 1872-1936 Life: 64 years	1900 Jane Wynne Gwladys b.1902, Florence, Emlyn b.1909	Miller for 36 years from 1900 (aged 28) to death in 1936 (aged 64).

do not survive to age 20. Average age of death for men is now 74 and for women is 80. (Note 3.4)

Reverting to the family of Edward Hughes II, his widow, Margaret Hughes, returned to her parents' home at Rhiwlas which is on the road that connects Llanarmon Dyffryn Ceiriog with Oswestry and is on the edge of Ceiriog land. Here she took her four children and later remarried. Her eldest son at the time of this move was 16 years old and he must have had meal dust in his veins for by age 20 he was married and living at Llwynmawr. His name was John Hughes (1825-93), a determined and dynamic young man and whose life was once more connected with his place of birth – Felin Lyn .

This John Hughes married in about 1845 a Sarah Hughes (1815-97) who was the sister of John Hughes (Dol) and exactly ten years older than her new husband. Sarah came from a family connected with corn milling, weaving, and maybe malting and brewing. So it would have been considered quite a natural alliance for these two milling families to have become united through marriage.

The 1851 Census shows John and Sarah Hughes to have three children of whom the eldest was five years of age. This same Census provides another clue; in the entry for 'Llwynmawr Public House' there are eight people listed in the household, headed by John Hughes, aged 26, 'Publican and Miller'. Within the household are three servants, two of them being Humphrey Lewis, *Miller*, aged 20, and John Williams, *Mill Carrier,* aged 16.

So here is clear proof that young John Hughes was brewing beer and running the pub at Llwynmawr, whilst he had two assistants to run Felin Lyn. Astutely he had hired a younger man than himself as miller, most likely someone just out of apprenticeship, who was not of the Ceiriog and over whom he could assert his authority. The same 1851 Census showed that the millhouse at Felin Lyn was occupied by a 35 year old labourer, his wife and a one month old baby.

This situation of not having a resident miller at Felin Lyn carried into the 1860s for the 1861 Census shows the occupants to be a 79 year-old labourer and his 84 year-old wife. The title 'labourer' meant that the old man still had work of some kind and so was not listed as a 'pauper' relying on Parish relief.

There is no doubt that John Hughes ran Felin Lyn as any other rural flour mill would be run, but that he also took advantage of using it to kiln and then bruise his malted barley, as one of the first steps in brewing his beer at Llwynmawr.

John and Sarah Hughes and two generations of family after them continued to run Llwynmawr Inn/Hotel until

1947 when it was sold. By this time the inn had been upgraded to a small hotel catering to the well-to-do who fished the Afon Ceiriog. It has been successively known as the Sportsman's Arms and the Golden Pheasant and is now a well-appointed hotel of 19 bedrooms.

At what date John Hughes divested himself of the tenancy of Felin Lyn is not known but it was sometime between the 1861 Census and a document dated 1867. Thereafter Hughes concentrated all his efforts on running the Llwynmawr pub and attached brewhouse. In due course he or the next generation controlled or owned four other pubs within a two-mile radius and supplied them with beer brewed at Llwynmawr to as late as 1930. These other pubs were the 'Butcher's Arms' at the Graig, the 'Queen's Head' at Dolywern, the lonely 'Star' on the main road halfway between Dolywern and Glynceiriog, and the 'New Inn' at Glynceiriog, later known as the Glyn Valley Hotel. (Note 3.5)

The first Evans miller was an Evan Evans (1815-c1880s) and the 1851 Census shows him, aged 36, living with wife Anne and four children at Scythie Ucha. This was a 16-acre upper hillside farm lying about one mile north of Felin Lyn; it has not existed for a long time.

Sixteen years later, in 1867, Evans is shown as occupying Felin Lyn and also renting seven acres of nearby Nantgwryd Farm; this is the same ancient farm of 'villa de Nant Goryt' listed in a 1391 Chirk Castle document.

The 1871 Census confirms that Evan Evans, aged 56, widowed, is 'Miller & Farmer', rents 12 acres and has four of his children living with him. They are: Godfrey, 23, who is a carpenter and joiner; Mary, 20, who is presumably now acting as housekeeper; Ellis, aged 16, mill carrier; and Abraham, 12, listed as 'scholar'.

This reference to schooling is of interest and it is thought that Abraham went to a voluntary attendance school in Pontfadog. At this date there were schools at Chirk, Pontfadog, Glynceiriog, and Llanarmon. They were all run by the Church of England as were 90% of the schools throughout Britain, and the teaching centred on Anglican doctrine followed by the three Rs – Readin', 'Ritin' and 'Rithmetic. In the previous year of 1870 Parliament had introduced the concept of universal, free and compulsory education but the task of providing

Edward Evans II and his son, Emlyn, with his cart fitted with high-sided attachments to carry pigs, pulled by faithful Flower; *about 1925.*
The late Mrs Gwladys Jones.

buildings, facilities and teachers was so daunting that a national scheme with all these aspects was not achieved for another twenty years.

It is probable that Abraham paid for his attendance on a weekly basis at the rate of between ld and 3d per week, plus a levy for coal in the winter months. Attendance fluctuated as there was no compulsion and class size probably ranged between 10 and 20 pupils. At the age of 12, Abraham was considered a senior because even in 1880 the compulsory top age limit was 10. The school at Pontfadog was housed in a building opposite the church, which became the village hall when the County Council built a new primary school in 1908. (Note 3.6)

When Evan Evans first took to milling is a matter of speculation. Perhaps at first he helped Hughes' miller at busy times and slowly became acquainted with the trade. Possibly he became the full-time and resident miller of Felin Lyn when John Hughes gave up his tenancy, at a date prior to 1867. Certainly from this time on the miller and the occupier were one and the same till the Mill's closure.

In 1872 Evan Evans retired and transferred the job of miller to his eldest son, Edward Evans I (1841-1912), then aged 31. At this point we can hand over the narrative to the late Mrs. Gwladys Jones (FL), a miller's daughter born at Felin Lyn in 1902. In 1982 she wrote:

"My grandfather, Edward Evans [I], was born in 1841. I cannot say if he was born at the Mill or not, but I do know from my father that he was trained by my great-grandfather to be a miller. He became miller about 1870, married (Glynceiriog Baptist chapel) at the same time, and had two sons .

My father, Edward Evans [II], was born in 1872 and my Uncle Dick a few years later. Both sons worked at the mill and were trained as millers and farmers. In 1900 my grandmother died and my father was married (Llangollen Baptist Chapel) and took over the Mill. Then my grandfather and uncle Dick left Felin Lyn and went to a farm in Llwynmawr called Glan-yr-afon, about 3/4 mile away. My grandfather died in 1912."

When Mrs. Jones wrote the above she did not have the benefit of having seen the Census details, and it is remarkable that her personal recollections dovetail so well with the official records. The two sources complement one another and help to give us a clear picture of how three generations of one family lived at Felin Lyn. Only on one minor detail is there disagreement between the two sources, and it relates to the existence of daughter Sarah Anne in the 1881 Census returns. When queried about this Mrs. Jones reiterated that there were only two sons and said that in the family records contained in her grandfather's copy of 'Taith y Pererin' (Pilgrim's Progress) there is no mention of a daughter, though another son is listed who was born in 1877 but died within months. Yet another example of the high infant mortality rates of previous centuries.

From these personal details, one general conclusion can be drawn. The trend was for the eldest son to take over the running of the Mill at about the age of 30, with the father miller moving out at about age 60. The carrying of sacks weighing in excess of 200lb. was a strenuous and necessary part of a miller's life and so it was an impossibility to cling on to the job into old age.

This is an appropriate place to mention that all the millers of Felin Lyn spoke Welsh in the home and to their neighbours and customers. This applied to the very end of the Mill's existence and beyond to when it was a smallholding in the 1950s.

In 1891 nearly half of the population of Glyn Traian spoke only Welsh, another 40% were bilingual, leaving 14% with English only. That meant that nearly nine people out of ten spoke Welsh. Sadly, this situation changed over the decades so that by 1931 a mere 4% spoke Welsh only in the Parish, a figure identical to the average for the whole of Wales. However a solid two-thirds (62%) were bilingual to offset the one-third (34%) who spoke only English. The decline of spoken Welsh continues, for the 1991 Census showed that only 27% of the Parish population were bilingual. Out of 785 residents in 284 households, 214 persons spoke Welsh. The data no longer distinguishes between monoglot Welsh and bilingual speakers, but the 1961 Census revealed that there were 13 persons who spoke only Welsh in the Parish of Glyn Traian. (Note 3.7)

The Evans millers were Baptists and attended the chapel at Dolywern, one mile away. Baptists, as their name implies, hold that baptism is only for believers and only by full immersion, and is withheld until a person is relatively mature. The chapel records at Dolywern show Edward Evans I, was baptised on 6th May 1860, when he was 19.

Mrs. Jones (FL) also readily supplied details of family life and circumstances at Felin Lyn in the 20th century. She said:

"In my family there were three children, my sister Florence who died in 1980, my brother Emlyn tragically killed in a tree felling accident in 1930 aged 21, and myself, Gwladys.

My father was extremely keen on education and saw that his children had a college education, and this continues, for my daughter Megan has lived all her life in England but she can speak, read and write in Welsh, and was bilingual before she first went to school. I am glad she can understand me when I speak Welsh to her. She has an Honours Degree in Fine Arts from Durham University and it is Megan who produced the two paintings of Felin Lyn, one in oils and the other a watercolour back in the 1950s.

My father was very keen on everything Welsh, a very patriotic Welshman, a Baptist, a keen Liberal and a great admirer of David Lloyd-George (who became British Prime Minister 1916-22) . *We did not see the famous man but we did see Mrs. Lloyd-George a few times because she was a visitor to Brynhyfryd, the first house up the Graig lane. Your grandfather [i.e. the author's] used to fetch her from Chirk in what we called the 'dog cart', a little round cart pulled by a pony."* This would have been prior to 1914. (Note 3.8)

The last miller, Edward Evans II, purchased in 1926 a neighbouring small farm of 22 acres called Pandy Bach. It lay but 200 yards away on the opposite side of the river and consisted of a house, farm buildings and some five or six fields. It was his intention to retire there when the time came, but unfortunately his health broke in 1935 and he never lived to enjoy it; he died in March 1936. His daughter says that at Pandy Bach he increased his holdings of cows, bullocks and sheep, and started to specialise in the breeding of pedigree pigs which included Large Whites and Gloucester Old Spots.

The name Pandy Bach is of interest for 'pandy' means 'fulling mill' and 'bach' is 'small'. Fulling is one of the processes in making woollen cloth and involves the cleaning, thickening and shrinking of the cloth so that the woven pattern ceases to be visible. It was the first process to be mechanised, in the 1300s, because the work was so strenuous. The medieval fulling mills in the Ceiriog are documented between 1334 and 1516 and Pandy Bach is not included amongst them. On the other hand nothing is presently known about the former fulling mill locally, so this would suggest it was at work sometime between 1500 and 1800.

In the first half of the nineteenth century there lived in the neighbourhood a one-eyed fuller called Dafydd but it is fairly certain he worked in one of the woollen mills at Glynceiriog.

Comprehensive view of Felin Lyn taken by the author in 1942 when it was no longer a mill but just a country small-holding. At left are farm buildings including the barn at rear; at centre is the principal building holding mill on left and miller's house on right; at right is cottage of Glyndwr, formerly called Glandwr. *White gate leads to mill yard and between it and the Mill is the miller's garden. All that remains in the 1990s is Glyndwr and small outbuildings. Author.*

Mill Helpers

Mills the size of Felin Lyn were usually run by the miller and his family but at certain times of the year and for certain jobs extra help was needed.

When Felin Lyn had a kiln attached to it prior to this century the kiln required a man's full attention whilst it was running, as the miller would be fully occupied inside the mill.

Custom varied as to how the kiln was manned. Sometimes it was the responsibility of the farmer, whose grain was being processed, to provide the fuel and to do the kilning. In other places the miller hired a man to look after the kiln and charged his customers for the use of the facility. It is not known what happened at Felin Lyn.

In the cycle of a year, the miller's busy period was from after harvesting in October to the end of winter. It is highly likely that at times he was much pressed and needed another pair of hands to help him out. This was no problem as there was surplus farm labour at this time of year but in some years perhaps he could call upon growing sons or a recently retired father for assistance.

Sometimes there were also 'pressed' helpers. The late Tom Davies of Llwynmawr remembers when as a boy he, and others, became involuntary helpers at Felin Lyn. *"Ned y Felin always had youngsters doing chores for him and running errands. Many times I was collared going home from school, as I went past the Mill, to scoop corn and meal into sacks from large troughs. At first it was fun to be a miller's assistant but after a while it became tiresome but in those days no child could refuse a reasonable request by an adult. After a time I found another way of getting home."*

Another person that a miller needed was a carrier who would sell the mill products in the neighbourhood. It was the responsibility of a farmer to bring his own grain to a mill and carry back the meal and flour, but it was naturally up to the miller to sell his own products. Before the age of shops, the miller was the local corn-and-meal retailer.

The Census returns of 1851, 1871 and 1881 show that there was a carrier at Felin Lyn. In 1851 he was a 16-year-old employee, in 1871 he was a 16-year-old son whilst a decade later he was a 12-year-old employee. The 1891 Census shows no carrier at the Mill – at least he was not living on the premises as had previously been the case. It looks as if the newly established grocer/baker at Llwynmawr and grocer at Pontfadog were eroding the miller's household sales and there was no need for a retail roundsman.

It appears customary for all Ceiriog watermills to have employed a carrier. John Hughes (Dol) reminisces that when he was 17 (in 1819) he acted as carrier to his miller father at Felin Wynn below Glynceiriog. He made deliveries on both sides of Afon Ceiriog from Dolywern upstream to Glynceiriog and Nantyr and used a long coaching horn to announce his arrival. In 1851 this mill continued to use a carrier who was aged 13.

J. W. Davies in his 1941 review of Ceiriog watermills says that the mill at Tregeiriog (Mill No. 3 in Appendix V) had a carrier until the closing decades of the last century and the last occupant of the job was called Alun y Cariwr. Thus the job of mill carrier in Britain passed into oblivion at the turn of this century. The task of supplying households with their cereal needs was now usurped by the emerging country grocery store.

The reminiscences of mill carriers are so rare that it is worth including the following though the events took place 12 miles to the south-west of Felin Lyn in the Tanat valley. The narrator was the late Ernest Ellis who lived as a boy at Felin Fach (little mill) at the village of Pen-y-bont Fawr. He was born in 1892 and said: *"We had a pony and cart and three donkeys for carrying the grain and the flour. My younger brother and I looked after the donkeys, which were used as pack animals. We made journeys with the donkeys to outlying farms, often up steep hills, during the evenings in summer and on Saturdays in the winter.*

I started these visits when I was 9 or 10 years old. Donkeys do not have a shoulder like a horse and so it was difficult to keeps sacks on the donkeys on steep hills. We would often have to turn the donkeys around to stop the sacks from slipping off.

I remember one particular isolated hill farm where I had to collect two bags of wheat in the wintertime and on arrival found they had not been filled. The farmer started filling the sacks using a peck – a round vessel with two handles – from the wheat on the granary floor. He would level off the top of each peck with a board called a strick, with the exception of the last peck which was piled up.

The morning was particularly cold and I was jumping around to try and get warm as I waited. The farmer shouted out to me: "Don't stamp your feet, lad – you're shaking the peck. He was afraid the corn would settle and more end up in the sack than normal."

The demise of this small Tanat mill is worth relating as being typical of the period. Ernest Ellis recounted *"...in 1904 a railway was built up the Tanat valley giving easy access to Oswestry and equally brought competition from large town mills, which could process grain and feeding stuffs more cheaply than our watermill. Father could see this coming and in 1905 he acquired a farm in Llanfechain in the next valley and moved into full-time farming. After that Felin Fach slipped out of regular working."*

Reverting to Felin Lyn in the last century, as well as a carrier the mill household needed a female domestic servant. In 1881 she was a girl of 13 who helped care for a two month-old baby and assisted with the innumerable chores of house and farmyard. In 1891 she was Susannah Davies aged 14. A teenage girl could be hired in the country for the equivalent of room and board and not even pocket money. The parents of a poor family would regard her employment as a blessing since it gave the girl some household training and was one less mouth to feed at home.

In the middle of the last century there were three-quarters of a million indoor domestic servants in Britain and they constituted the second largest occupational group – exceeded only by agricultural labourers. At the beginning of this century domestics had risen to one-and-a-quarter million and one girl in three aged between 15 and 20 did this kind of work.

Landlords

As previously mentioned, Felin Lyn was never owned by the miller of the day, though the last miller to run it did himself become the landlord of a small farm. This was the norm, for as late as 1910, 90% of British farmlands were worked by tenants. It was not until 1962 that the property, by then only a smallholding and not a mill, was purchased by someone who contemplated living on the premises.

The dominant landlord in the life of Felin Lyn, and its medieval predecessors, was the Lord of the Manor of Chirk, or more simply put, Chirk Castle Estates. It is highly probable that all the mills in the Ceiriog were owned by Chirk Castle in earlier centuries.

Chirk Castle is well known locally and perhaps regionally, but not until recently has it come to national notice. It can claim several distinctions, amongst them being continuous habitation since its construction c1310; an unchanged external silhouette of walls and towers; and ownership by one family for the last four hundred years. This family, the Myddletons and their descendants, was in possession of the castle from 1595 to 1978, when the property was purchased by the nation and then conveyed to the National Trust.

In the period that concerns us, that is beginning from the mid-1700s, Felin Lyn was owned by Richard Myddelton (1726-1795) of Chirk Castle and it is most likely it was he who authorised the construction of the Felin Lyn of this history. But it has to be appreciated that Felin Lyn was but one of several hundred properties in north-east Wales which comprised the Chirk Castle Estates.

At the death of Richard Myddelton uncertainty prevailed in the family for about a decade, for the succeeding son died unmarried within a year and the large estate passed to his three unmarried sisters. After protracted legal negotiations the Estate was divided into three unequal portions. This may explain why 'Estates' is used in the plural form.

The eldest sister held the Manor and Lordship of Chirk and the core of the original estate, which comprised close to 20,000 acres. Maria Myddleton, the second sister, received those parts of the Estate that lay in Holt, Wrexham, Ruabon, Llangollen, Llansantffraid Glynceiriog and Llanarmon Dyffryn Ceiriog.

As a result of this partitioning, Felin Lyn became the property of Maria – in theory. In practice Maria never owned it because before the legal settlement was made, she married the Honourable Frederick West in 1798 and he in due course became the legal owner of Felin Lyn since wives were not allowed to own real estate. Frederick West was the third son of John, 2nd Earl de la Warr. This alliance explains the origin of the name of the hotel at Llanarmon, the 'West Arms'.

Frederick and Maria West spent the first years of their married life at Chirk Castle, then moved to the Quinta which was a large country house at Weston Rhyn and one-and-a-half miles south of the Castle. In 1826 they took the ruins of Ruthin Castle and built a mansion adjoining it, living there in splendour with a staff of 18 house servants. Much of Ruthin had been part of the original Chirk Castle Estate and had reverted to the Wests; in 1850 they owned 60% of the town.

Maria West died in 1843 and her only son – also called Frederick and then 44 years of age – became the owner of Ruthin Castle. He and his wife were dissatisfied with the 1826 design of the mansion and between 1849 and 1852 they partially demolished it and in its place erected a rectangular three-storey home. It can still be seen, and even lived in, for it is now the luxurious Ruthin Castle Hotel of 60 bedrooms. (Note 3.9)

This magnificence cost much money and to finance it Frederick West, Junior, (1799-1862) sold pieces of his large land-holdings. This appears to be the motivation for the sale of Felin Lyn.

Considerable portions of Estate property in the lower part of Dyffryn Ceiriog were sold in the period 1849-52. John Hughes (Dol) says *"...about 1849 the Honourable*

Frederick West sold most of his land in the Glyn, my brother Samuel bought his farm about 1850".

In 1852 Felin Lyn itself was sold. On 4th June of that year an auction was held at the Cross Keys Inn, Oswestry, to sell some 600 acres of Estate farms and lands in the townships of Nantgwryd, Hafodgynfor, Cilcochwyn, Erwallo and Crogen Iddon. The Estate solicitors, Longueville & Williams of Oswestry, acted for the vendors. Lot 19 was simply listed as *"Mill, Dwelling-house, Garden, and Lands at 5 acres, 3 roods, 16 perches."* It is interesting to note that some years later the Ordnance Survey calculated the self-same area to be 4.7 acres. The location of the Mill property was given as being in the *"Townships of Crogen Iddon, Hafodgynfor and Nantgwrid* (sic), *or some of them"*, suggesting that the precise junction of these three townships on the property was unclear. Written details of the sale price and the new owner have not survived, but it is presumed that the latter was a John Jones, who will be introduced shortly. Sixteen days later there was another auction of Estate lands grouped around Glynceiriog, but this time it was held at Llangollen.

So after five-and-a-half centuries of feudal and aristocratic ownership by the Lordships of Chirk, Felin Lyn was to be owned by a 'common man', albeit a member of the gentry.

It should be noted that this was an early dated example of the dismemberment of large estates which continues to this day but which peaked after World War I. For a local example, the entire village of Chirk was owned by Chirk Castle Estates until it was put up for auction by lots in 1911.

The nineteenth century was the era of large estates. A government survey of 1871 showed there were 27 estates in north-east Wales of more than 3,000 acres. At this date Ruthin Castle Estate possessed 5,617 acres whilst Chirk Castle Estate held 6,953 acres. These paled into insignificance when compared with the vast Williams-Wynn Estate, whose family seat at Wynnstay Hall, Ruabon, was 6 miles north-east of Felin Lyn, and whose estate measured 87,919 acres, plus 54,000 of woodlands and sheepwalks.

For the remainder of its working life, Felin Lyn had only two owners, named Jones and Davies. The first was John Jones and because of the prevalence of such a name in Wales, the author had the greatest difficulty identifying him. At first all that was known about him was that he was a cut above the farmers of the area. This was because in the 1867 Property Valuation his name carries the suffix 'Esq', whilst other landowners are plain 'Mr'. A surviving boundary stone, inserted in a wall marking the boundary between the Mill's Erw field and Brynhyfryd, is carved '*J. J. Esq – 1888*' and confirms the distinction.

In the times of the Crusades and earlier, the title 'Esquire' had meaning but by the beginning of the eighteenth century it implied no rights or privileges and was used by lesser gentlemen to give themselves some sort of social standing. Later still, it was used by anyone who wanted to appear respectable. John Jones seemed to fit this category but was an enigma. His place of birth on the Property Valuation was a cryptic 'County of Denbigh', whereas most other people gave their Parish.

The sleuth that ran this anonymous John Jones to earth is Mr Robert Owen Jones of Glynceiriog; of the same name but unrelated. Mr Jones is carrying out family and local history research and, aware of the author's problem, promised to keep a weather eye open for possible clues. His diligence paid off for recently he found two sources (linked by a common home address) that led to and then positively identified owner John Jones. So grateful thanks to present day Robert Jones for his timely perseverance.

The first source is contained in the newspaper *Llangollen Advertiser* of 17th August 1894. It recorded the ceremonial opening of a small iron bridge spanning the Afon Ceiriog at Pontfadog and adjacent to Felin Lyn; it was replacing the ancient ford. The bridge had been erected by the Llangollen Road Improvement Board, who contributed half the cost whilst the remainder had been raised by parishioners and friends. It was obviously a local community project.

The account provides an all important clue; *"On the 2nd inst. the bridge was formally opened by Mr J. Jones of Send, Surrey, one of the landowners in the district and a generous supporter of the bridge scheme."* There follows a description of a simple but charming summer scene to honour the opening of this 32 feet long bridge which had become part of a public road. A procession was formed of carriages and (two-wheeled passenger) traps, followed by school children, and all crossed over the new structure – presumably with much exuberance! Everyone then entered the Mill meadow *"...kindly lent by Mr Ed. Evans, Felin Lyn"*, where the children were entertained with sweets and nuts. The author found the account nostalgic because as a young boy he crossed or idled on the bridge nearly every day and long ago saw the commemorative plaque, which is placed underneath the span on the northern abutment.

The second clue appears in "Bye-Gones" of 15th September 1909. This was a weekly column in a Shropshire local newspaper, the *Oswestry Advertiser.*

"Bye-Gones" covered a miscellany of topics connected with local history throughout Wales and the Border and in

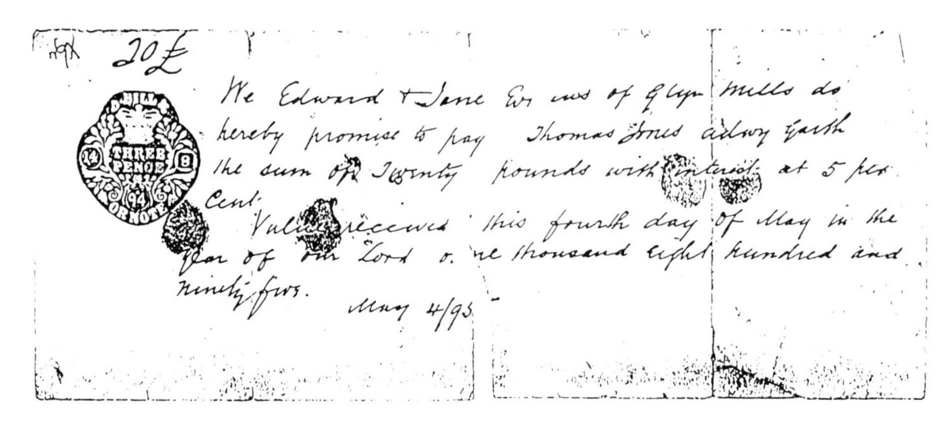

20£

We Edward & Jane Evans of Glyn Mills do hereby promise to pay Thomas Jones Adwy Garth the sum of Twenty pounds with interest at 5 per Cent.

Value received this fourth day of May in the year of our Lord one thousand eight hundred and ninety five.

May 4/95

Promissary Note for £20 reads: "We Edward & Jane Evans of Glyn Mills (sic) promise to pay Thomas Jones, Adwy (Derfyn), Garth, the sum of Twenty pounds with interest at 5%. Value received this 4th day of May in the year of our Lord 1895."
Very little is known about this transaction which represents about a quarter of the year's income for an average worker of the period. The lender was a quarryman who lived at Glynceiriog, who in normal circumstances could ill afford to make such a loan. It would have made more financial sense if the parties had reversed their roles. Edward Evans I was miller between 1872 and 1900. *Mr Robert Owen Jones, Glynceiriog.*

this particular issue was an obituary for a John Jones, who lived at Send in southern England.

This Jones was born in 1815 and his forebears came from the Ceiriog but no details were supplied, and there was nothing about his youthful years. His father owned a jewellers and watch & clockmaking business in the Strand, London. This is a prestigious address to this day, in the heart of the Metropolis and adjacent to Trafalgar Square, and so suggests a high-class retail shop. Young John joined the family business in 1837, aged 22, and eventually assumed its management and ownership, retiring at age 70 in 1885.

John Jones was much interested in technical education, was a Vice-President of the British Horological Society, Fellow of the Royal Geographical Society, sometime member of the London Metropolitan Board of Works, shareholder of the Bank of England, a proprietor of the East India Company, and a renowned after-dinner speaker.

He was also a Liveryman of the City of London for 70 years in the Worshipful Company of Turners, becoming its Master in 1861 at the relatively young age of 46; at the time of his death he was its 'Father'.

Landlord Jones was therefore a wealthy man of wide attainments and interests, and esteemed in public life. He had a sister who married a solicitor in Oswestry but he remained a bachelor all his life. He was 37 years old when he purchased Felin Lyn and was 90 years of age when he sold it. Only with this very recent knowledge, does it become clear that it was John Jones who was responsible for upgrading the Mill in the 1870s, a work described in some detail at the end of Chapter 4.

John Jones died, aged 95, at his retirement home, the Manor House, Send, which is a village two miles south of Woking, in Surrey. His estate amounted to £57,000, a large amount for the times. (Note 3.11)

Whilst searching for the true John Jones, several possible candidates appeared and one of them should be mentioned as having a tenuous connection with the history of Felin Lyn. He is John Jones, senior partner in the 1870s, of the Oswestry firm of solicitors, Longueville & Co.(founded by a Jones in 1803) and Secretary of the Glyn Valley Tramway for 17 years in its horse-traction era. This law firm (Longueville & Co, now Longueville Gittins) has acted for the Chirk Castle and Ruthin Castle estates since the early part of the nineteenth century. Substantial groups of records from the offices of the firm, including documents relating to these estates, have been deposited at the National Library of Wales and are known as the *Longueville Papers*. One substantial deposit is covered by the 1960 preliminary schedule; later ones have been sorted and are largely covered by working lists. If any documentation exists to establish Felin Lyn's building date, then it might lie within these records.

In 1905 owner John Jones sold Felin Lyn to a 44-year-old Liverpool solicitor. The new owner was Alfred Thomas Davies and though Welsh with forebears who had lived on the Denbigh moors, he had no previous connections with the Ceiriog except that he had acquired the house, *Brynhyfryd*, above the Mill, in 1902.

Davies was a contemporary and friend of David Lloyd-George, for they were both young Liverpool lawyers of the 1890s and knew each other's families. Lloyd-George, now a politician, appointed Davies in 1907 to take charge of the newly-created Welsh Department of Education, which separated the function from that of England. This post he held until his retirement in 1925.

Alfred Davies quickly grew very attached to the Ceiriog and he and his wife were largely instrumental in the creation of the Ceiriog Memorial Institute in 1911 at Glynceiriog, which still serves as the valley's principal community centre. In 1918 he was given a Knighthood for services to Welsh education and for setting up educational courses for British prisoners-of-war in their camps abroad. In 1921 he was appointed a Deputy Lieutenant of the County of Denbigh.

In 1931 Sir Alfred Davies' second son, Llewelyn, acquired the properties of Brynhyfryd and Felin Lyn, living in the former until the beginning of World War II. The last landlord of Felin Lyn, by then no longer a watermill, was a John Smith of Wrexham, who purchased it and its fields in 1962 for £1,600. He never took up residence, or had a tenant, and in the mid-1960s disappeared completely. If he is dead, no one knows if his death was accidental or by foul play; it is all a mystery. It was the owner's absence and ensuing neglect that led to the Mill's eventual demolition.

The title deeds to Felin Lyn, which would have been so useful to examine when compiling this history, were in the hands of the Chester solicitors acting for Mr Smith at the time of the purchase. However they were returned to Mr Smith in March 1963 and their present location is unknown.

In the next twenty or so years after the disappearance of John Smith there grew up in the neighbourhood of the former mill a 'tongue-in-cheek' tale that he was in some way connected with the Great Train Robbery. This very major crime occurred in August 1963 when a night mail train from Glasgow to London was ambushed by a gang and nearly £3 million was stolen. The anonymous name of Smith, the juxtaposition of dates, the disappearance of the new owner, and the fact that one of the twenty persons charged with the crime was a Smith, have all helped to produce the connection. It makes for good drama but seems to have little substance. If the Felin Lyn was meant to be a cache for part of the loot, it seems to have been a poor choice for it was easily observed by the neighbouring cottage and after a period of non-occupancy any activity would have been remarked upon.

A summary of owners is as follows:

Chirk Castle Estates

(a) Richard Myddleton (1726-1795) Chirk Castle. Landlord: 1747 to 1795.

(b) Honourable Frederick West (1767-1852) Ruthin Castle. Landlord: 1798 to 1852.

Gentry

(c) John Jones (1815-1909). London and Surrey. Landlord: June 1852 to August 1905.

20th Century

(d) Alfred T. Davies (later Sir) (1861-1949) Liverpool and London, with house at Pontfadog.
Landlord: August 1905 to July 1931.

(e) T. Llewelyn Davies (son of above), (1892-1978). Various, Pontfadog and Border country.
Landlord: July 1931 to July 1962.

(f) John R. Thompson Smith, Wrexham.
Landlord from July 1962 to ???.

Rural Craftsmen

Until the late eighteenth century the machinery of all mills was made solely of wood and was built by the local joiner and carpenter, or by a specialist called a millwright.

Iron components were first tried out in Britain in about 1780 and it took the next 50-100 years for the practice to spread to most of the watermills in the land. But to the very end of rural milling, it was rare to find a mill with machinery made entirely of iron. It was better to alternate the parts of the transmission between wood and iron, as the former yielded to the latter and gave smoother and quieter running. It also prevented sparking which could lead to a fire and possible total loss of the premises.

It is probable the machinery of Felin Lyn was made entirely of wood when the Mill was built, and that at varying times in the nineteenth century pieces requiring replacement were converted to iron. Maybe at the time of the renovations of the 1870s the proper mix of wood and iron components was achieved, if that state had not already been reached.

At all times in the eighteenth century a carpenter and a blacksmith would have been available at Chirk, and possibly at Llwynmawr. Certainly from the mid-nineteenth century such craftsmen operated their trades at Llwynmawr. There is a smithy at the cross roads of that village, built in 1873 and still in use. The fourth son of Evan Evans, the miller of Felin Lyn, became the blacksmith of this smithy in about 1890. It has remained in family hands ever since – followed by John, then Absalom, and now Tecwyn: although the last named now works with welding equipment, he still calls himself a blacksmith – 'gof' in Welsh. A new and additional smithy opened in Pontfadog c.1880 but closed about 1950. As a small boy, the author knew the latter well as it was one of the village 'hang-outs'; he still remembers having a hoop and guide rod made to his requirements in front of his very eyes at the forge.

These smiths would have been capable of fabricating and repairing any small ironwork required in the Mill. The only job that could not be tackled would be failures of castings caused by fractures and teeth stripping. In such cases replacements would have to be cast at any one of several foundries in the district.

In practice a good smith could, and did, make permanent repairs to casting breaks by making splints or straps and securing with bolts or some device. Replacement gearwheel teeth could be hand-forged and likewise secured in place. Ingenuity was the keyword. This alternative was cheaper and more expeditious than seeking replacement castings.

No doubt the carpenter at Llwynmawr did all the necessary wooden repairs to the Mill prior to about 1870, but at this date the work passed into the hands of the miller's family. The fourth son of Evan Evans became a blacksmith, as noted, and his second son, Godfrey became a carpenter and joiner, and the third son became a builder. As described by Mrs Jones (FL) earlier, the builder and carpenter operated a business out of the barn and this probably lasted from about 1875 to about 1890. It is said that they built the Rectory at Pontfadog in the 1880s and as a result of this and other experiences went out of business or became bankrupt.

Another craftsman, not essential to milling but useful for emergency repairs and cart making, was the wheelwright at Llwynmawr. Traditionally called wheelwrights, their true trade was of wagon-wright or cartwright. At Llwynmawr he was a joiner, cartwright and funeral undertaker, since wagons were never built in the Ceiriog. The last person to do this as a lifetime occupation was Richard Jones (1850-1929); he was regarded locally as an excellent craftsman. The shop, located in a part of the old tithe barn, continued to be run until 1933 and again between 1942 and 1950 when it finally closed. It was Richard Jones who made the two-wheeled cart that was used by the last miller at Felin Lyn, Edward Evans II.

The local joiner at Glynceiriog, Jonah Phillips (1858-1929), also did work at the mill in the first two decades of this century as shown by the extracts from his account book in Chapter 1. Jonah Phillips was also a man of some local standing, being a Justice of the Peace and a Baptist lay preacher, variously at Glynceiriog, Dolywern and Castlemill. He traded from a building known as the Old Pandy (former water-driven fulling mill) close to Pont Bell at Glynceiriog. In his son's day, the business expanded into a small building firm and is still in existence, managed by grandson Melvin.

In Phillips' account of work done at Felin Lyn in 1919 he lists 'working with the millwright'. Unfortunately there is now no local recollection of the names or personalities of any regional millwright. In that same year a trade directory for Gloucestershire listed only two millwrights, so the presumption is that Denbighshire also had only two or three at that date. One of them is known. He was David Williams (1861-1953) who trained as a millwright, sawyer, carpenter and joiner near Mold and who spent the last year of his apprenticeship in Liverpool. He then emigrated to Texas, USA, and did all kinds of building work in wood but returned to Wales in 1894. In 1900 Williams purchased Pentre Mill, Loggerheads, near Mold, which was both a cornmill and a sawmill but the emphasis was on the latter function. David Williams and his mill both ceased working in 1942. (Note 3.12)

Yet another craftsman essential to milling was the stone-dresser. Millstones need to have their faces dressed at intervals, otherwise their shearing action becomes blunted and poor quality meal is produced. The problem with French burr stones is that the 'lands' become glazed at the skirt after too much grinding, and reduces both quality and quantity of the meal. The time between dressings depends on several factors, such as type of stone, type of grain and running hours and the subject of frequency of dressings is somewhat akin to the question, 'How often do you sharpen your pencil?'. It all depends upon the type and quality of the pencil, what it is used for, and the demands and expectations of the writer. One unidentified source claimed that a burr was dressed about every 300 hours and after producing 15 tons of fine flour or 25 tons of coarse meal; another source quoted 50 tons of flour and 80 tons of meal.

Mrs Jones (FL) recollected, *"The stones were dressed two or three times a year by a trained and experienced stone dresser who travelled around the district."* The late Mrs Humphreys of Pontfadog usefully added that *"...after World War I this was done by a Mr Williams of Selattyn"*, which is a village with a mill some four miles to the south-east.

At first sight, Mrs Jones' recollection shows a very infrequent dressing of the millstones. A possible explanation is that it relates to the French burrs, which for equal tonnage, require less frequency of dressing than the softer monolithic stones. Also in the twentieth century Felin Lyn was milling much less wheat than in the two previous centuries, so reducing the burr running time. This frequency is echoed by the miller of Hundred House Mill, Radnorshire, who said that his stones were dressed twice yearly in the 1920s.

The time taken to dress a pair of stones depended upon the diameter, hardness, and amount of bluntness, but a rough and ready guide would be two or three days for dismantling, dressing, reassembly and balancing of a pair.

Another stone dresser lived in the district in this century. He was Alfred Peate of Glynceiriog who worked at this trade until he was in his early seventies; he died in 1953 aged 76. Mr Peate did not work at Felin Lyn but it is known that he dressed the stones of watermills at Chirk, Erbistock and Rossett, travelling by bicycle. Despite the identical name, he was not connected with Peates Mill at Maesbury, just south of Oswestry.

Customers

Before reviewing the customers of Felin Lyn in an objective and somewhat impersonal fashion, it might be of interest briefly to describe the social fabric and the countryside in which these people lived.

The first point to make is that many parts of Wales, Scotland and Ireland do not have the compact villages that are such a characteristic of England. The tidy mix of manor house, church, pub, village green and surrounding houses and cottages, created by feudalism, is not a feature of the Celtic countryside.

Such was the case with the area about Felin Lyn. This mill was not a village watermill; it was a mill built in the countryside, in isolation, serving an area of farms. Before about 1850 there really was no such place as Pontfadog, only a stone bridge called Pont Fadog (Madoc's bridge). At no time, whilst it was working as a toll-mill, did anyone ever think of Felin Lyn as the mill of Pontfadog or Llwynmawr. In this century, for ease of reference and mail delivery, it was associated with Pontfadog.

Since everyone who lived within about a two-mile radius of Felin Lyn – before the end of the last century – was a customer of the Mill, it is legitimate to describe the whole community and the land on which they lived and from which they made their living.

The countryside immediately around the Mill was devoted solely to farming. It was the only activity and everybody worked at it in some capacity or other. That is, excepting about a tenth of the local population who provided services for the majority that worked the land. It was still the age of local self-sufficiency.

Farming was mixed, but the raising of livestock such as cattle, sheep and pigs, was dominant, followed laggardly by dairying. Crops, such as hay, cereals and roots, were grown through necessity but the acreage devoted to them was relatively small.

From data listed in various documents of the nineteenth century it has been possible to build up a picture of the territory of Felin Lyn and the people who lived there. There were about 70 farms ranging in size from a five-acre smallholding to units of about 200 acres, but the average sized farm was of 35 acres and was worked by the family, with the help of one servant in many cases.

An equal number of people in the community did not live on farms. They lived in houses and cottages with ample gardens, and in such places as smithies and pubs. Some of these people were old and retired and in the 1851 Census some of them were listed as paupers, meaning that they received some Parish relief.

Contrary to popular image, the size of households, whether they were farm or otherwise, was not large. Most ranged between two and seven people and could include in-laws and servants; such households accounted for four-fifths of the community. Persons living alone were rare.

Nowadays we would talk about live-in employees but 150 years ago these were classified as 'servants', irrespective of type of work or sex. At that time about one-eighth of the local community fell into this category and worked as farm labourers, cowmen, dairy maids, apprentices, and domestics. They were invariably found in all farms of over 50 acres in size and 'service' households such as smithies and inns. They were also frequently found at farms of 20-50 acre size.

Jobs performed by the 'non-farmers' remind us how self-contained were these country communities. The 1851 Census shows that within the Parish of Glyn Traian there were: Shoemakers, 7; butchers, stonemasons, wheelwrights, publicans, and dressmakers, 4 each; basket makers, bailiffs, blacksmiths, joiners, tailors, 2 each; and one each of the following – canal carrier, chandler, grocer, lime merchant, midwife, *miller, mill carrier*, milliner, shopkeeper, salter, washer-woman.

When this list was first extracted, the author was surprised to see it headed by shoemakers and thought perhaps he had stumbled upon an enclave of shoemakers, but when reading randomly about other British villages with tradesmen data, he came to see that shoe/boot makers usually headed the list numerically. There seemed to be about one shoemaker for every 125-200 persons. A curious omission in the above list is the trade of saddler for every farm had harness. It is presumed a shoemaker would do any light repairs, leaving a town saddler the specialised work.

In the same vein it seemed there was one rural miller to every 500-700 head of population. As will be presently seen the miller at Felin Lyn serviced about 550 territory inhabitants in the last century.

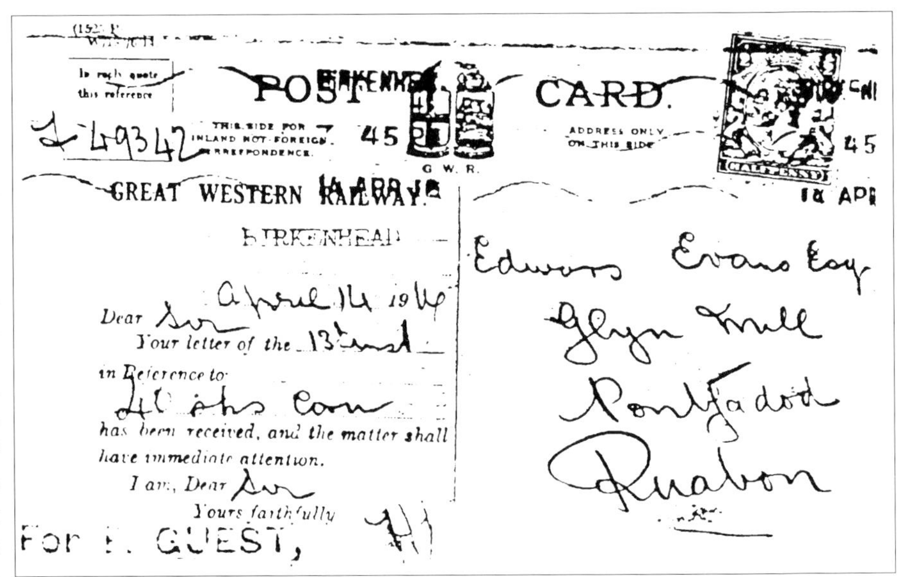

In reply quote this reference
L49342

POST CARD.

THIS SIDE FOR INLAND NOT FOREIGN CORRESPONDENCE.

ADDRESS ONLY ON THIS SIDE

GREAT WESTERN RAILWAY

BIRKENHEAD

Dear Sir April 14 1916

Your letter of the 13th inst

in Reference to 40 qrs corn

has been received, and the matter shall have immediate attention.

I am, Dear Sir

Yours faithfully

For F. GUEST,

Edward Evans Esq

Glyn Mill

Pontfadog

Ruabon

A typical example of 'confirmation of order' postcard received by the miller of Felin Lyn in April 1916, mailed from Birkenhead, Merseyside. Forty Quarters of corn (possibly maize) amounts to 320 bushels and would have been delivered in 90-120 sacks; whether by canal or railway is undetermined.

The late Mrs Gwladys Jones.

Within a two-mile radius of Felin Lyn there were five *nuclei* or hamlets, but certainly no village. The largest and most important was Pentre Cilgwyn which, after the clearing of the great grove or bushland, moved its centre a quarter of a mile down the slope and called itself Llwynmawr. In mid-nineteenth century it boasted a blacksmith, wheelwright, butcher and an inn. In the name Cilgwyn it is thought that 'gwyn' is a corruption of an older Welsh word 'gwydd' meaning trees or glade. 'Cil' means 'recess/corner/retreat' so there comes the concept of a shady and sheltered spot and that is what it is to this day. Extant property deeds of the area have the spelling 'Pentre Cilgywdd'.

The nearest hamlet to Felin Lyn was the Graig (crag or rock) which perched on a steep hillside a quarter of a mile to the north-east. During this period it could claim an inn with shop attached, the 'Butcher's Arms', plus a tailor, shoemaker, dressmaker and stonemason.

Mrs Jones (FL) remembered a tailor in the Graig but of this century. He was called Lot-y-Teiliwr (Lot the Tailor) and always wore a tail coat. She recounted: *"He used to come to the Mill for a week or so to make my father's corduroy trousers and corduroy waistcoat with linen sleeves and linen back. My mother would clear the mats and Lot would sit cross-legged on the floor and draft out the material with white chalk. As a child I used to be fascinated watching him as he worked so deftly."* This places the scene circa 1910.

An adjacent hamlet, separated only by the Afon Ceiriog and lying on flatter land, was Pentre Pont Fadog but it had only a Methodist chapel (1806) and the Swan Inn.

George Borrow, the author of *"Wild Wales"*, visited both Pentre Pont Fadog and the Graig in the summer of 1854, when he made Llangollen the starting point of his famous walking tour in Wales. The recognisable description of his visit is contained in Chapter XI of his book. He remarks upon the beauty and the silence, meeting only two persons in these two hamlets. One is Thomas Davies, shoemaker aged 50, in the Graig and the other is a *"...good looking woman"* at the Swan Inn, Pontfadog, called Jane Edwards, aged 22. Here he had some ale in a neat sanded kitchen.

The fourth hamlet no longer exists, a victim of being bypassed by better roads. It was called Garth Obry (below the enclosure) and lay $1^1/_4$ miles west of Chirk Castle on the north side of the river. In 1851 it possessed five cottages and a wheelwright and close by was a grocer and a shoemaker. The 1914 edition of the Six Inch Ordnance Survey map, and even more recent maps, honour its existence by the fact that Garth Obry is written in the same size lettering as Pontfadog and Llwynmawr.

The fifth and final hamlet was Castlemill, just to the west of Offa's Dyke and in the valley below Chirk Castle. It had four cottages and an inn which George Borrow also visited and described as being formerly the mill of the

Castle. In the immediate vicinity lived a joiner and a wheelwright. The place has declined in size and is now not even a hamlet.

The whole area was very Welsh. All the place names down to names of dwellings were in Welsh, except two. Ninety-five percent of the households were Welsh, and the language of the home, field, chapel, marketplace and inn was Welsh.

Jones was the dominant surname and if this had been a Scottish glen it would have been occupied by the clan MacJones, for a quarter of the inhabitants carried that name. Another half of the people shared but six surnames; in descending order of occurrence they were: Edwards, Davies, Roberts, Hughes, Evans and Parry. The 'Sais' or Saxons were kept firmly on the other side of Offa's Dyke. (Note 3.13)

This paucity of Welsh surnames is due to the use of patronymics in Wales until 250 years ago – John ap (son of) William, ap Edward, ap Thomas, and so on. As a result there are few Welsh surnames and most of them are derived from Christian names; Jones is but a corruption of John's son. This explains the Welsh habit of using unofficial identifiers to differentiate people with the same name, such as 'Jones the Shop' (village store), 'Alfred the Grate' (A. Jones, chimney sweep), or 'Jones Pen-Craig' (farm).

As to land tenure at the beginning of the nineteenth century, it appears that much of the land was owned by Chirk Castle, but Sir Watkin Williams-Wynn, another large North Wales landowner, had properties in the townships of Nantgwryd, Talygarth, and Hafodgynfawr. However, unlike parts of England, this land holding by the large estates was not total and there were scattered pieces owned by occupiers. For example, John Hughes (Dol) says that his father rented the watermill at Dolywern but owned Accerfawr (big acre), Ddol Isa (lower meadow) and Ddol Uchaf (upper meadow) .

There was a certain independence to these people, partly a racial characteristic, and partly due to the social equality of the local community. Added to this was a Celtic wit and a teasing sense of humour. There was no local squire and no big house or manor. The only house that fits that description in the Parish of Glyn Traian is Plas Tan-y-Garth (hall below the enclosure) but this was built in 1915 and its cost so crippled the owner widow that she sold it within six years.

With regard to religion, this part of Wales was as much affected by the popularity of Non-Conformism as anywhere else in the Principality. It offered a democratic religious and educational organisation run by local lay leaders and had instant appeal for the labourer and tenant farmer. This contrasted with the 'Church of England', in Wales, which was regarded as part of the English establishment and was dominated by the large landowners and the gentry. The first Non-Conformist chapel in the Ceiriog was built by the Baptists in 1762, and the first built within the territory of Felin Lyn was by the Wesleyan Methodists at Pontfadog in 1806.

The second half of the nineteenth century saw changes to the life style of the area so far described, slow at first but accelerating as this century was reached. The initiator of the change was the Church of England which, in 1848, created a new parish and in 1847 built a church at its geographical centre and not 300 yards from Felin Lyn. Then in the 1860s a toll road was built along the valley floor, which altered the focus of living. Instead of climbing hills to get out of the valley, people now proceeded along the flat to Chirk where there was a railway. In 1873, as already described, a horse tramway was built beside the toll-road and this in turn was upgraded and converted to steam traction in 1888.

At first Llwynmawr had more amenities than Pentre Pont Fadog but the latter had eclipsed the former by 1900 because it was on the main road and could also boast a railway halt and the telegraph. By this time both villages had a village store-cum-post-office, pub, chapel and smithy. Such is the backcloth against which we will examine the customers of Felin Lyn in more clinical style.

Customers are the reason for, and the very life blood of, any business and without them a business withers, as almost all watermills in this century discovered. It would be negligent not to take stock of the customers of this Mill, but the author has to admit he experienced difficulty in writing the rest of this Section and views his findings as tentative. The problem is partly a matter of interpretation and the reader is asked actively to question the contents and come to his own independent conclusions. The tonnage figures at the very end of the Section are open to question.

With this cautionary note, an examination is now made of the two groups of customers – humans and animals – served by Felin Lyn.

Human Customers (19th century)

For the human customers, we have an accurate count for the whole of the nineteenth century, thanks to the national Census taken at ten year intervals since 1801. The Census counted people and dwellings in the Parish of Glyn Traian and by taking 60% of this data we have the numbers of people and dwellings in the territory of the Mill for the whole of the century. To reduce the amount of statistics in the table below, details have been listed at 30 year intervals.

Table 6
People and houses in the 19th Century – Local

Year of Census	*Parish of Glyn Traian*		*Territory of Felin Lyn*	
	Persons	*Dwellings*	*Persons*	*Dwellings*
1801	805	153	483	92
1831	868	178	520	107
1861	975	202	585	212
1891	935	198	561	118
Century Average	896	183	537	110

So without getting too technical, we know that Felin Lyn's task in the human food chain was to provide milled grains for an average of 540 persons, who lived in 110 dwellings.

It is important to remember that until 1873, when a horse tramway was built in the valley and when North American wheat was about to enter Britain, all residents were customers and conversely all customers were residents.

From about 1875 onwards there was an erosion of this pattern, slow at first and then quickening, which resulted in the Mill losing all its human customers – except for a handful – by 1920 at the latest when a bakery was in operation at Pontfadog.

In the heyday of local food production nearly half of all the households in Glyn Traian grew cereals of some kind. If one excludes houses and cottages with only gardens attached and smallholdings of nine acres and less, then it can be said that nearly all of the farms grew grain.

A field of two acres of wheat could adequately feed the average-sized family of five for 12 months. In medieval strip farming crops were grown on acre lots and there must have been a relationship between the size of the lot and its capacity to feed the family that tilled it. It is also interesting to note that a 1589 Statute stipulated that a cottage built for a labourer must also have four acres of land attached; this area being assessed as being sufficient to provide food for one family. It also forbade the division of the cottage into two halves. The Act was not repealed until 1775. (Note 3.14)

That farms of perhaps 10 to 20 acres in size grew cereals should really come as no surprise. As well as the grain, straw was needed to feed and provide litter for the family's milk cow. These small farms had room only to grow one type of grain each year and because of the necessity of crop rotation, it meant that the farmer had to purchase any other grains needed.

The small size of the operation was a virtue, rather than a liability. A small farmer could not afford equipment and almost all the operations of soil preparation, sowing, and harvesting were done by the farmer and his family, and a borrowed horse if he was not fortunate enough to own one.

It is fairly certain all Ceiriog farms of over 20 acres grew cereals. The 20 acre farms probably grew one or two acres of oats only, whilst a 50 acre farm probably grew 5 or 6 acres of corn, of which oats was the dominant grain.

The composition of the size of land holdings in the territory of Felin Lyn is unknown, but a synthetic model can be produced by using the national statistics for England and Wales in the late nineteenth century. It is felt it would have this kind of profile:

Table 7
Number of holdings, acreages and persons

Size of holding	*Less than 1 acre*	*1-19 acres*	*20-40 acres*	*50-149 acres*	*150-299 acres*	*300+ acres*	*Grand Total*
Growing grain	None	Some	◄—	Grain growers		—►	—
No. of holdings	30	33	20	23	4	1	111
Combined acreage	30 (1.5%)	330 (7%)	700 (15%)	2,300 (49%)	900 (19%)	400 (8%)	4,660 (100%)
Persons (probable)	90 (17%)	165 (31%)	100 (19%)	138 (26%)	30 (6%)	12 (2%)	537 (100%)

Assuming thirteen of the thirty-three holdings shown in the '1 to 19 acres' size were of 10 acres or more and grew grain, then it is reasonable to assume some 60 local farms grew grain and took some of it to Felin Lyn to be ground.

It is probable farms of less than fifty acres took back in entirety their milled products to feed their households and their stock. This would apply to about 30 to 35 farms and smallholdings.

On the other hand, the larger farms produced an excess of grain based upon their own needs and it is quite possible that some or all of this excess was sold to the miller at Felin Lyn, or in the case of barley to the maltster at Dolywern. The miller, in turn, would process it and sell it to those families of the neighbourhood who rented or possessed no farming land, or who worked a smallholding of less than ten acres. It has been deduced from the table that this group consisted of about 190 persons or some fifty households and accounted for 35% of the population of Felin Lyn's territory. A list of all the known dwellings in the territory is given in Appendix VI.

From this review, it becomes strikingly clear how Felin Lyn acted as an intermediary in the redistribution of grain within the community. The bulk of the human food requirements was for wheaten flour for bread-making, though some oatmeal and a small amount of barley were also needed.

Bread consumption in the last century was about one pound per day for an active adult and more for a late teenager. It requires about one-and-one-third pounds of wheat grain to produce one pound of wheaten flour, and about three quarters of a pound of flour to make one pound of bread. To simplify the arithmetic, let it be assumed that one adult needed 365lb of wheat annually to give him or her one pound of bread daily.

The average population in the nineteenth century of Felin Lyn' s 'territory' was 537 persons so the total weight of wheat required annually to feed this population was: 537 persons × 365lb = 196,000lb or 3,266 bushels (at 60lbs/bushel) This wheat requirement was well within the projected harvest yields as shown in Table 3 and suggests an annual export of the surplus as grain or flour, perhaps up-valley to areas where more inclement weather and higher altitudes would produce less wheat.

Barley was sparsely used in cooking and it is unlikely that the local population would consume more than two tons in a year. However, barley was also used to brew local beer and later chapters show that 15-20 tons of the harvest was diverted for this use. Such an amount has not been included in the 'Human Food' table below. Turning to oats, it has been estimated that a Welsh person in the last century would consume daily not more than two ounces of oatmeal in porridge, soups, cakes and other dishes. The arithmetic gives us:

537 persons × 2oz × 365 days = 24,500lb
or 765 bushels (at 32lb/bushel)

All the foregoing shows in rough and ready terms that the human customers ate a third of the cereal harvest.

Table 8
Human food as a percentage of harvest

Cereal	*Average harvest*		*Human food*		*As % of harvest*
	Bushels	*Tons*	*Bushels*	*Tons*	
Wheat	3,960	106	3,266	88	83%
Oats	7,520	107	765	11	10%
Barley	5,075	109	100	2	2%
Totals	*16,555*	*322*	*4,131*	*101*	*31%*

Animal Customers (19th century)

Animal husbandry and grain farming have co-existed for a very long time. In most primitive circumstances, or when a harvest was particularly bad, all the grain was eaten by the family and none went to the animals. Then through centuries with improved productivity, excess grain was fed to the animals to improve their meat or their performance if they were in draught. When horses displaced oxen in the mid- to late-eighteenth century, it became imperative to feed the horses oats when they were at work.

By the nineteenth century, the advantages of feeding grain to animals was a fact of farm life. But desire and fulfilment are not the same thing and an upland farmer, working not the best of lands, would be careful as to how he doled out grain to his animals; only in the case of horses would he be sweet reasonableness, for it was a case of 'no oats, no work'.

The influx of cheap imported grains, chiefly wheat, at the end of the last century reduced the price of home-grown cereals and this encouraged a trend to feed more barley and grain to animals. The importation of maize, as animal feedstuff, was also an innovation of the second half of the last century. The trend to feed animals on grain has continued unabated to this day and now includes wheat, a cereal never given to animals until recent decades.

We now come to a tightrope situation. The fundamental question is in what state and in what quantities was this grain fed to animals in the territory of Felin Lyn? The only grains to be considered are barley and oats, since wheat was then never fed to animals.

A reasonable estimate can be made of the animal population in the territory of Felin Lyn. Statistics exist for the animal population of Denbighshire for 1918 which may be a trifle inflated because of the war, but they remain our only guide. The pig population looks surprisingly low and it is thought that it should be at least double the amount shown. Possibly the wartime returns came only from farms and so excluded the smallholdings and cottages that also kept pigs. (Note 3.15)

Table 9
Animal population of the 'territory'

Animal	*Denbighshire in 1918*		*Territory at Felin*
	Per 1000 acres	*Acres per animal*	*(at 4,700 acres)*
Sheep	1,117	0.9	5,250
Cattle	236	4	1,110
Pigs	76	13	357
Horses	29	35	136

Experiments have shown conclusively that cattle, sheep, and especially pigs, thrive on crushed or 'rolled' grains. In the case of horses this is not so and they perform equally well whether fed with whole or bruised grains.

On the other hand, working horses have to be fed some grain to make them efficient hauliers, whereas other animals can survive without grain. It is left to the farmer's discretion as to how much grain he will feed such animals and depends upon the availability and price of such feed and current market prices for sale animals.

Nowadays it is difficult to grasp what a multitude of horses existed in Britain in the previous 200 years, working on farms, country roads and town streets. In 1811 there were $1^1/_4$ million, 2 million in 1871, $2^3/_4$ million in 1891, reaching a peak of 3.4 million in 1901. Horses did almost all the heavy farm work and local haulage of people and goods. Even in 1924 when the 'infernal' combustion engine was firmly in the ascendancy in the life of Britain, there were still just over 2 million horses at work. (Note 3.15)

It has been said that nearly a fifth of Britain's fields were needed to feed its horse population in the late nineteenth century, remembering that at least a third of the horses were stabled and worked in urban areas and rarely saw green pasture. Of the cereals, horses ate only oats and this explains why Welsh farms felt less of the agricultural depression – starting in the 1880s – than did many English farms where wheat had been the mainstay. Oat fields then were what oil fields are now – fuel providers.

A shire horse consumed from 7lbs (light work) to 16lbs (heavy work) of oats per day, whilst a lighter Welsh cob would eat a third less. When out on pasture at rest no grain would be fed. Calculations show that the average horse of the last century ate a daily average of 4lbs of oats, or about 1,500lb annually. For the estimated horse population of Felin Lyn's territory at 134 horses, this works out at about 6,300 bushels or about 85 tons of oats each year. This, coupled with human requirements, would absorb most of the oat harvest.

The vital question at this stage is how much of the oat feed for horses went to Felin Lyn for crushing or bruising? The answer has the wide range from 'nil' to '85 tons'.

We turn now from oats to barley. Twentieth-century experiments show whole barley as being 15% less digestible than rolled barley when fed to cattle. However, it is imperative the barley must be coarsely ground and any fine particles removed because the barley 'flour' causes stomach bloat. Whether a nineteenth century Welsh farmer knew this from trial and error or from the wisdom of generations is not known; but it is certain he bruised some of his barley. For these hypothetical calculations it will be assumed some 75 tons of local barley was bruised or converted to coarse meal each year.

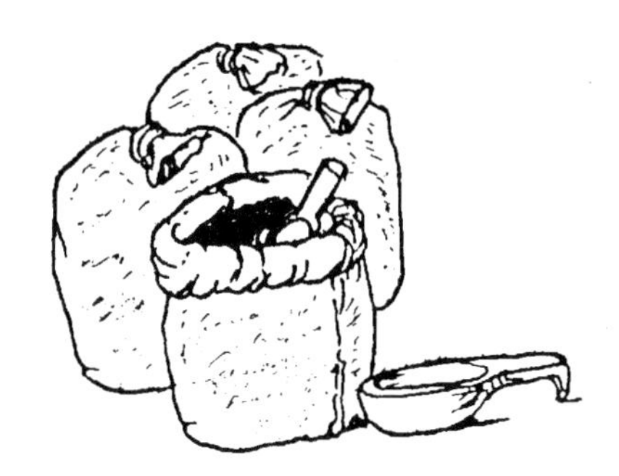

A residue of brewing is spent malt, which is to beer as tea leaves are to tea. It is an unwanted residue originating as barley, but unlike tea leaves it makes good animal feed. Llwynmawr Inn made its own beer until about 1930, and so always had malt mash ('soeg' in Welsh) to dispose of. It is known that the last miller of Felin Lyn, Edward Evans II, would give it to his pigs and sometimes they got drunk on it!

As an etymological aside, it is worth noting that the words 'barn' and 'beer' both derive from the Anglo-Saxon word for barley, a barn being a place where barley sheaves were kept. It should be noticed in this story of Felin Lyn that the topic of beer intrudes every now and then, for there has always been a connection between milling and brewing.

Combination of Human and Animal Customers

By combining the commentary on humans and animals it is possible to form a reasonably clear idea of what types and tonnage of grain were handled by Felin Lyn in an average year of the mid-nineteenth century, and for whom the products were destined.

The problem of oat processing cannot be resolved, so an arbitrary decision has been made that half the oat harvest went to the Mill for processing, i.e. 42 tons.

In the case of all three grains, a deduction of 10% has been made to provide seed for the next year's planting. Twenty tons of barley have also been added to the 'Humans' column to make local beer.

Table 10
Cereal consumption by humans and animals (in tons)

Grain	*Average harvest*	*Deduct seed*	*Available to use*	*Humans*		*Animals*		*Both*	
				Tons	*%*	*Tons*	*%*	*Tons*	*%*
Oats	107	10%	96	11	11	42	44	53	55
Barley	109	10%	98	22	22	75	76	97	99
Wheat	106	10%	96	88	92	Nil	Nil	88	92
Totals	*322*	*32*	*290*	*121*	*42*	*117*	*40*	*238*	*82*

As previously mentioned, caution has to be exercised in using the results of this table, but in general it appears to be realistic.

To sum up: the territory of Felin Lyn in the mid nineteenth century grew some 325 tons of grain a year in an average harvest, and after seed grain was set aside there were 290 tons available for some kind of use. It is possible four-fifths of this available grain went to the mill for processing.

Despite the fact that in the last century literally hundreds of cornmills worked in Britain, no data (if it has survived) has been published on this very fundamental aspect. The only three tonnage details known to the author tend to confirm that the estimated Felin Lyn tonnages are acceptable.

First, a reference to Pentrefoelas mill in south-western Denbighshire, which had three pairs of stones and was identical to Felin Lyn in this regard. The late George Heald, whose father ran the mill from 1920 to 1949, says *"I would roughly estimate production to be one ton per day, but during World War II there were certain days when it ran uninterrupted for 24 hours, and others when it ran all day except for stopping for a short lunch break. During this period perhaps 300 to 350 tons per annum was processed, and it could have been more."*

The second reference comes from a renovated uplands mill at the village of Little Salkeld in Cumbria. This watermill has two pairs of stones and currently produces between some 150 and 200 tons of flour annually.

The last reference comes from Church Minshull in Cheshire where the mill worked until 1954. This mill had two undershot wheels and each drove three pairs of stones. Towards the end of its life it was producing about 2 tons per day of barley, oats, split corn, poultry & cattle feed, or one ton per waterwheel per day.

It is with a sense of relief that the summary can be presented in pictorial fashion as a flow chart. The false precision of the arithmetic has happily given way to approximations.

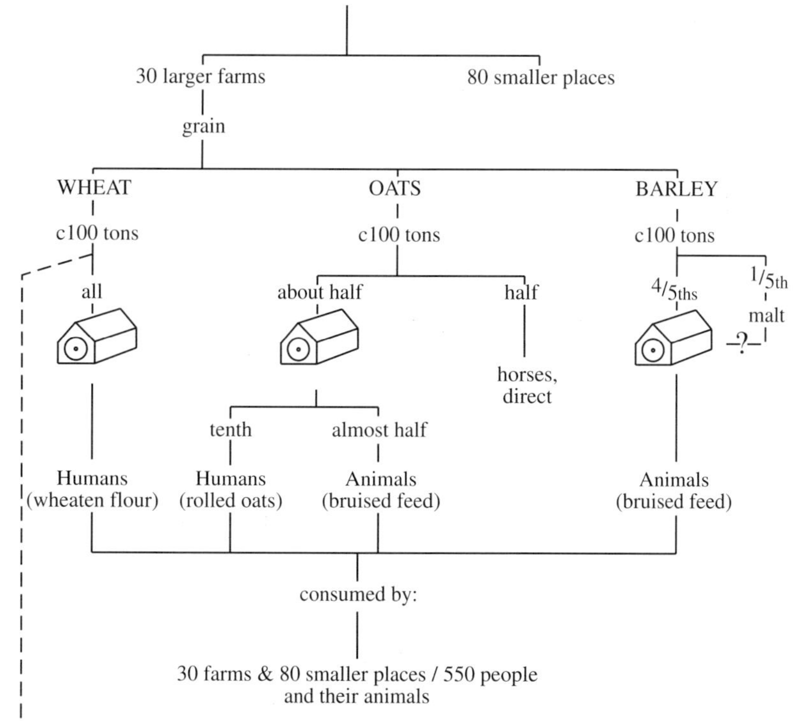

NOTES

3.1 **Mrs Gwladys Jones**, nee Evans (1902-92). Eldest daughter of Felin Lyn miller Edward Evans II. Recollections contained in several letters written 1981-85 to the author.

3.2 **Disappearance of Tombstones:** No malicious act need be attributed. Earlier tombstones were made from slab stones or slate and these eventually disintegrate with weathering. This has happened to tombstones of the author's forebears buried in Nantglyn churchyard, Denbighshire, in the last 50 years.

3.3 **Infant Mortality**. The author can attest to this. His great grandmother, Annie Davies, bore seven children between 1861 and 1872 and only two of them reached adulthood. The successive deaths were at 18 months, 3 months, 15 months, 2 months, and 14 years; the last child dying of typhoid fever.

3.4 **Life Expectancy**. See '*English Life Tables*' No 1 (issued 1845) and No 14 (issued 1987) by Registrar-General of England and Wales, both published by HMSO.

3.5 **Newsletter:** "*Hel Achau, No 31*", Summer 1990, Clwyd Family Historian, ISSN 0260 1975, Ruthin. Article 'Hughes – Glynceiriog' by Angela Downs, p.4 & 5.

3.6 **Education in Ceiriog**. See appendix 'Education' in booklet "*The Ceiriog: One Piece in Historical Jigsaw Puzzle of Welsh-English Border*". David Ll. Davies (same author as this book), Chirk, Chirk Local History Society, 1991, 42pp.

3.7 **Welsh as a Current Language.** One example of spoken Welsh in the Ceiriog. The Glyn Valley Tramway Society (history & artifacts) started an oral history project in 1992 to record memories of the narrow-gauge roadside railway by people who had been its employees or passengers. By the end of 1994, 4½ hours of interviews had been recorded, of which 70% were given in Welsh. It should be mentioned that this Society has recently purchased and restored the Tramway 'station' (a simple waiting room) at Pontfadog, built in 1894.

3.8 **Book:** "*The Lloyd-George I Knew*" Sir A. T. Davies, KBE, CB (author's grandfather), London, H. E. Walter Ltd., 1948, 146pp. Photo on p62 shows Mrs Lloyd-George at Brynhyfryd, close to Felin Lyn.

3.9 **Landlords of the Glyn at 1839**. Preamble to an Enclosure Act of 14 May 1839 affecting parts of the Parishes of Llangollen and Llainsaintfraid (sic) Glyn Ceiriog lists the following landlords: "Charlotte Myddelton Biddulph, widow, Lady of the Honour or Lordship of Chirk and Chirkland; Honourable Frederick West; Sir Watkin Williams Wynn, Baronet; Robert Myddelton Biddulph Esq; William Ormsby Gore Esq; Richard Jones Esq.; and several other persons".

3.10 **Sale of Felin Lyn in 1852**: Handbill/catalogue advertising auction held 4th June 1852, Oswestry. Contains details of 30 Lots sold. Document privately held, and is a sale particular measuring 14" by 9" and contains 3 maps with one page printed both sides giving Lot Numbers, description of the property, tenants and quantities. The solicitors dealing with the sale were Longueville and Williams, Oswestry.

3.11 **Obituary, John Jones, 1909**: See p.111 (15/9/09) of Vol XI, *"Bye -Gones"* (Anon), 2nd Series covering 1909 & 1910. Published by Thomas Woodall, Minshall, Thomas & Co, Oswestry & Wrexham, 1911, 300pp. Copy held by Oswestry Public Library.

3.12 **Denbighshire Millwright**. See booklet "*The Last Miller, Pentre Mill, Loggerheads, Mold*" by grandson J. Idris Davies. Clwyd County Council, 1986. 28pp.

3.13 **Names of Heads of Households in Parish of Glyn Traian in 1851**. (Source is 1851 Census, held 30th March.) In 171 households within the Parish, 162 households held one of 23 Welsh surnames, and 9 households each carried an English surname. Dominant Welsh surnames, in descending order were: JONES (25%), EDWARDS (13%), DAVIES (9%), ROBERTS (9%), HUGHES (8%), EVANS (5%), PARRY (4%), WILLIAMS (4%). These names accounted for 77% of all household head names. GRIFFITHS, MORRIS, ROGERS, WYNNE, FFOULKES, and OWENS were found in two to five households each. There were single instances of: ELLIS, HOWELL, LEWIS, LLOYD, MORGANS, PHILLIPS, PRICE, THOMAS and TUDOR.

3.14 **Estimate of Annual Grain Needs of One Family** (pre-18th century). Would not have changed significantly over the centuries, whether B.C. or A.D., except for introduction of potato in 16th-17th century. Adults and teenagers used to eat 1lb of cereals per day or 350 to 400lb per annum. Family of 5, consisting of 2 adults, 1 teenager and 2 children, would need 1,400 to 1,600lb each year.
Assuming family lived in Ceiriog and grew equal weights of oats and barley and put aside one-tenth of crop for seed, then its yearly needs were 30 bushels of oats and 20 bushels of barley. Assume yield was 15 bushels/acre, then 2 acres of oats and 1-1/2 acres of barley were sown and harvested. Add the output of another l/2 acre to cover wastage in harvesting, storage and for poor harvests, so total acreage needed is 4 acres. This represents a per-capita annual consumption of about 9 bushels of grain. This happens to fit comfortably with an ancient Welsh land unit, the tyddyn (small farmstead) which possessed 4 erw (acres), and that 4 tyddynnod made one rhandir (shareland). Most tyddynnod possessed two oxen, and so a rhandir was capable of supplying eight oxen to pull the communal plough.
These notes have been put together by the author and are offered for discussion, rather than as fact.

3.15 **Book:** "*Agricultural Atlas of Wales*". Howell, J. P., Southampton, Ordnance Survey, 1921.

3.16 **Book:** "*English Agriculture – An Historical Perspective*". David Grigg, Oxford, Blackwell, 1989, 255pp. See pages 150-1 'The Age of the Horse'.

Chapter 4

*i*nside *t*he *m*ill

Felin Lyn was well-sited at a point where one level of the valley floor gave way, by means of a 10 to 20-foot bank, to another and lower level. By this natural and advantageous siting, a good head of water for the wheel was obtained.

The Mill building was rectangular in shape with no pretensions to beauty, an attribute often bestowed on watermills. Rather, it suggested utility and strength; it faced almost due north.

Externally the building measured 41 feet × 22 feet and consisted of two floors with an attic above. The whole was divided vertically into two unconnected parts with two-thirds of the space allocated to the mill itself and one-third to the miller's house. From here on in this chapter, the mill itself which contained the machinery and processed the grain will be referred to as the 'mill' with a small 'm'.

The walls of the mill building were 30 inches thick and 18 feet tall, and the roof crest was estimated to be 28-30 feet high. The walls were made of stone and slabs of slate-stone; this latter material does not produce slates but is suitable for building purposes. In a slate quarry it would normally be discarded as waste. It is quite likely the stone came from Craig-yr-oryn quarry, which in the late 1700s was owned by Richard Myddleton of Chirk Castle. The quarry, situated a mile away on the Gwryd hillside, was later worked as a slate mine and closed about 1896. It is probable that the first slates used to roof Felin Lyn also came from this quarry. (Note 4.1)

In most circumstances a roof is a roof and that is the end of the matter, but in this instance we are fortunate to have some technical details. The very last tenant of the smallholding of Felin Lyn was a stone mason and slate roofer and one of his sons used to help him. As a result we know precisely the type of slates covering the buildings in the 1950s.

The ex-mill and house carried Caernarfonshire slates, the barn had Ffestiniog slates, and the cowhouse and pigsty were covered with local Glynceiriog slates. It is a curiosity that each of these roofs provides an example of three types of slate beds to be found in Wales. Caernarfonshire slates were the most favoured because they were so durable, followed by Ffestiniog. The slates of Denbighshire came from the Silurian rocks and were the softest and weathered faster than the others; this explains why the production of Denbighshire slates never exceeded 2% of the total Welsh output. The last local slate mine at Glynceiriog closed in 1947.

The mill had an external frontage of 26 feet and the miller's house 15 feet but both had an external depth of 22 feet. Internally these two parts were divided by a wall of timbers, lath and plaster. There was no internal access between these two parts on any of the three floors.

On the south wall of the mill, and at its easterly end, projected the oat kiln, with a gable that ran at right angles to that of the mill. Externally it measured 18 feet by 10 feet and consisted of two floors of which the lower was about 3 feet above the level of the ground floor of the mill. The lower floor of the kiln was the fireroom containing a grate and above it was the drying room. Access to the latter room was by an external doorway with stone steps leading to it from the rear lane, and was so designed as to bring the floor of a cart level with the doorway platform.

To the rear and also at the south-west corner of the miller's house were later additions (called Annexes 'A' and 'B'). Date of construction is not known but is probably the second half of the nineteenth century.

Annex 'A' was single storeyed of one room, which acted as scullery, wash-house and bakehouse for the miller's house. Annex 'B' was two storeyed, with a combined dairy and larder on the ground floor and a bedroom above.

Miller's House

As previously stated, this occupied a third of the mill building and when originally built consisted of three rooms, one above the other. There was no internal access between the house and the mill.

At ground level was the kitchen/living room, 12 feet wide and 17 feet deep, with a porch and front door (75" × 40") on the west wall beside the large chimney. The floor of this principal room was covered with stone slab. A window (60" × 48") looked out onto the kitchen garden, beside the mill yard. This was a lofty room having a 9 foot ceiling and an exposed supporting beam (10" × 10") which ran the length of the room.

In the twentieth century the deep chimney hearth was occupied by an iron range consisting of fire grate, water boiler, oven, and range top. It survived, as did the bread oven, until the Mill was razed in 1981.

This range carried the name 'Dale Excelsior', which identifies it as having been made by the Coalbrookdale Company of Shropshire, and was probably installed in the 1870s. The Company had registered the design in 1869. From the early 1700s it produced for two centuries a wide range of domestic and industrial cast iron articles.

In the southwest corner of the kitchen/living room was an open stairway, 32 inches wide, that turned through a right angle in its climb to reach the main bedroom above which was essentially the same as the room below. Above this bedroom was an attic, reached by a staircase of black oak, poorly lit by one skylight.

Behind the kitchen was a scullery, or back-kitchen, which was a later addition. This was used for washing, laundering, bread-making and sundry other domestic chores. In 1905 piped water was brought into this scullery from the millrace nearby and to the very end this was the only water supply inside the house or mill. In 1911 the landlord constructed a private water supply by tapping a spring on the opposite side of the valley to his house, Brynhyfryd. A branch line was run off to the Mill and a tap was fitted outside and close to the front door of the miller's house which gave the convenience of pure wholesome water year-round. This tap was shared with Glandwr.

In one corner of the scullery was a bakeoven which also dated from the general improvements of the 1870s. It consisted of a cast iron oven (very likely Coalbrookdale) with internal dimensions of about 24 inches wide, 18 inches high and 36 inches deep, set in terra cotta brickwork with a fire box underneath. The oven was heated with brushwood and after firing for one or two hours it would have reached a temperature of 400-500°F. All the ashes were then removed and a damp cloth cleaned it out. Next the temperature was roughly gauged by someone putting an arm in the oven to a count of ten. If this could not be tolerated then the oven was still too hot for the dough, which was placed inside with a wooden shovel. The bread took some 60-90 minutes to be baked and by that time the oven temperature had fallen to 200-250°F, the temperature difference having been absorbed by the loaves. (Note 4.2)

Mrs Jones (FL) had childhood memories: *"The big oven was heated by piles of wood and when the liner bricks got white hot, the fire was raked out and the dough for the 4-5lb loaves and the bara brith were put in. This oven was for our own needs as we did not bake for profit."* Bara brith is speckled bread or a type of currant cake, containing dried fruits, candied peel, spices, eggs and brown sugar.

At the southwest corner was another addition of two storeys, identified as Annex 'B' on the plan, and built prior to 1900. The ground floor consisted of dairy and larder and above was a bedroom, which became the subject of contention. For some unknown reason in about 1910 the landlord annexed this bedroom and transferred it to Glandwr permanently. This caused much inconvenience to the miller's family and as Mrs Jones said with feeling, *"Many a time my father told me how upset he and my mother were that one of their two bedrooms was taken and added to Glandwr. It left the Mill with one bedroom which my parents divided into two, and the attic. The lost room was always referred to as Uncle Dick's bedroom, for that is where he slept prior to his departure from the Mill in 1900."*

The ground floor room was a larder and a cool place fitted with heavy slate shelves. It was aptly named because a larder was originally a place where products of the pig were stored, such as salted pork and lard, and this was where the meat of the millers' pigs was salted down. It also stored butter, bread and some other items of food.

Mrs Jones referred to the dairy as the 'bwtri' as this was where the butter was stored. On the shelves sat shallow pans of milk and when the milk and cream had separated, the cream was skimmed off and used to make butter. Most of the skimmed milk was fed to the pigs. The butter churning was done in the mill itself and is described later in this chapter in the section headed 'Ancillary Machinery'. Mrs Jones said *"this rich butter was for home use only though occasionally my mother would sell some to a shopkeeper. She would always imprint a picture of a cow on the butter, using a wooden stamp or mould; unfortunately this got thrown away when my mother left the Mill in 1937."*

Artificial lighting was originally from home-made rush lights and then by the middle of the last century from factory-produced candles; still later came paraffin lamps. In the winter time this lack of lighting tended to make people go to bed early and a retiring time of between 8 and 9 p.m. was common for country dwellers; anyone with responsibilities for animals had to be up and about by 6.00 am, if not earlier.

Better illumination, better education, and the introduction of leisurely evening pursuits for the common man has eroded our quota of nightly sleep. In rural areas in 1890 the average person had about 9 hours of sleep but this has now declined to some 6 to 8 hours for the majority dweller of today's Britain – the urbanite.

This paucity of lighting in the winter nights was a prime factor in the maintenance of an oral tradition in which details of family history, lore, farming wisdom, stories, and much else, were passed down from one generation to another. The erosion of this oral tradition started with better lighting and universal free education, and has continued with the help of mass-produced newspapers, radio and television. Within one hundred and fifty years it seems the Ceiriog has gone through a winter evening recreational cycle of talking, (gossip, oral tradition), reading (newspaper, Bible, few books), listening (wireless), and now watching (television and videos).

The exact form of lighting in the mill itself is not known. Some 1919 repair accounts mention 'glass for lamp' which implies flat and not curved glass and is suggestive of a fixed lamp box to guard against draughts and fire. Some mills had candle or lamp recesses built into the walls but none of these were seen at Felin Lyn. It was also the practice in some British mills to use the miller's candlestick. These were made of iron with a handle on one side and a long sharp spike on the other which was stuck sideways into sacks or a convenient wooden beam, but it is not known if these were once used at the Mill. (Note 4.3)

The landlord introduced electrical lighting to his own house in 1936, with poles across the miller's field, but the Mill never had electricity. As to sanitation, the lavatory was at all times on the outer perimeter of the farmyard and was of the earth closet type. (Note 4.4)

In its final deserted and dilapidated days, the miller's house looked gloomy but Mrs Jones casts back to her early years at Felin Lyn and remembers it as a cheerful and happy home. *"I know it was not modern but I remember it with great affection. When we lived there, it was lovely with all the antique furniture, brasses, copper, Staffordshire figures, hams hanging from the massive oak beam, and a glowing fire in the grate. Right now as I write, I have many things to remind me of that home – the Welsh dresser, grandfather clock and brasses."*

Oat Kiln

The use of heat to help remove the husk of a grain is of ancient origin. Neolithic woman used naked fire to parch, toast, roast, or scorch the outer covering of grain seed to get rid of it, and the method is still in use today in many primitive parts of the world. It was last practised in Britain less than two hundred years ago in the outer isles of Scotland. (Note 4.5)

By contrast, the use of a kiln to help remove the troublesome husk of an oat can be considered a sophisticated device. In such kilns the oat is mildly toasted so that the husk becomes brittle and with a light milling or bruising it splits and falls away.

Though kilning assisted in the process of hulling the oats, the principal reason was to reduce moisture in the grain. Otherwise, during milling, the stones would become clogged and ineffective with 'damp' meal. Oat heads, when attached to a sheaf and stored in a barn or rick, held about 15-18% moisture but after kilning this was lowered to almost 5%.

Since the uplands of Britain were the prime areas for growing oats, it came about that all upland mills were equipped with oat kilns and these were to be found in Wales, parts of England, and Scotland. British watermills can be placed into one of two categories in relation to their altitude. The arbitrary dividing line is at about 600 feet above sea level and those below and above this level are called lowland and upland mills, respectively. By this definition Felin Lyn, at 435 feet altitude, was a lowland mill, but because it possessed an oat kiln was firmly in the 'upland' mill category. Until about 1800 it was the practice to have the kiln located somewhere on farm land rather than at the mill, and in 1984 the remains of just such a kiln were discovered at an abandoned mountain top farm called Bryn Bugeilyn which lay $1^{3}/_{4}$ miles south-west of Felin Lyn at 1325 feet altitude. The kiln was separate but close to other buildings and was 12 foot square.

Then in the late eighteenth century there was a trend to move the drying of the grain to a mill and away from farm and field. It is not known if Felin Lyn was in advance of its time and had the kiln built at the same time as the mill, or if it was an addition made later.

Welsh kilns varied but all of them consisted of two parts; below was a fire-room with grate and above a drying chamber. The two were separated by a floor honeycombed with tiny holes, so tiny that an oat seed could not penetrate one of them but would allow hot air to pass upwards. This floor was either made of tiles or perforated iron plates.

To kiln the oats, a fire was lit and the chamber preheated for about two hours. Oats were then poured onto the floor to the depth of about four inches. The heat applied was in the range 100-150°F and for the next three or four hours the grain was turned every twenty minutes with a short-handled wooden shovel. A metal tool was considered injurious to the taste of the oats. After this the oats remained untouched for the next half day to slowly cool and they emerged with a lovely brown or golden colour. This operation gave off steam and other fumes and reduced the moisture in the oats to about 5% from 15-20% when first placed on the kiln floor. The flavour of oatmeal was affected by the way in which oats had been kilned, so great care had to be exercised in the process to avoid scorching parts of the batch. (Note 4.6)

Naturally our knowledge about kilning at Felin Lyn is meagre since no living person ever saw it take place. We do know the internal measurements of the kiln room were about 15 feet by 9 feet which would permit between 25 and 35 bushels of grain to be kilned at a time. This would amount to between half and three-quarters of a ton of oats and nearly a ton of barley .

Our sole information comes from Mrs Jones (FL) who says; *"We called that room 'Y Cul', meaning the kiln* (note interconnection between the words 'kiln', 'kitchen', 'cul' and 'culinary'). *My father mentioned it was heated and oats were laid on its floor. Whatever was done was not done in my father's time (post 1900) but his father would have known about it."* In 1982 Mrs Jones found an old man in Glynceiriog who knew through his family that the Mill's kiln used to be worked.

The running of the kiln was not the miller's responsibility – he merely provided the equipment – for he did not have the time to properly oversee the work. The responsibility lay with the owner of the oats to do the kilning and provide the wood, which seems to have been the usual fuel. The grain owner was a farmer and sometimes he did the work himself but more frequently handed it over to the local expert called 'crawswr' ('crasu' means *to bake*) who did such work on a part-time basis.

It is most probable the kiln was also used to kiln the barley malt required to make beer (see Chapter 5) and in the case of Felin Lyn all the evidence shows that the man who did this lived at or close to Dolywern, one mile away.

Footwear in a kiln was always clogs as the heat would soon ruin leather boots, and one or more pairs of clogs were usually seen at a kiln door. When George Borrow was in the Ceiriog in 1854 he came upon an Englishman at Pandy, four miles upstream from Felin Lyn, who was cutting alder into crude blocks of wood. These were then sent to Bolton in Lancashire to be fashioned into clogs for people working in the textile mills. Indefatigable Borrow reported that such clogs were sold for 2/- a pair, whereas leather shoes cost 10/- to 12/- a pair. Presumably, some clogs were fashioned locally in the Ceiriog, as clogs were used as workaday footwear in many parts of Wales up to the present century. (Note 4.7)

Dewi Jones of Llwynmawr discovered two unbroken kiln tiles in the 1980s at the former farm of Bryn Bugeilyn, already mentioned. As they may have been similar to those in use at Felin Lyn, their details will be of interest. The tiles were not crudely made but were closely dimensioned and well finished and are believed to have been machine moulded. Each tile was made of yellow clay, measuring 13" × 13" and of 2" thickness. The underneath side had 81 recesses, each almost $1^1/_2$" square and each contained 5 holes that penetrated to the upper face. These holes had a diameter equivalent to a thin kitchen skewer and provided 405 holes per tile. (Note 4.8)

If these tiles had been laid in the kiln at Felin Lyn, about 120 of them would have been needed. It was usual to fill the cracks between the tiles with cow dung, this being found better than mortar. Sometime in high summer when the kiln was not in use, the miller's children were put to work cleaning out the 46,000 or so hot-air holes. This was done with a dibber with five nails attached.

The kiln, together with the mill, was demolished in 1981 but externally was not altered during its life. However its function and its internal features were changed at a date thought to be about 1873-80 when the mill swiftly changed its function to that of a Trader.

The kiln room was converted to a bulk grain store by the building of a four-sided hopper made of yellow brick which sloped to a pointed central base at about four feet depth. Across the top of the hopper were two parallel iron rails likely supporting a plank bridge, which was level with the threshold of the doorway, and probably level with the floor of the mill attic. There was no access between the kiln and the mill except for a six-inch square hole which permitted a flow of grain/maize from garner to mill; originally this lack of inter-communication was to ensure a fire barrier. The presence of the yellow brickwork suggests the kiln was converted to a garner at the same time as the other improvements to the mill were made.

The cessation of kilning meant that the arduous, time consuming and fume laden labour was gone but there also disappeared a long-standing custom. Bachelors and youths used to drift into the fireroom of the kiln building on chilly winter evenings to talk about their betters, local scandal, politics and even to sing. A view of Felin Lyn's kiln is preserved in an 1908 photograph which shows a louvered ventilator and staining of the slates below the ventilator. This was characteristic as the toasting released sulphur and the smell of oats being kilned could be detected a mile away if the wind was in the right direction.

The doing away with the kiln from 1880 onwards raises an interesting question. If it was needed before, why not subsequently, as the mill ground oats up to the mid 1930s? The only explanation that readily comes to mind is that prior to 1880 oats were ground finely for humans and coarsely for animals. Humans needed the husk to be removed and the kiln was the first step in the process but animals are less fussy and will eat both husk and kernel, though preferably in a bruised state.

After that time flooding imports of good quality and cheap wheats caused such a shift in cereal diet in the Ceiriog that demand for oat flour and oatmeal fell away to such a point that it became uneconomic to produce it, for its production was quite labour intensive. Furthermore the kiln building was needed to store a new and upcoming product – maize.

The mill Itself

Externally the mill itself (holding the machinery) measured 26 feet by 22 feet, which made it dimensionally an average-sized watermill in the Welsh border country. Mills in the region could range from a 14 feet by 14 feet farm mill to a 36 feet by 30 feet small-town mill. It appears that builders favoured even numbers of feet when setting down their external dimensions – with 20 feet. as the most frequently seen measurement. Lengths or breadths of 18 feet, 24 feet, 26 feet and 30 feet were also fairly common. The internal dimensions of the mill at Felin Lyn were 23 feet long (west-wall was wood not stone) by 17 feet wide, giving about 400 square feet per floor.

The ground floor or 'meal' room was floored with stone slabs and had a ceiling height of about seven feet clear of joists. In its south-west corner was an upward flight of four stone steps which led to a door, giving on to the lane at the back of the mill. At right angles to the top stone step was a set of seven steepish open wooden stairs which reached the upper floor or 'stone' room. At the time of the Mill's demolition, the wooden steps were about half worn.

The dimensions of the upper room were identical with the one below. The floor consisted of one main cross beam of 10" × 10" section (lying north-south), upon which joists of 6" × 3" were mounted, and on these in turn were laid floor boards of 6" × $^{3}/_{4}$" tongue and grooved. Headroom was six feet to attic ceiling joists and nearly seven feet elsewhere.

The attic above was itself entered by vertical ladder from the 'stone' floor. It could not be examined in 1980 because of its precarious state but it appeared to have a central gangway and remnants of dividers, which would have created corn bins. In the days of Toll milling these would have separated each farmer's parcel of grain.

The sack hoist operated into the attic and the trap door for it was still in position in 1981. This attic was carried on

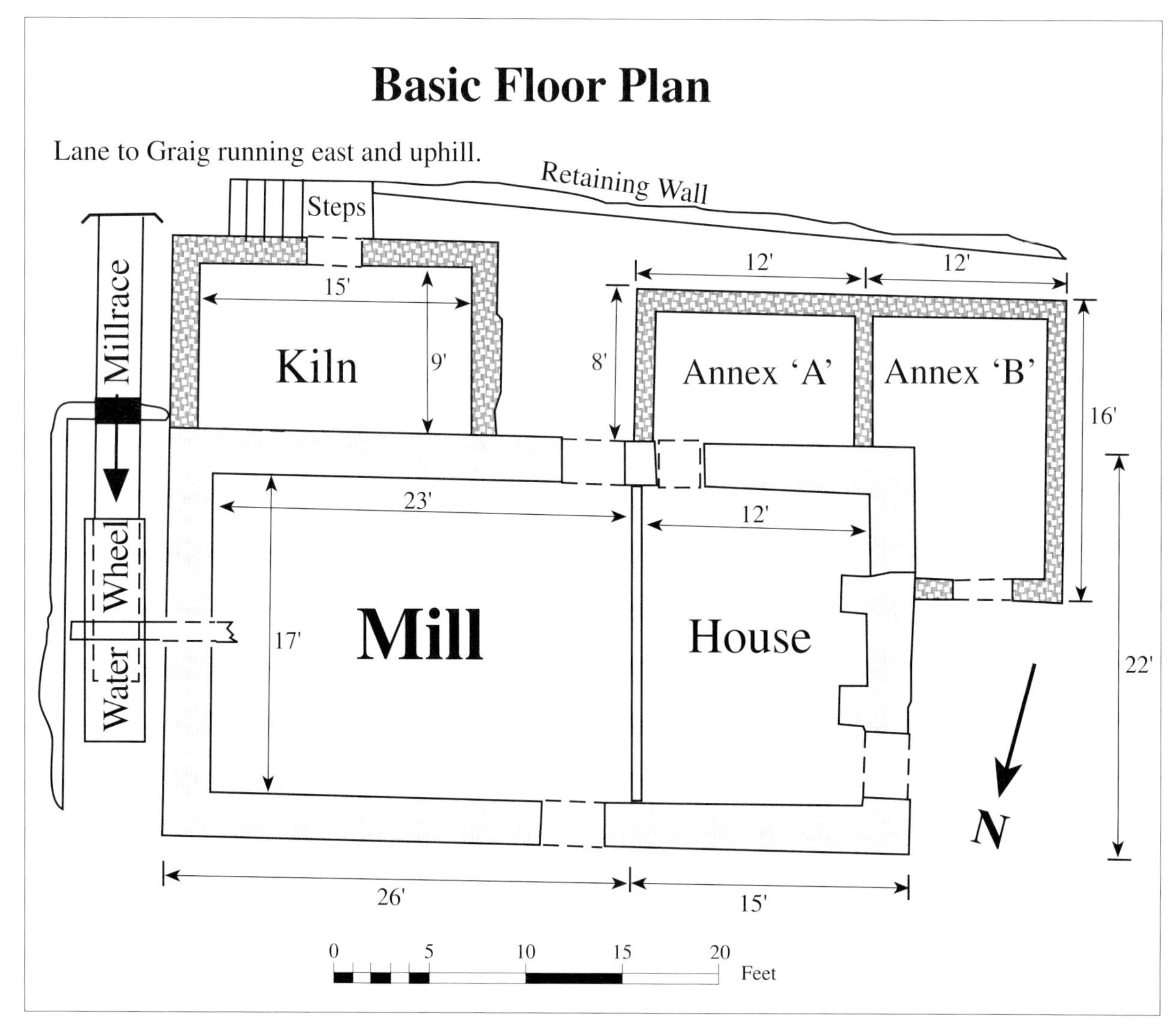

floor joists of varying dimensions but averaging 10" × 8". This detail suggests these were the original hand-hewn joists used when the mill was erected, whereas the floor below had timbers sawn by machinery and almost certainly date from the renovations of the late nineteenth century.

Access to the mill was at two points. The principal door was on the ground floor, at the front of the mill, and led directly to the mill yard; it was a two-part stable door and measured 42 inches wide by 68 inches high. Through it went all incoming grain except oats in the days of kilning and maize in the days of trading, and outgoing all the products of grinding. The second exterior door has been already described, being at the rear of the mill and halfway between the ground and first floors. Kilned oats in sacks entered the mill through this second door, but it had other uses for it gave ready access to the top level of the barn and for external examination of the waterwheel.

Natural lighting was somewhat deficient by present day standards but normal for the times. The ground floor was lit by a 30 inches wide window on its north side sited close to the stable door, plus of course light from the top half of the stable door which was usually open. Some light also filtered through the waterwheel shaft hole which was on the east wall and measured four feet high and 31 inches wide. On the front wall of the first floor was one medium and one small-sized window, and on the gable wall was a third one to allow the miller to view the water flow in the launder and the movement of the waterwheel. The attic was ill-lit as it had only one small gable-end window and one very small skylight.

Machinery

Mill machinery, though ponderous looking, is essentially simple. It takes rotative power from the waterwheel, which runs at very low revolutions per minute (rpm), and multiplies it by two steps of gearing to increase the speed of the revolutions about tenfold. This provides a speed suitable for grain to be ground between two stones, the top one revolving and the bottom one fixed.

The machinery is commendably compact and at Felin Lyn occupied an area no larger than 14 feet by 11 feet on each of two floors, one above the other. A mechanical comparison can be drawn between a motorcar and a watermill. Each has fuel (petrol/water) and a prime mover (engine/waterwheel). With the car, the power is transmitted by shafts and gears to the driving axle but in doing so the revolutions are decreased because the engine runs at a constant speed which is much too high for the road wheels to use. In a watermill the reverse takes place with the revolutions being increased. Finally in both cases, it is necessary to be able to interrupt (not stop) the supply of power even though the prime mover continues to run and this is done by a device called a clutch; in a car it is used to start and stop the vehicle and in a mill it can theoretically start and stop the millstones. At this juncture the analogy ceases to apply because a clutch in a car is used constantly but in a mill acts only as a safety device and cannot be operated when the prime mover is working. A mill is put out of gear only at night or for longer periods when no milling is to be done. With car and mill the prime mover can be 'killed' by denying it fuel – petrol for the car and water for the mill.

The basic design of the machinery in any waterwheel has but few variations. The most dominant design in Britain in the 19th century was the under-drive spurwheel gearing, and this was used at Felin Lyn. Details and dimensions of this machinery will vary from mill to mill because each mill was built individually by some master craftsman and was a unique creation, but the essentials were common to all mills.

The machinery of Felin Lyn with its basic dimensions, could be found in countless upland watermills of Wales, but it is improbable that any other mill was identical in every regard. (Note 4.9)

When the Mill was built it is possible that all its machinery was built of wood but it is equally possible that a few of its components were made of iron. The casting and forging of iron was well known in the region for there were furnaces near Wrexham and at Ironbridge, and five miles to the east of Felin Lyn there was a forge close to where the Ceiriog meets the Dee. Chirk canal aqueduct has a minor niche in engineering history for when designed in 1795 it was to be a stone structure carrying an iron water trough, the second ever such innovation in Britain; it is still functioning today. The use of iron must have had a certain common knowledge in the vicinity and it is presumed that a local millwright, who conventionally worked in wood, may have started to use iron experimentally for the small pinions.

Slowly through the nineteenth century, more wooden components would have been switched to iron, usually when failure was imminent or had happened. The prime candidate for conversion to iron was the waterwheel and its axle shaft; this was because a wheel was intermittently wet and dry and this is the fastest way to induce rot in any woodwork. Wooden gear wheels were often replaced with iron, particularly those of small diameter which were difficult to make in wood and yet retain their strength.

Pinions made in iron had a distinct advantage as casting was easy and strength was improved. However, some wooden gears were retained, meshing with iron to give smoother and quieter running. The larger iron wheels were made without teeth and in their place were cast rectangular slots at the periphery. Into these slots were driven wooden cogs, so creating a 'wooden' pinion. The design clearly had advantages over an all-iron piece for it produced quieter running, and wear and breakages could be attended to immediately by the miller. A broken cog could be repaired within the hour, but a missing iron tooth created a major stoppage.

On the subject of quietness, Mrs Jones (FL) says that as a child she does not recollect any excessive vibration or noise being felt in the Millhouse when the mill was at work. This was due to a fundamental design seen in all watermills. The gearing and the millstones are supported on a strong wooden frame called a hursting and all the weight, thrust and vibration are carried down into the ground below and not into the walls, which in Felin Lyn's case were over two feet thick.

Since all the machinery in the mill, except for a short length of launder, was removed in about 1956, nothing survived by 1980 to indicate by whom or where it had been made.

In ten instances the author knows of a mill and the location of the foundry that supplied the mill with castings. With but one exception the distance between mill and foundry did not exceed 10-12 miles. This suggests that foundry work for watermill machinery was not the preserve of a few regional specialists but was practised by a great many local foundries, in the nineteenth century. There was no shortage of iron foundries within a ten-mile radius of Felin Lyn for they lay in a quadrant to the east; Cefn Mawr and Ruabon to the north-east, Ellesmere to the east and Oswestry to the south-east. (Note 4.10)

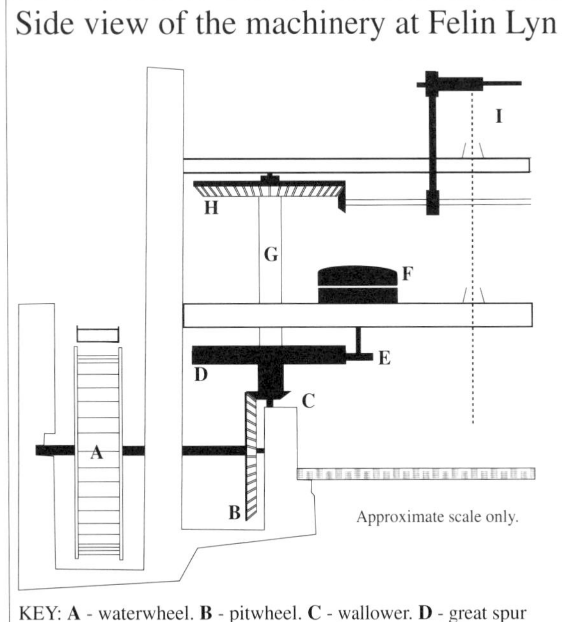

KEY: **A** - waterwheel. **B** - pitwheel. **C** - wallower. **D** - great spur wheel. **E** - stone nut. **F** - millstone pair. **G** - main shaft. **H** - crown wheel. **I** - sack hoist.

In the last century Cefn Mawr's principal industries were iron-making and clay products such as bricks, tiles and chimney pots. It was home to the then famous Plaskynaston Iron Foundry and the New British Iron Works but such large firms would not have bothered themselves with making individualised transmission components for a watermill. Such would have been left to Ruabon Iron & Brass Foundry or some small jobbing foundry in the district, now lost and long forgotten. The Ruabon foundry, run by R. & W. Jones in the last half of the nineteenth century, made the waterwheel and launder for the surviving (and open to the public) Pentre Mill at Loggerheads, 12 miles north of Ruabon, so here was a foundry with known milling machinery expertise. It also supplied ironwork for a sawmill at Welshpool in 1844.

At Ellesmere was Clay's Iron Foundry (1810-c1910) sited on the town's wharf arm of the Shropshire Union Canal. Also called the Bridgewater Foundry, it was well known locally for production of its Cockshutt ploughs and for all manner of iron fittings required by the Canal Company and the Ellesmere estate of the Earl of Bridgewater.

Finally, at Oswestry there were at least three foundries in the second half of the 19th century. Foremost was J. Ellis & Son of Victoria Street calling itself 'Engineers, Iron and Brass Founders'. Its 1868 advertisement is of interest and is quoted almost verbatim: *"Beg to call attention to their portable and fixed steam engines (2-30 hp),* ***portable and fixed flour mills*** *(author's emphasis), patent portable threshing machines, circular saw benches, mortar mills, 2 & 3 speed gears for driving chaff cutters, turnip pulpers, bone mills, kilning mills; also continuous fencing, hurdles and gates in iron."*

Some time in the early 1880s, this firm was absorbed by W. Clay & Sons who, as mentioned above, worked the foundry at Ellesmere, but the foundry continued to function at Oswestry as a branch plant. The two other foundries were run by John Nield and Richard Mason, respectively, and were both situated at Castlefields. An 1879 advertisement by the latter foundry states: *"...all kinds of portable, vertical and horizontal steam engines, agricultural, mining, and other machinery made and repaired."*

Obviously, it is not possible now to determine who made the iron machinery components for Felin Lyn, but the review shows that several competent foundries and machine makers were available within a radius of a dozen miles.

All the machinery at Felin Lyn was removed in 1956, at a time just prior to the emerging popular interest in all things of yester-century such as canals, railways and relics of early industrialisation. As a natural consequence, none of Felin Lyn's machinery was examined, measured and recorded for historical purposes. The slight residual evidence was inspected and noted in 1980-81 and from it a reasonable deduction can be made as to what the machinery looked like when intact in the twentieth century.

Stan Jeffreys, quoted earlier in the book, and who grew up at the ex-mill makes these interesting comments: *"The mill machinery was intact when our family became tenants in 1952 but it had not been worked for years. As young boys, we 'repaired' the waterwheel and one day when our parents were not at home we managed to make it turn half a revolution. It made such a noise and vibration that it frightened the life out of us and we all took off, and it had much the same effect on Miss Parry who lived next door at Glandwr.*

"In about 1956 Mr Davies the landlord who then lived in Radnorshire, made an agreement with a scrap metal merchant to sell the machinery to the latter. As I understand it, part of the agreement was to repair and renew the floors after the machinery had been removed. What actually happened was that the scrap merchant gutted the place, taking everything of salvage value, leaving an awful mess and repairing nothing.

"The three runner stones were smashed to get at the brass bearings and the pockets of lead used as balance pieces. My father, Bertie Jeffreys, being a stone mason, used the broken pieces of these runner stones to repair the wall leading to the farmyard and they are still there now. The landlord tried to trace the merchant but he had no luck."

(i) Waterwheel

This was of the overshot type, common to hilly districts, where the water fell onto the wheel. Overshot wheels are worked by the weight of water in the buckets and not by the impulse of a stream striking the paddles as in the case of undershot wheels.

It is an axiom of hydraulic motors that they should work efficiently irrespective of the quantity of water supplied to them. Turbines and waterwheels are hydraulic motors. The overshot wheel adheres to this requirement as its efficiency is highest in times of low water, for then the buckets are poorly filled and empty closer to bottom dead centre than when amply filled. Overshot wheels also possess the highest efficiency of all types of waterwheels, being able to convert about 65% of the energy presented to them into useful work. This compares most favourably with an undershot wheel which has an efficiency of about 20% to 35%. Quite clearly Felin Lyn was fortunate in having such an efficient type of wheel to drive its machinery.

Felin Lyn's waterwheel was positioned on the centre-line of the east wall and gable-end of the mill. Measurements of the depth of the wheel pit below the axle line suggested a radius of about 6 feet which gives a wheel diameter of 12 feet. This was quite a popular diameter in Wales. A list of the diameters of 50 overshot wheels obtained randomly by the author shows a diameter spread of 8 feet to 26 feet with an arithmetical mean of 13 feet and a median of 12 feet; the next two most popular and equally shared diameters were 10 feet and 14 feet followed by 18 feet.

The wheel pit which housed the waterwheel was built of stone on three sides and was 64 inches wide. Since the launder that carried the water to the wheel was 32 inches wide, it is probable that the waterwheel was 36 inches wide. This would provide a 14 inches clearance on either side of the wheel, just enough space for a man to squeeze in to inspect or repair the wheel or clean out the pit. There are several recorded deaths of men and boys throughout Britain who were crushed to death by a waterwheel due to this lack of clearance; in many cases they had gone into the pit to remove an obstruction that had prevented the wheel from turning and were then trapped when the wheel started to move. A specific Denbighshire example of such a fatality befell the uncle of the last miller of Felin Segrwyd (see Note 2.12) in the early years of this century.

The rims and the axle of the wheel were made of cast iron, the former being made up of bolted and braced segments. It was usual to make the spokes of oak and these usually numbered six or eight pairs to a wheel, thus giving an assembly of six or eight segments. The 1919 repair details quoted in Chapter 1 suggest however that the spokes then being fitted were of larch; maybe oak was unobtainable after four years of war.

The buckets of the waterwheel were almost always wooden boards fitted into slots cast in the wheel segments. This was done to keep weight to the minimum and to give the whole assembly a marginal flexing. The bucket boards were usually made of elm – also coffin material – as this wood will last a century when kept perpetually wet, but not half wet.

A miller disliked his waterwheel standing unmoved for several days, because wood that is alternately wetted and dried out will rot at a faster rate than if permanently kept dry or damp. In totally wooden wheels it also produced imbalance when first restarted because the dried-out and wet sections weighed differently, resulting in jerky revolutions.

A launder is a wooden or metal trough that delivers water to a wheel and to a casual observer a leaking launder looked liked poor maintenance. But many millers created it intentionally so as to keep the waterwheel moist at all times. If a miller had to close down his operation because of major repairs to internal machinery, he took good care to keep his wheel constantly wet.

The waterwheel at Felin Lyn probably had 36 buckets since its circumference was $37^1/_2$ feet, and each of these buckets would have held about 8 gallons of water when full. However a waterwheel is never meant to operate with full buckets and a third to a half filling is considered practical and economical. It is thought that the buckets of Felin Lyn's wheel each carried a working maximum of 4 gallons and a minimum of $2^1/_2$ gallons of water. Once the inertia of a standing waterwheel was overcome, it operated something like a flywheel and needed little effort – read water – to keep it running.

At any given moment the wheel would have held water in 15 of its 36 buckets with the others empty or almost so, and the weight of this water would have totalled about a $^1/_4$ ton. The wheel itself probably weighed $2^1/_2$ - $2^3/_4$ tons, so when at work the revolving structure weighed close to 3 tons.

It is believed the natural speed of Felin Lyn's waterwheel was about 10 revolutions per minute(rpm). At this speed it used between 1,000 and 1,500 gallons of water a minute. It could also run as slow as 8rpm and as high as 12rpm with water requirements ranging between 750 and 1750 gallons. These volumes were well within the capacity of the headrace to supply except at some periods in the low water months of July, August and September.

Since Felin Lyn could grind about 6lb. of meal per minute, it appears that between 100 and 200 gallons of water were needed to produce 1lb. of flour. Attempts have also been made to assess the nominal horsepower of Felin Lyn and differing computations have yielded a 5hp to 9hp range; perhaps 7hp would be realistic.

The low-breast iron waterwheel of the old mill at Dolywern (one mile upstream on the Afon Ceiriog) still survives and, though its origins and installation date are unknown, it is worth comparing its measurements against those deduced for Felin Lyn; they are: diameter of 10 feet, width of 34 inches, 34 buckets.

The water in the headrace reached the waterwheel by going under the Graig lane in a culvert which had its upstream face covered by a grating. This collected all the larger pieces of floating debris to prevent damage to the wheel. The point should be made however that waterwheels could work with water that was muddy and contained small debris and weed, whereas the more mechanically efficient Pelton turbine needed clean water to work properly.

The author clearly remembers this section of the millrace because near the grating cattle had broken down the sides of the bank to make a drinking spot and it made an ideal place to retrieve 'boats' of sticks or paper which he had launched higher up the stream.

On emerging from the culvert, the water was carried in a launder or trough which was so positioned as to have no more than a foot clearance above the top of the wheel. The launder was extended for about 16 feet so that its end projected well beyond the axle line of the wheel and allowed the water, when the wheel was not working, to cascade some 16 feet into the pit below. The bottom of the pit was faced with flag stones to prevent erosion.

The launder was made of $^1/_2$-inch thick iron plate, 32 inches wide, having 10 inch high sides, and was supported by old lengths of standard gauge rail laid across the pit. In 1980 a six foot length of the launder was still in position, having been left there by the scrap merchant to allow the runoff water to fall harmlessly into the empty wheel pit. This residual ironwork was not worn, pitted or rusted.

This characteristic immediately identifies it as wrought iron, a material unsurpassed for its resistance to corrosion. It was much favoured for ironwork at the seaside and in ships as it resisted corrosion in salt air and salt water to a degree which is quite beyond the capacity of modern steels. It is a type of iron no longer produced in Britain because its production is very labour intensive and primitive. Wrought iron had superb welding properties and when cherry-red hot could be beaten into any shape or attached to another piece so to become as one. It was much used by the country blacksmith and often came to the aid of a miller when repairing or improving his machinery.

Wrought iron was produced near Wrexham in Denbighshire and at Coalbrookdale in Shropshire till the middle of the last century, with barstock being made at both locations and sheet at Wrexham – not 35 miles from Felin Lyn.

To set the wheel in motion, the miller pushed a rod which opened a trap door or hatch in the launder. This hatch was hinged to the bottom of the launder and was

Denbighshire, North Wales, 1808

by Baugh

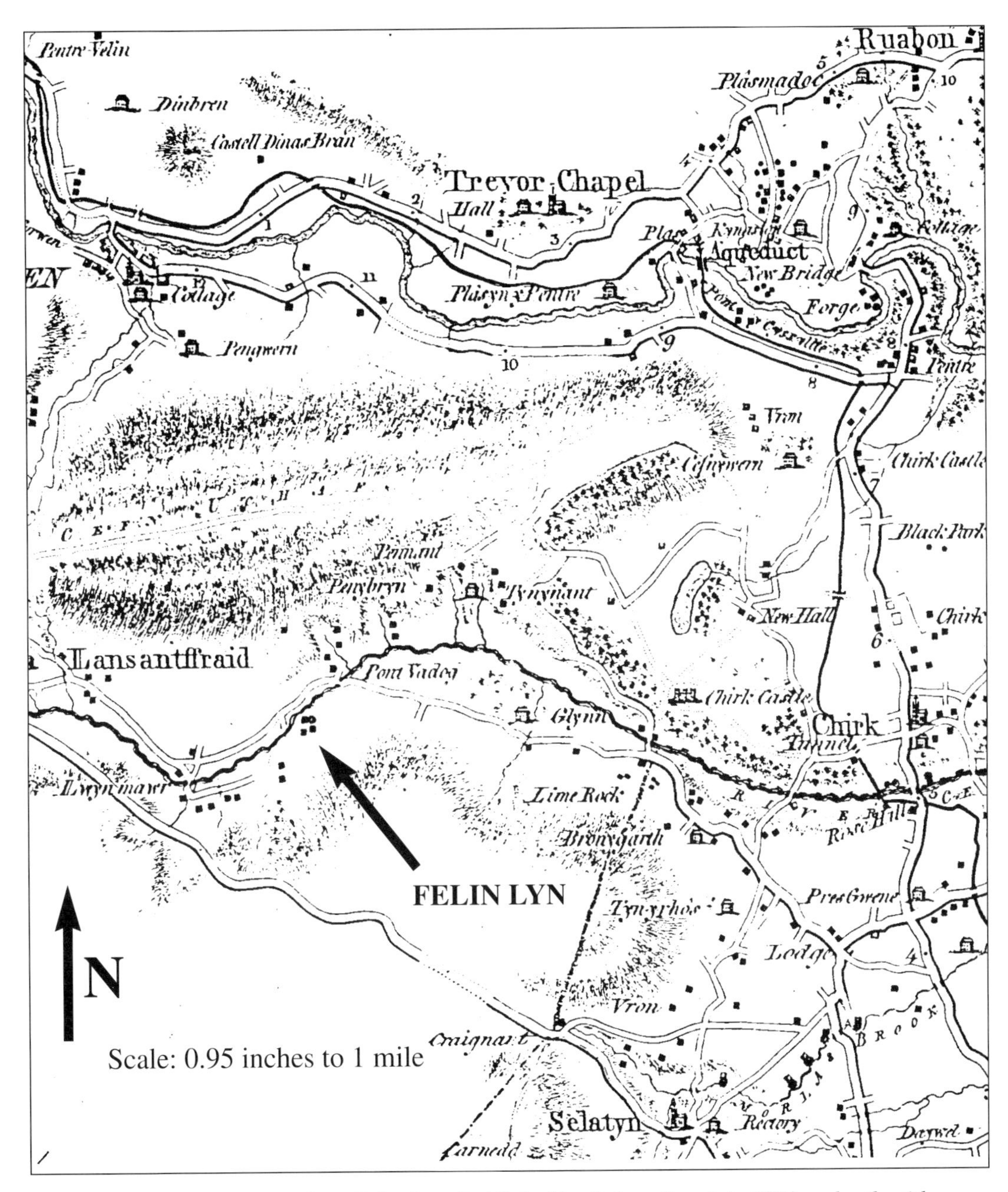

One of the earliest maps to show Felin Lyn. Published by Robert Baugh in 1808 under the title 'Shropshire' and dedicated to 'Edward, Earl of Powis, Lord Lieutenant of the Counties of Salop and Montgomery'. Fortunately, this bottom segment of Denbighshire was included.

Clwyd Record Office (Ref. PM/5/13)

Felin Lyn & surroundings c1825

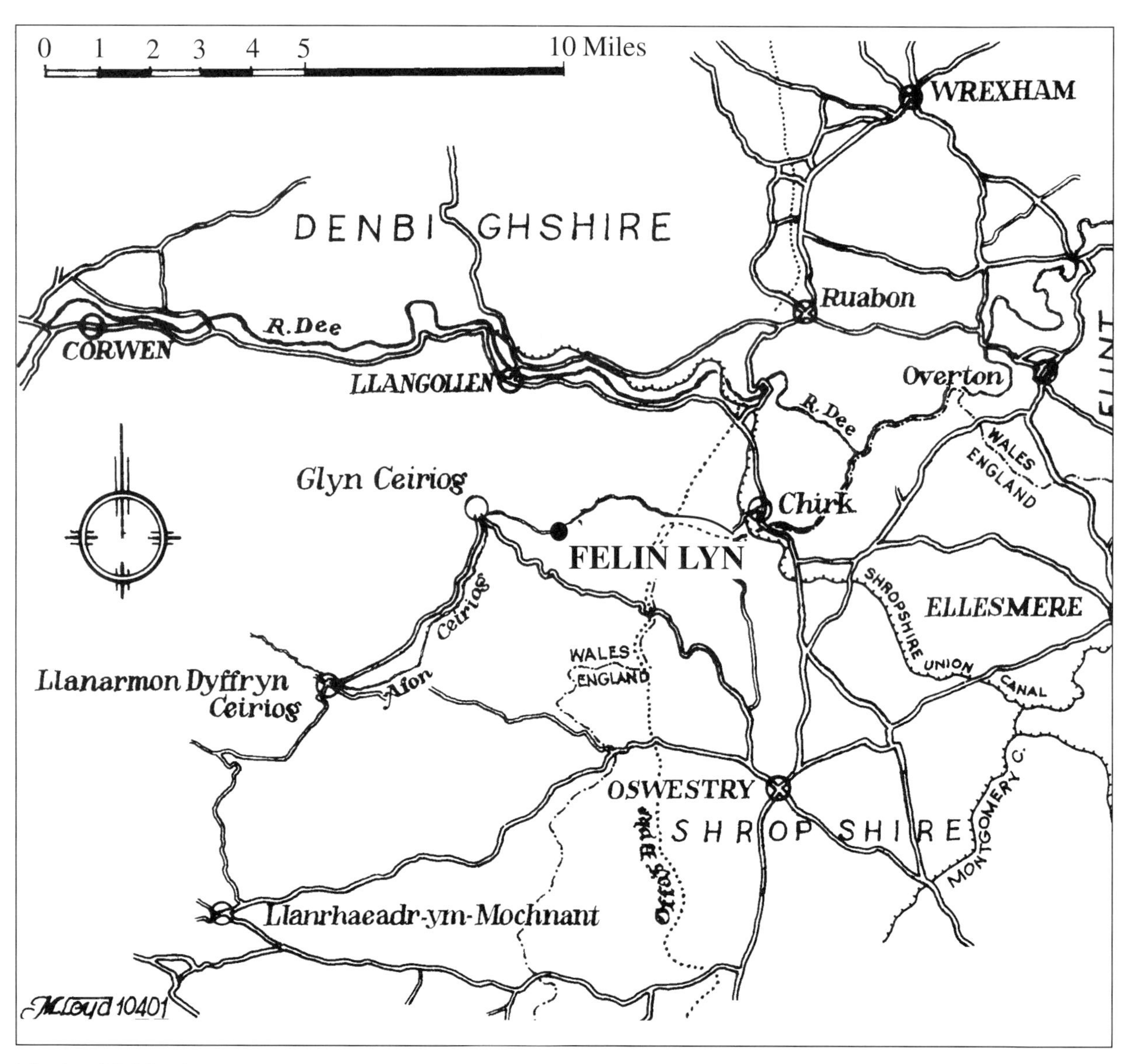

The late M. Lloyd.

The 'territory' of Felin Lyn

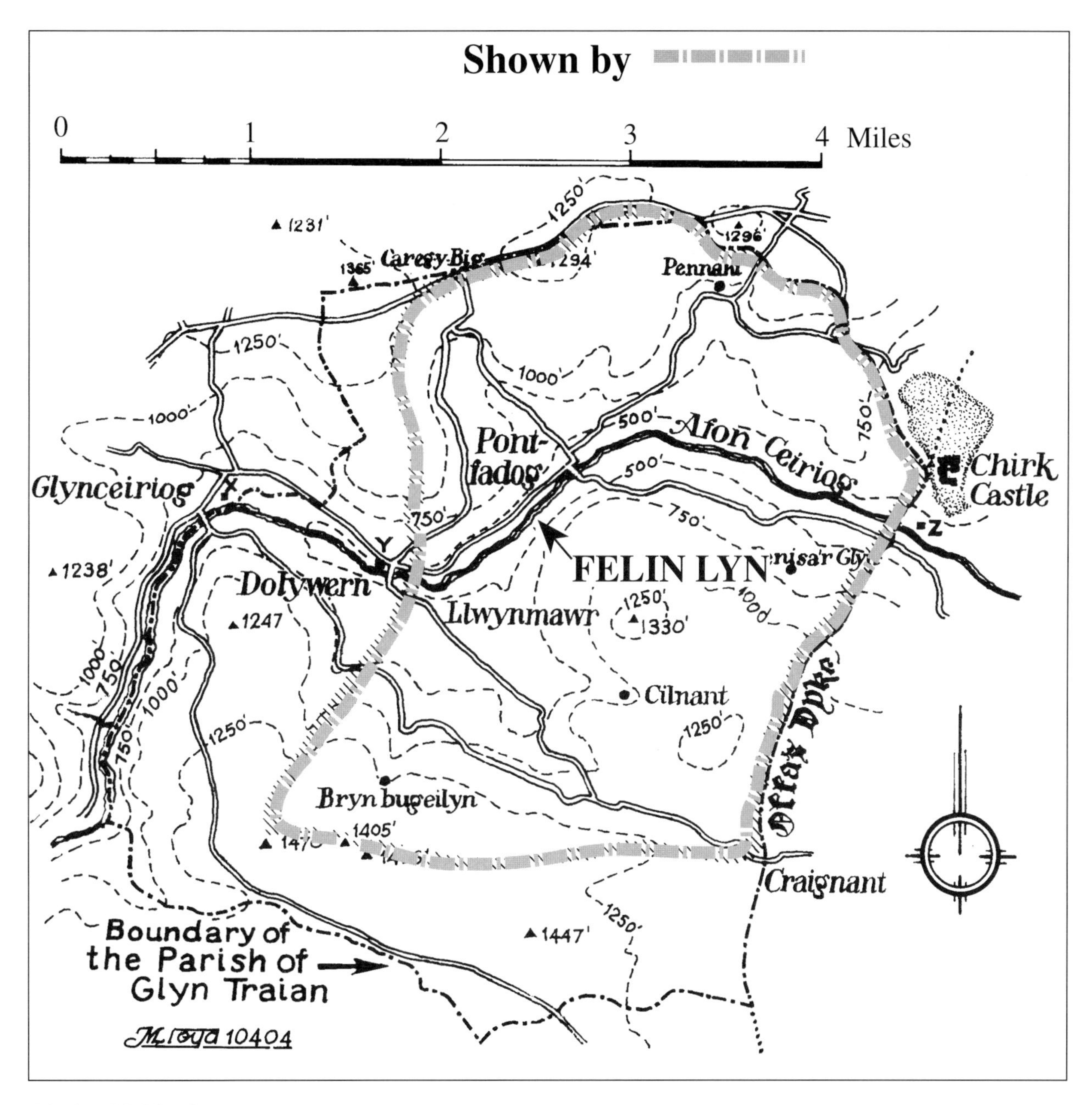

The late M. Lloyd.

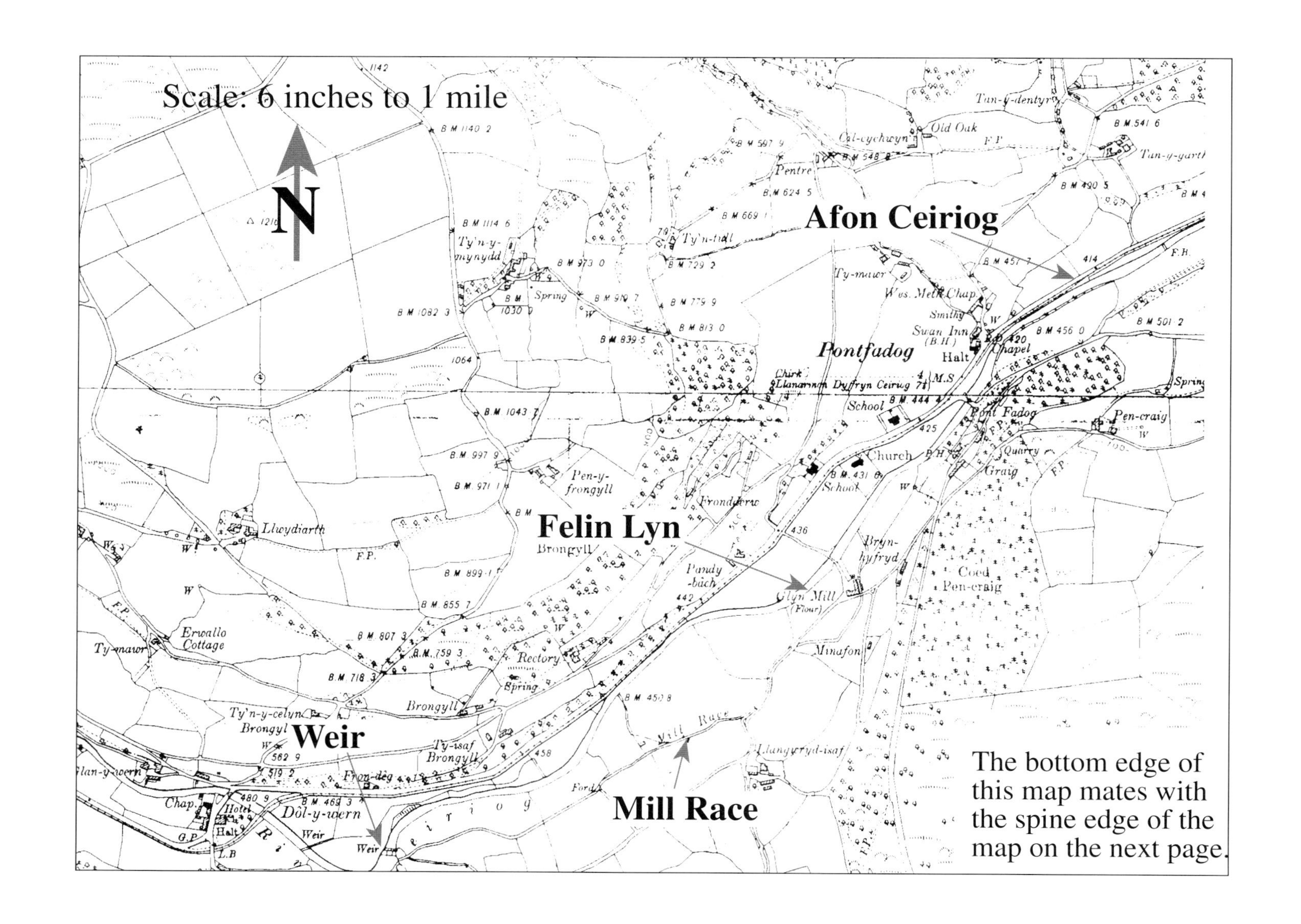
Scale: 6 inches to 1 mile
N
Afon Ceiriog
Pontfadog
Felin Lyn
Mill Race
Weir
The bottom edge of this map mates with the spine edge of the map on the next page.

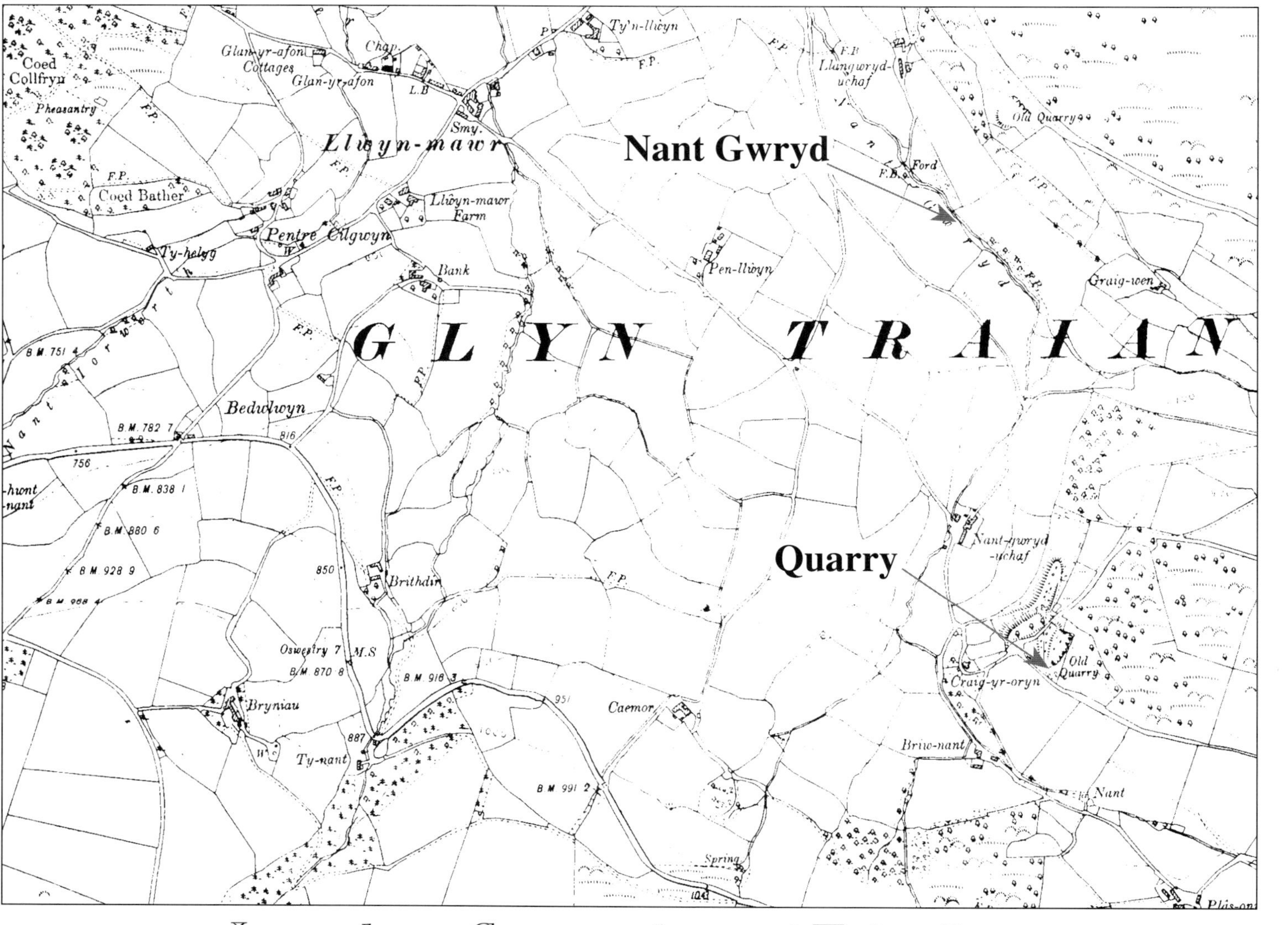

Immediate Surroundings of Felin Lyn

Taken from the Ordnance Survey map of 6 inches to 1 mile, 3rd Edition 1914 and originally surveryed 1872/4 and revised 1909. Sheet: Denbighshire XXXIX-S.E.

Smallholding of Felin Lyn/Glyn Mill

Mill premises and four fields.

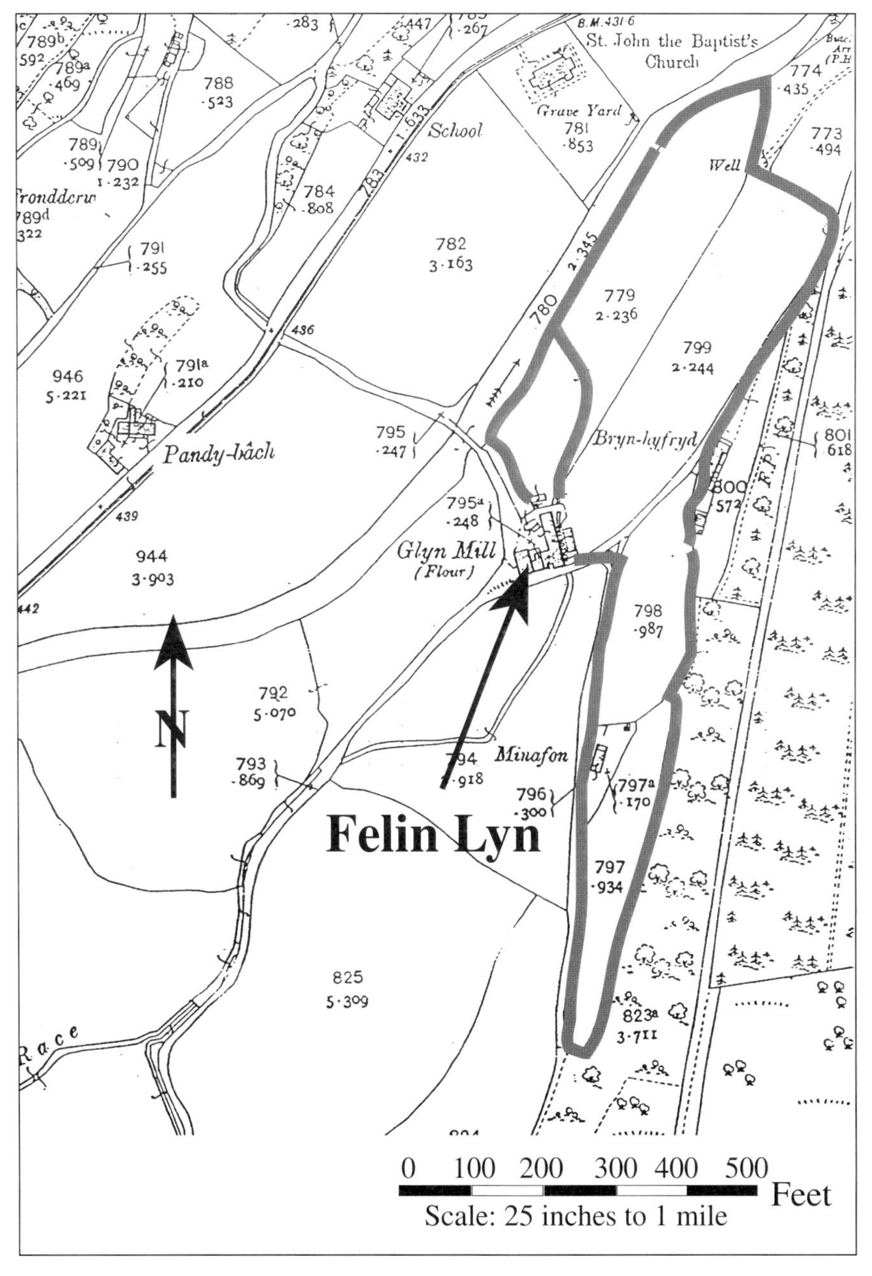

Taken from 25 inch to one mile Ordnance Survey, Sheet: Denbighshire XXXIX-12, 2nd Edition, 1912.

By permission of the National Library of Wales.

Felin Lyn

Water delivery at 1850.

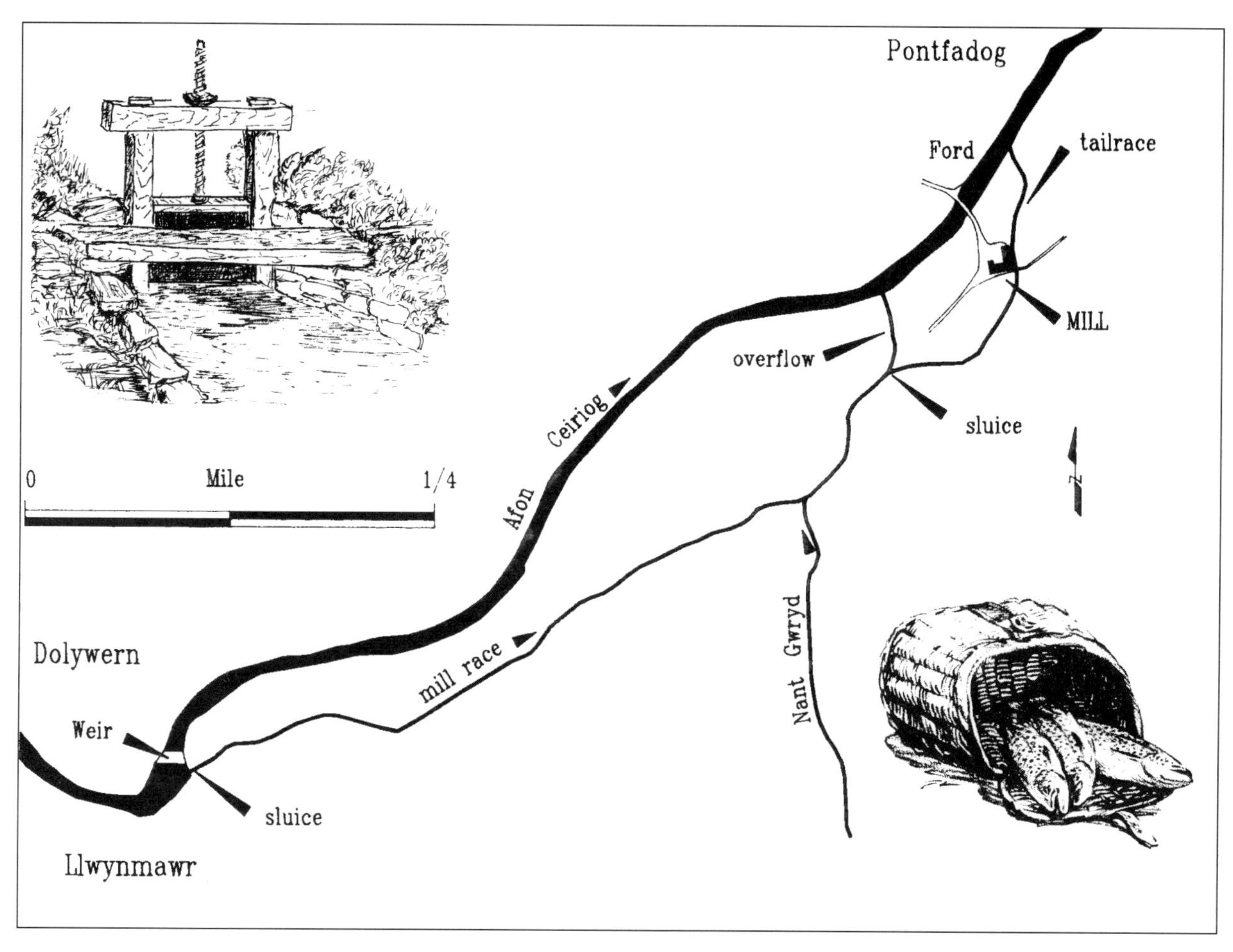

Author.

Felin Lyn

Detail site plan at c1920.

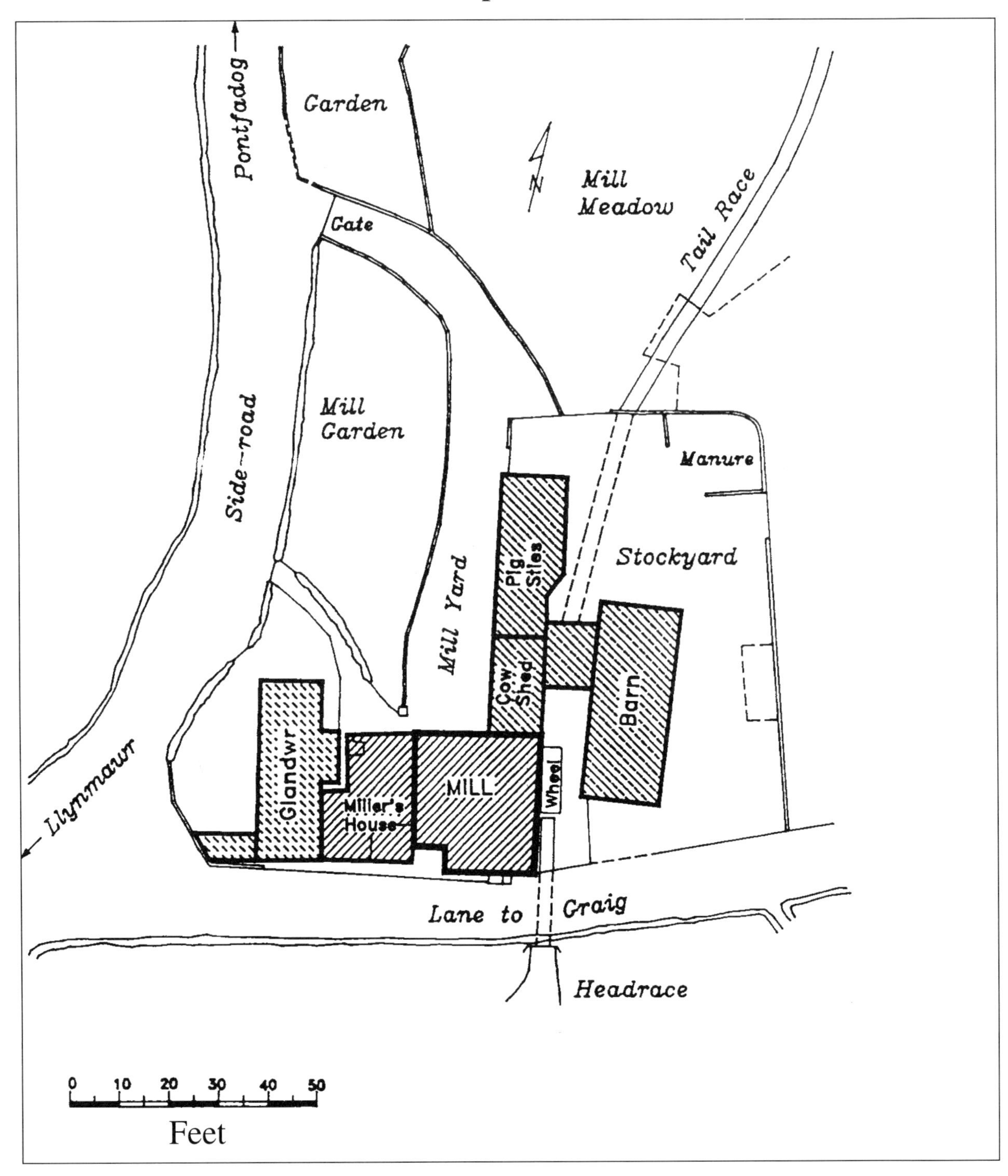

Author.

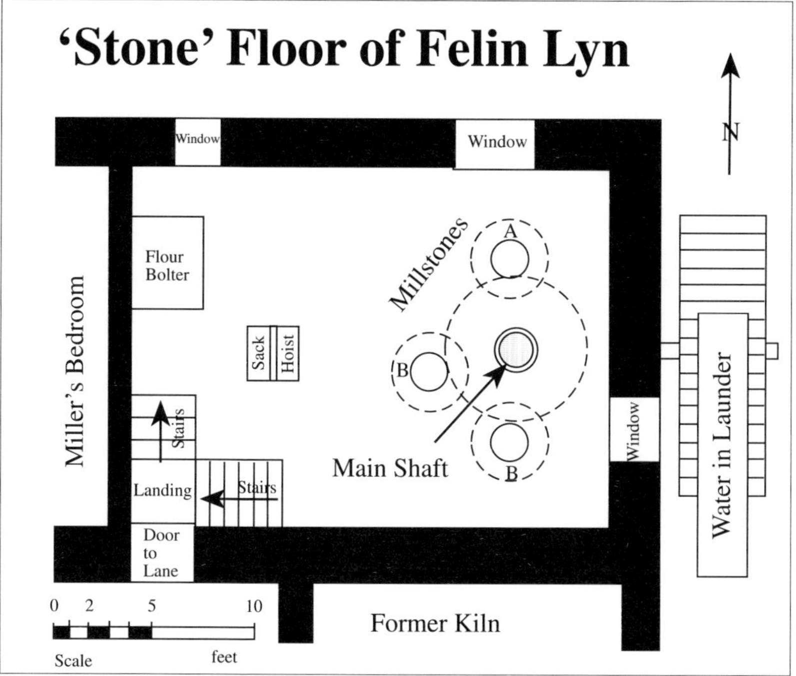

wheel and having the launder finish at the point where it is desired the water should fall on the wheel. At Felin Lyn the hatch, which was moved upwards from a horizontal flush fitting position to a near vertical angle, was always closed unless the mill was grinding.

The Felin Lyn launder and hatch design may have been determined by the unusual flood control arrangements. All watermills must have some form of flood control to remove excess waters from the mill; the normal arrangement is a sluice gate that diverts water into a by-pass channel which skirts the mill.

Felin Lyn was unusual in that it had no such by-pass. However it did need flood control and this was achieved at a point 150 yards away where the headrace passes under the Llwynmawr road. Here there were two sluice gates,

sited just beyond top dead centre of the waterwheel or at a 'one o'clock' position when looking into the axle line of the wheel from outside the mill. The miller was able to finely adjust the size of the opening of the hatch, and this would determine the amount of power he desired. For example, the de-husking of oats was a 'lightweight' operation and would require less water than, say, milling wheaten flour which would need more water to produce the power required. In reality, the rod that actuated the hatch was the throttle of the mill 'machine' and was in constant use throughout the working day with start, stop, and power variations. Inside the mill it took the form of a lever sliding over a quadrant drilled with holes, so that a peg could hold the lever at any desired position.

It should be mentioned that the author, as a boy, took a photo of the wheel in 1942. It lacks clarity because of an inferior camera and the deep shade of the subject, but there is enough detail to be able to say that the essentials of the description above are correct. When looking externally at the east wall of the Mill, with the wheel in front of it, the launder came in from the left or south side. The photo confirms that the wheel was the normal overshot type running in a clockwise direction and not a pitch-back wheel (which runs anti-clockwise) with the launder hatch at the 11 o'clock position. It also reaffirms that the waste water was taken in the launder across the top of the wheel and allowed to fall beyond its circumference, to the right or north side. This is in contrast to the practice of inserting a wastewater hatch in the launder before reaching the

one stop-gate straddling the race and the other an excess water escape just upstream of it and set into the bank of the race. In flood conditions the stream sluice was partly closed and the overflow sluice opened to its maximum extent; in summer drought the positions of the gates would be reversed.

This arrangement shows that the use of the conventional launder design would have been risky. An excess of water reaching the mill could overwhelm the capacity of the hatch and the excess would fall on the wheel causing it and the machinery to turn without any form of regulation. No owner or tenant miller would permit such a situation to arise, hence the reversal of the normal launder design thus allowing controlled but excessive waters to crash harmlessly into the pit beyond the wheel.

When the waterwheel needed to be examined or repaired, the stopgate was fully closed and all the waters were diverted via the overflow sluice back to the Afon Ceiriog.

The effects of freezing weather on Felin Lyn's waterwheel is unknown, for there is no recorded comment. Presumably the wheel was occasionally locked in ice when weather conditions became severe. John Hughes (Dol) mentioned that the neighbouring mill at Dolywern was never locked in by frost. This may have been attributable to *"...springs and wells of water rising strongly"* whose warmer waters prevented the formation of ice in the headrace.

(ii) Transmission

As previously mentioned, when the mill was first built all the gearing may have been made of wood. By the end of the nineteenth century it was a mixture of wood and iron and the description that follows relates to this period. It is a theoretical reconstruction since few pieces of evidence about the transmission remained in 1980, but is thought to be reasonably accurate.

The revolving speed of any overshot wheel is always slow – a law of physics – and as a consequence such wheels tend to deliver power at high torque. For example, the water wheel at Felin Lyn would have delivered five or six times the torque found in a motorcar. As a result the axle had to be immensely strong and in the days of wooden construction the wheel shaft or 'axletree' was just that, a tree with a finished diameter of 15-24 inches.

In this century the axle of Felin Lyn's waterwheel was of iron and was perhaps of about 8-inch diameter. It was extended as a shaft into the mill for a distance of three feet measured from the inside of the east wall and ended in a vertical bevelled gear wheel. This was called the pit-wheel and ran parallel to the waterwheel; it was called the pit-wheel because its lower part was forced to revolve in a pit dug out of the ground floor of the mill. It was almost certainly made of iron fitted with oak cogs, with a diameter of about 104 inches and some 96 teeth. Often the pit-wheel had an odd number of teeth to mismatch the even number of teeth of the next engaging gearwheel called the wallower. This ensured that differing cogs mated at every revolution, so making for more even wear and smoother running.

At this point the rotative power was transmitted from the horizontal to the vertical plane, through bevelled gears, and carried by a mast-like timber called the main-shaft. This vertical main-shaft extended from a raised stone base on the ground floor, through the next floor, and ended underneath the floor of the attic. It is presumed it had a total length of about 13-14 feet, and is estimated to have weighed about 450lb. When the two gear wheels, called the wallower and the great spur, were attached to it, the assembly would have weighed over half a ton.

The torque or twisting force developed in such a shaft was considerable and over the centuries millwrights had evolved a rule-of-thumb thickness for such shafts. Fortunately we know the dimensions of the main-shaft at Felin Lyn because in 1980 a 5 feet piece of it still lay on the floor. It was of hexagonal shape, with each face about seven inches wide and with a diameter of 17 inches. At one end still survived a bearing which was quite primitive but obviously effective. It consisted of an iron cap and collar bolted to the wood in four places which ended in a projecting iron pin of three inch diameter and 6-inch length. This presumably was held within a primitive stone, iron, or hardwood bearing block.

Attached to the base of this main-shaft was a bevelled pinion that made contact with the pit-wheel and in so doing turned the transmitted power through 90 degrees. This pinion, called the *wallower*, was considerably smaller than the pit-wheel and always made of iron. Its usual diameter was between 30 and 40 inches and in this theoretical exercise it is assumed to have had 33 teeth. Since the ratio between the pit-wheel and the wallower was of the order of one to three, it follows that the vertical main-shaft revolved at three times the speed of the waterwheel.

Attached to the main-shaft at a point just below the ceiling of the ground floor was a large horizontal gear wheel called the great spur-wheel. It was of 80 inch diameter, as this could be computed from the positioning of the three bedstones that lay *in situ* until the mill was demolished in 1981. It was either made entirely of wood or was of iron fitted with wooden cogs and is estimated to have carried 72 cogs.

This great spur-wheel, in turn, drove three identically sized pinions at points on its circumference. These pinions were called stone-nuts and their dimensions varied little across Britain. It is most likely they were one-piece iron castings of about 15 inch diameter and 16 teeth. This second and final gearing step made the stone nuts revolve $4^1/_2$ times as fast as the main shaft, or 13 times as fast as the waterwheel. This would have produced a most satisfactory speed to grind grain at Felin Lyn.

Directly above each stone-nut, but set on the floor of the room above, was a set of millstones. The lower millstone was fixed and did not move but the upper stone was free to rotate. It was turned by an iron spindle that ran from the stone-nut upwards through a hole bored in the centre of the lower or bed millstone. The miller's stone-nut was the first clutch to be developed in the world and was operated by moving it vertically and so disengaging it from the great spur-wheel. This effectively cut off the power between the waterwheel and the millstones but, unlike the sophisticated motor vehicle, it could only be operated when the transmission machinery was at rest. The transmission was usually put out-of-gear at the end of the day's work. This was to prevent the millstones being accidentally put in motion for sometimes a waterwheel would turn in the night due to an ill secured launder hatch lever, a flash flood, or the inevitable prankster.

Though Felin Lyn was a three-pair millstone mill, these

pairs were never run simultaneously. Either the 'hard' pair of stones was run by itself to grind wheat or the 'soft' sets of stones were run together or independently to produce milled oats or barley. When grinding oats it was customary to run both sets of 'soft' stones with the first pair doing the hulling or de-husking and the second pair the coarse grinding. It was technically feasible to run a 'hard' and a 'soft' stone simultaneously and was so done at Pentrefoelas Mill, Denbighshire, as a standard practice. But many mills had difficulty in getting the two pairs of stones to 'balance' and the combination was never attempted.

The terms 'tooth' and 'cog' appear to be synonymous in the milling trade, but there was the suggestion that a tooth was an integral part of a gear wheel (as in a casting) whilst a cog was a detachable piece inserted in a gear wheel.

A typical wooden cog consisted of a head and a tapered shank which was driven into a mortise within a gear wheel. The top of the head measured about 4 by $1^1/_2$ inches and it stood proud of the mortise by about 2 inches. When fashioned, the head of the cog was left in the rough. The piece was then driven into the empty slot in the gearwheel with a sledgehammer and afterwards the head was carefully shaped. Because of the constant wear involved, it was always made from a slow growing hardwood such as fruit trees, beech, holly, hornbeam or hawthorn.

These woods were favoured because they had a cross grain and a resin or oil within them which helped to lubricate and keep the cogs cool. Oak, though a hard wood, was avoided because it had no natural oil and soon heated up though it was sometimes used as a pit-wheel cog and was lubricated by the splashes from the waterwheel.

Hornbeam was reputed to be the hardest of British woods but was scarce, and the author has been told that some millers always relied upon old discarded fruit trees as a steady source of cog material. Such timber was not given away but had to be bid for, since wood workers used it for treen ware. Wild cherry grows naturally in parts of the Ceiriog, so it is possible local millers made use of it.

In the twentieth century there was a beautiful hawthorn tree growing beside the waterwheel and close to the launder at Felin Lyn, which produced a mass of deep-red flowers; the author knew it well. Any other tree would have been cut down as an interference and a stone wall disturber, but maybe the miller regarded it as a 'miller's tree' and let it grow under his protection. A more prosaic reason has been offered by an old miller. He says the shade provided in summer kept the waterwheel moist and thus helped prevent the alternating shrinking and swelling of the timbers.

Cogs were set round a wooden gear wheel at a spacing of about $2^1/_2$ - $3^1/_2$ inches between each of their centre lines. The designer millwright often avoided simpler gear ratios by adding a 'hunting' cog. This ensured that each time a revolution was made, different cogs meshed and so promoted even wear in a pair of gear wheels. A miller would always keep a stock of cogs on hand so that an instant replacement could be made should one or several be damaged. These he would fashion on a winter's evening or on summer days when work in the mill was light.

It is quite impossible at this date to be precise about the gearing ratios and the operating revolutions at Felin Lyn. However they are fundamental to the working of the mill and are of general interest, so a hypothetical set of figures has been prepared by way of illustration.

It should be explained that peripheral speeds of waterwheels and millstones hold the key to the running of a successful watermill. Small diameter waterwheels always turn faster than large diameter wheels and vice-versa but their peripheral speeds are about the same. Felin Lyn had a 12 foot diameter waterwheel and its natural or optimum speed was about $9^1/_2$ - 10rpm.

In the same vein, the upper millstone (runner) of a pair needed to have a certain peripheral speed to grind the grain properly and this was also a constant. This meant that a smaller runner stone ran at a higher rpm than did one of a larger diameter. The most popular diameter for runner stones in the British Isles appears to have been 48 inches and this requires a grinding speed of 120-150rpm. Felin Lyn's runners were larger at 55-57 inch diameter and this called for a lower speed of about 100-130 rpm.

Part of the millwright's designing expertise lay in juggling the gearing ratios to ensure that the natural waterwheel speed was able to drive the runner stone at its correct speed. An attempt will now be made to emulate the millwright's calculations.

$$\frac{\text{Pit-wheel of 96 teeth}}{\text{Wallower of 33 teeth}} = \text{Ratio of 1 to 2.91}$$

i.e. every time waterwheel turns once, main vertical shaft turns 2.91 times.

$$\frac{\text{Great spur-wheel of 72 teeth}}{\text{Stone-nut of 16 teeth}} = \text{Ratio of 1 to 4.5}$$

i.e. every time mainshaft turns once, stonenut and runner stone above turns 4.5 times.

If the waterwheel is turning 10 times per minute, the sum is: $10 \times 2.91 \times 4.5 = 131$ rpm for millstone.

Felin Lyn's waterwheel speeds could be marginally altered by supplying it with less or more water, so altering the grinding speeds as shown in the table below.

Waterwheel rpm	7	8	9	10	11
Millstone rpm	92	105	118	131	144

Finally, one mundane but important aspect of all transmission machinery – lubrication. The gears were lubricated with a coarse tallow which may have been made from the fat renderings of cattle or sheep; pig fat, though plentiful, was unsuitable. Some millers had a preference for beef suet. What was important was that no mineral oil be used as this could contaminate grain or meal that chanced to come into contact with it. In some mills it was the practice to force sheep's wool into the bearings to act both as packing and as a primitive fat or oil sponge.

(iii) Millstones

Felin Lyn had three pairs of millstones for grinding for much of its life. A pair of millstones consists of a bed stone that does not move and an upper or runner stone which revolves, with both of them having the same diameter.

In the uplands of Wales, one or four pairs of millstones were very infrequently seen, two and three pairs being the norm. On this basis, Felin Lyn's grinding capacity was typical.

Within the last 200 years two types of millstones, depending upon their hardness, were installed in mills. For operations that required light milling, a 'soft' stone was used and this was quarried as a monolith from some location in Britain. In England there was a marked preference for stones that came from the English Peak district in Derbyshire, being grit stones of a fine gravel, but in Wales most monoliths came from Anglesey or Monmouthshire.

Hard milling, such as the production of wheat flour, demanded a harder stone but it was found that the British Isles were incapable of supplying it. A hard quartz stone found near Paris established its supremacy in western Europe and virtually all British mills needing hard stones purchased this type which was known as a 'French burr'. Unlike the 'soft' stones, the French burr was not monolithic but was assembled by putting a shaped collection of smaller burr stones in a bed of plaster of Paris or cement. A hoop of iron was then shrunk around its edge to contain tangential forces. These composite millstones were manufactured near Paris and some French channel ports, and as a later development at several British ports. In the latter part of the nineteenth century, Liverpool was the nearest such port to Pontfadog. (Notes 4.11 and 4.12)

The three pairs of millstones at Felin Lyn were not uniformly positioned around the great spur-wheel, and one possible explanation is that the Mill started its life as a two-pair mill. It is probable that the addition was at the apex position, to the west. What is not known is whether the original two pairs were 'soft' stones or one 'soft' and one 'hard' and there are persuasive arguments for either configuration. Two pairs of soft stones made for a highly productive oatmeal mill for, whilst one pair is hulling, the other pair is producing the meal. On the other hand a mill with one hard pair and one soft pair is versatile and is capable of dealing with 'hard' wheat and 'soft' oats or barley. On balance, the author is inclined to think Felin Lyn was set up with the latter formation to take its part in the agricultural improvements of the late eighteenth century already discussed in Chapter 2.

The French burr stones at Felin Lyn had a diameter of 57 inches and the bedstone surviving in 1981 was fitted with 13 pieces of burr. The author has seen other burrstones in Britain that have ranged from 7-21 pieces with about 15-17 pieces as the norm. Mrs Jones (FL) wrote: *"The wheat was ground on a different set of stones to the other grain. If I remember rightly, my father told me they came from Brittany."*

The two pairs of 'soft' millstones were of 55 and 57 inch diameter respectively, but they did not come from Derbyshire. The stone was a form of sandstone with prominent embedded pebbles which ranged in size from half to one inch diameter, with one exception at 2 inches. This description fits Anglesey stones and it is fairly certain they came from there. Chirk Castle Estates had a partiality for these stones and the accounts of 1751 record that an employee was sent to Anglesey to buy a millstone.

Thomas Telford (1757-1834), civil engineer of renown, was apprenticed as a stonemason and possessed a thorough knowledge of British rocks and their uses. In assessing the worth of British millstones, he said Anglesey stones were *"...grey, soft and gritty, but of lasting quality."*, a good recommendation from such an expert. Telford made his mark on the Ceiriog at Chirk, where he was responsible for building the canal aqueduct (1796-1801) and the Mail Road (1822-24), both still in use.

There were several millstone pits in Anglesey, but the best-known quarry was at Enys, about two miles inland from Red Wharf Bay on the east coast of the island. It produced millstones and farm rollers for some 200 years until closure in 1939. Geologically, the stone was defined as a carboniferous millstone grit, a form of sandstone.

Only a small part of the quarry's output went to Welsh mills, there being a large trade within northern Europe – in particular Norway and Sweden. (Note 4.13)

In the eighteenth century these millstones, which weighed a ton apiece, would have reached Felin Lyn, first by sailing coaster along the North Wales coast to Connah's Quay, then possibly by small barge on the Dee as far as Holt; the final 20 miles had to be by road. The last part of this journey in the vicinity of the Ceiriog would have been arduous. In the late eighteenth century there was no flat valley-bottom road and all things had to ascend and descend the hill spines to reach Felin Lyn. In terms of sheer human effort the making and transporting of these four original mill stones must be considered one of the major tasks in creating the Mill. If the eighteenth century millers were susceptible to nightmares, then one would surely have involved the shattering of an Anglesey stone. (Note 4.14)

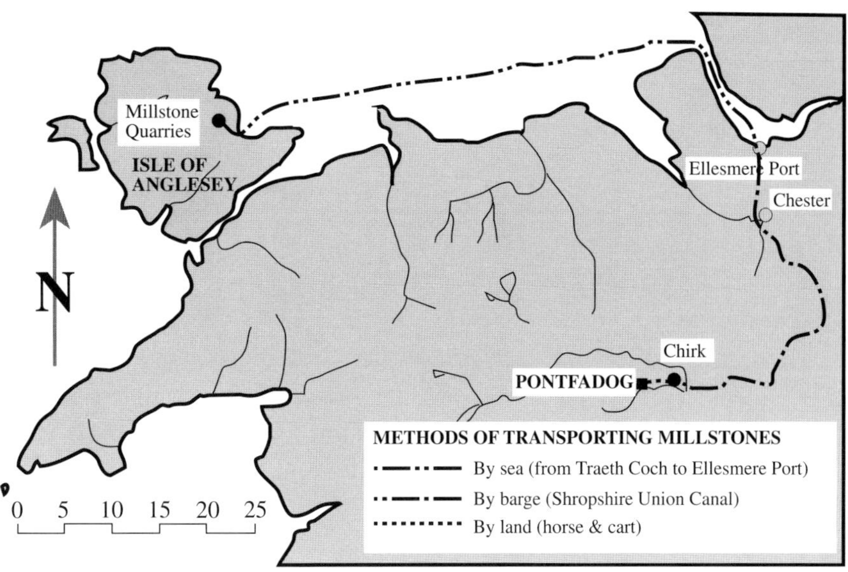

G Nash

For the whole of the nineteenth century and to at least 1920, the carriage was water-borne for all but the last four miles to Pontfadog. The first leg was by sea to Ellesmere Port on the Mersey and thence by Shropshire Union Canal to Chirk. It is almost a certainty that the Anglesey stones surviving to 1981 at Felin Lyn were transported by this route. Rail carriage was not considered because Red Wharf Bay in Anglesey was not served by a railway until 1908 and water transport was infinitely cheaper.

The diameters of the millstones at Felin Lyn, at 55 inches and 57 inches, were slightly unusual but were not a rarity. Millstones in Britain ranged from 32 inches to 64 inches, with 48 inches and 54 inches being the favoured diameters. A discarded but surviving millstone at Tregeiriog, six miles upstream from Felin Lyn, has a related diameter of 55 inches. It is of interest to learn that of the few millstones surviving at the small, abandoned quarries in Anglesey, in partial or finished state, some are of 55 and 56 inch diameter. All Anglesey stones had iron bands affixed to them and those at Felin Lyn were similarly treated.

When Anglesey millstones were new they possessed the following dimensions and weights. The upper or runner stone was 10 inches thick at the outer edge and 14 inches at the point where a 9 inch diameter hole was made through its centre; it weighed one long ton almost exactly. The stationary bed stone was a uniform 10 inches thick and was pierced by a smaller hole of less than 5 inch diameter; it weighed about 1,900lb or $^{7}/_{8}$th of a ton. The weights have been calculated on the assumption the natural rock weighed 140lbs to the cubic foot, though another source quotes 155lbs/cubic foot (granite and slate range between 164 and 170lbs). The upper face of the bedstone was always perfectly flat whilst the lower face of the runner was slightly concave to allow the meal to escape to the edge of the stones.

In a reasonably busy mill such stones wore down at the rate of a quarter inch or less per year, and could be safely used until they were three to four inches thick. Thus in a continuously worked and busy mill, a pair of stones had a minimum life of 25 years. However, many upland Welsh mills had two sets of these stones and, as they were not run at the same time, their life expectancy was often closer to 50 years. The bedstones at Felin Lyn were about eight inches thick in 1981 and had last been used actively in 1935. Their thickness suggested a busy life of 15-20 years or double that for a slower pace of work. This points to the likelihood that these Anglesey stones were installed new in the fourth quarter of the last century.

The three pairs of millstones at Felin Lyn were sited in a triangle with soft stones at the south angle and the west apex and the 'hard' burr at the north angle. Ten inches separated the circumferences of the two soft stones, 19 inches between the apex stone and the burr, and 15 inches between the burr and the east wall of the mill. The space occupied by these millstones, plus the limited access area between them and the east wall, amounted to 100 square feet, which was commendably compact and equal to a quarter of the room area.

When installed as new they collectively weighed $5^1/_2$ tons, and this formidable weight – as in all mills – was taken by a very solid wooden platform of triangular shape called a hursting. This hursting was supported by thick posts on the ground floor, which also enclosed the transmission machinery. At some late date an iron stanchion was inserted at the apex of the triangle to help shore up ageing timbers.

The faces of both bed and runner stones were intricately dressed with cutting edges and furrows in straight but tangential lines from the eye of the stones. These could be quite clearly seen in 1981 on the faces of the three surviving bed stones, once the accumulation of over 40 years of dirt had been removed.

The matching runner or top stones, as described earlier, were broken up by a scrap metal merchant in 1956 in order to acquire their metal fittings. So for a mess of metal pottage, these millstones – hewn laboriously from the solid rock and transported laboriously for 130 miles – were shattered in pieces within minutes by sledgehammer blows.

(iv) Ancillary Machinery

None of the ancillary machinery had survived to 1980 but there were enough pieces of minor evidence and one brief eyewitness report to be able to describe with accuracy what had been there.

The large wooden upright main shaft, described earlier, terminated in a bearing fixed to the ceiling of the first floor. Attached to its top end was another gear wheel which was about two-thirds the size of the great spur-wheel and was called the crown wheel – being the topmost gear wheel in the mill. The crown wheel meshed with a bevel gear and this rotated the power from the vertical to the horizontal and drove an iron lay shaft on an east-west axis about mid-ceiling. The shaft was attached by bearings to the underside of the bin floor above and evidence of the arrangement could still be detected in 1981. It is deduced that it drove at least three pieces of machinery.

Crown wheels usually had a diameter of about 56 inches with some 50 teeth and drove a bevel gear with some 10-20 teeth. What the dimensions were of this part of the power train at Felin Lyn is not known. It is presumed the crown wheel rotated at about 30 rpm so it is possible the layshaft turned between 75 and 150 times per minute. Ancillary machines require differing rpms and this was achieved quite simply by running pulleys and belting off the lay shaft in combinations of big to small pulleys for faster speeds and small to big pulleys for lower speeds.

The ancillary machinery within the mill itself at Felin Lyn, at varying periods, consisted of sack hoist, grain cleaner, flour dresser, oatmeal winnower, and butter churn.

The sack hoist was common to all mills of the nineteenth and twentieth centuries, having been introduced in the late eighteenth century. In theory grain and meal descends within a mill by gravity, but in practice there are some up-and-down movements. For instance, in a toll mill each farmer's delivery of grain had to be kept separate and sometimes it had to be given temporary storage in the attic, two floors up. If processed immediately it still had to go upwards. After the grinding of wheat, the meal was taken up once again to the first floor and fed into a sieving device called a bolter. So a sack hoist was in constant use in any mill, but it was a one-way device capable only of lifting sacks in an upward direction.

At Felin Lyn, trap doors were installed in the floors of the upper room and the attic, about midway between the north and south floors and 7 feet out from the west wall. Each trap measured 30 inches by 29 inches and was fitted with two half-doors with a 2-inch gap between them. These doors were fitted with leather hinges and could open only upwards. Fitted into the roof of the attic was a drum or barrel, onto which a rope was wound, and was powered by belting taken off the lay shaft mentioned above. At the end of the rope was a short length of chain which was used to put a running noose over the neck of a sack. A further length of rope was attached to the chain, because after every upwards movement the miller had to pull the rope down to the floor that he was working on.

In 1936 a mill enthusiast called Mitford Abraham, whom we shall hear more about later in the book, visited Felin Lyn and observed two ancillary machines, a cleaner and a dresser. In 1980 floor and wall marks suggested where these machines may have been located, both of them on the first floor. In the south-west corner of the room and on the south wall at shoulder height were marks of a 36-inch diameter wheel, the marks presumably made by the driving belt. Against the west wall was some device that was 53 inches long and 40 inches wide and of uncertain height.

Photographs of these machines taken in other small country mills suggest that the grain cleaner was underslung from the ceiling, just under the bin floor, whilst the dresser stood on the floor beside the west wall with its chutes feeding sacks set up on the ground floor.

The grain cleaner consisted of a drum about three feet long and of one foot diameter covered with fine wire mesh and inclined slightly from the horizontal. Inside this drum were rotating brushes or beaters and at one end was a primitive but effective fan powered by the pulley wheel, the marks of which have already been alluded to. The whole contraption was slung from the ceiling and was fed with grain by a chute coming from the attic. In operation the corn was forced against the wire mesh by the action of the beaters and all items smaller than the corn grains, such as dirt, dust, weed seeds, went through the mesh aided by the air blast. The grain then passed through a sieve which trapped larger items such as twigs, stones, leaves or perhaps a dead mouse.

A good husbandman could bring grain to a mill with as little as 2% impurities but with a neglectful farmer and a careless harvester this could rise three or fourfold. The rpm of this cleaner is not known. Its location ensured that the clean grain could fall by gravity into the hoppers of the millstones, the furthest being ten feet away.

The dresser was a sieving machine and in essence worked in the same way as the corn cleaner. It consisted of a four-foot long wooden cylindrical frame of about 16-18 inch diameter, fixed on an inclined axis. The frame was covered with wire mesh of different sizes, finest at the top and coarsest at the bottom. Inside this cylinder was a rotating shaft fitted with a series of brushes which lightly touched the wire mesh, at 300-400 rpm. Meal was fed into the cylinder at the top end with the fine flour separated first, followed by bran and 'thirds'. It was a popular machine with country millers as it made satisfactory grade separations simultaneously at a good rate. The machine usually came with internal gearing that doubled the rotational speed brought to it.

Another processing machine existed in toll milling days but was presumably discarded in this century. It was called an oatmeal machine (winnower) and was located on the ground floor at the foot of the hursting and took the oats as they came from the millstones. Its task was to separate oat husks from the oat grain, thus producing groats. It did all this using a vibrating sieve and an air blower. Its use is further touched upon later in the chapter.

The last ancillary machine to be found within the mill itself was a butter churn. Such devices were often found in watermills in the nineteenth century so its application at Felin Lyn was in no way unusual. John Hughes (Dol) mentions that his father and uncle some time between 1835 and 1850 carried out a joint venture at Dolywern of meadow watering, malt grinding and butter churning, so the practice was known locally. The butter churn at Felin Lyn was located on the ground floor of the mill and Mrs Jones (FL) had a childhood recollection of *"...a long pole that worked in the tub, which in turn was attached to the machinery. This pole went up and down, making a lovely sound. It was one of the jobs we could be entrusted to do as children."*

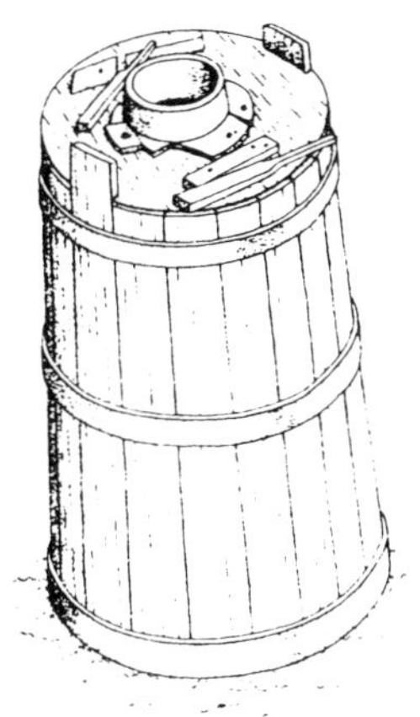

The churn that Mrs Jones refers to was a plunger churn that had been in use since the fifteenth century and was popular in Wales. It was a stoutly-built narrow barrel made by a cooper, tapering from bottom to top. It had a close-fitting lid held in place by clamps and through the centre of it passed a shaft to which was fitted a piston head bored with many small holes. At Felin Lyn the top end of the wooden shaft, which projected well beyond the barrel, was pinned with a crank to the edge of a wheel face. The wheel was driven by belting from the mill machinery and so imparted a reciprocating motion to the plunger inside the churn; the whole device might be described as having an elegant simplicity. The churn was half filled with cream and in a short time – with much agitation – it became butter and butter-milk.

Other essential, but unpowered, pieces of equipment were the weighscale and the two-wheeled sack truck. The scale stood near the main entrance door and in this century everything entering and leaving Felin Lyn by sack was weighed on it. On one side was the sack platform with a curved back, in the enclosed middle was the mechanism, and on the other side was another platform to receive weights. Such scales normally weighed up to a maximum of 4cwt. and had weights available in the 14, 28 and 56lb. range.

Two pieces of equipment that survived within the mill to 1980 are worth a mention. One was a thick canvas driving belt of 4 inch width, and the other was a wooden trough issuing from the granary hopper located in the former kiln and leading to where the hoppers would have been sited above the millstones; the mouth of this was 6 inches square.

There was also more ancillary machinery in the barn that performed farm work and had nothing to do with milling. Most watermills had a powered grindstone but this was always located away from the mill rooms because it was just possible that the sparks created by sharpening could ignite the potentially explosive dusts that were to be found in mills.

The grinding wheel at Felin Lyn was used to sharpen

bill-hooks, axes and the like; it was there for the convenience of customers as well as for the miller himself. This grindstone was located on the top floor of the barn and close to the doors that opened out onto the Graig lane. The late Tom Roberts (1906-1987), former farmer and Felin Lyn customer, remembered that he availed himself of this service, particularly when hedges were being re-layered in the winter or trimmed in the summer.

It would certainly have been used by the stone dresser, who was constantly resharpening his mill-bills and picks as he worked on the millstones. In the last days of Felin Lyn the author can vouch for it also being used by the Forestry Commission woodsman who looked after the plantation on the hill to the south. This hill was called Bryn Perkins by the Welsh, Brown Billy by the English, and nameless by the mapmakers.

The woodsman lived at Dolywern and each morning cycled over to Felin Lyn where he left his bicycle in the barn, and then walked up the hill for a mile to his job. This is a happy recollection of the author's because the big man and small boy were good friends.

Also in the barn, driven by the same line shafting, was a chaff cutter and a root (turnips, swedes, mangolds) pulper.

This array of ancillary machinery and equipment shows a surprising sophistication for a small country mill, and was not anticipated when the research first started.

(v) Timber Sawing

Until comparatively recent times, man's traditional method of obtaining beams or thick planks was to split a tree trunk by driving wedges in line down its entire length. The pieces suddenly split along the grain, producing a very strong load member and one superior to sawn timber which takes no notice of the grain. The beams were then shaped by adz and it is probable that the roof joists of Felin Lyn were fashioned in this way.

Hand sawn timber had been available since before the Middle Ages but such timber was very costly because it had to be laboriously cut by two experienced men (top sawyer and pitman) using a ripsaw and sawpit. This method produced one ten foot plank per hour or perhaps 8-12 planks a day, and the result was that their use was limited to objects requiring a flat surface such as doors, floorboards and table-tops. Prior to the sawing of wood by mechanical power at Felin Lyn, there were two saw pits in the parish of Glyn Traian, one on each side of the valley sited at Tyn-y-Graig near Nantgwryd and at Llwydiarth north of Dolywern .

It is believed it was the Dutch who first mechanised sawing in the late 1500s. In the context of timber, the

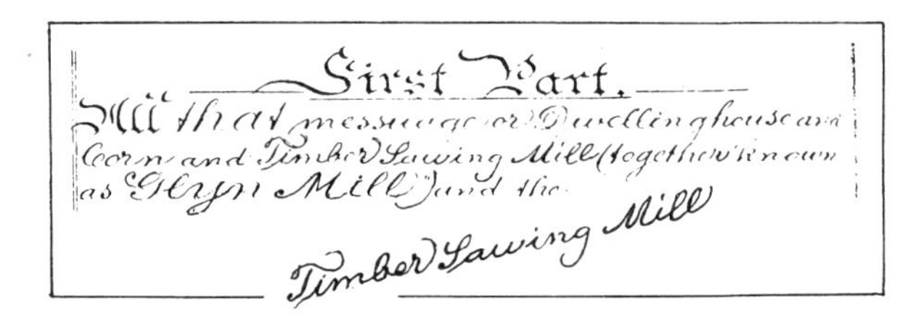
First Part.
All that messuage or Dwellinghouse and Corn and Timber Sawing Mill (together known as Glyn Mill) and the
Timber Sawing Mill

Dutch were then the equivalent of today's Japanese in that they had the technology and imported the raw materials. Amsterdam had 74 wind-driven sawmills by 1645, and at this period Holland was by far the richest country in Europe in proportion to its size and population. Such wind-driven sawmills continued to work into the beginning of this century, being slowly superseded by steam-driven machinery that first appeared c.1870.

The concept soon spread to Scandinavia and then to North America where timber stood for the asking but where labour was scarce and expensive. The first water-powered sawmill in North America is believed to be dated 1623.

The British were among the last to adopt this form of mechanisation, with the Scots taking the pioneering lead because they did have stands of native conifers. Water-powered sawmills were well established in Scotland before 1800 and by the middle of the last century there were about 700 of them.

In the early 1800s sawmills became a useful addition to many estates and sometime in the first half of the last century, Chirk Castle Estates set up a water-driven sawmill close to its home farm and within a mile of the Castle. This sawmill was certainly at work in mid-century because George Borrow, author of *"Wild Wales"*, was at Castlemill in 1854 and records that he met a man with a bandaged hand. Asking what was the matter, the man replied that he had lately lost three fingers whilst working at the sawmill up at the Castle. It is known that at the same period there was an estate sawmill at Glyndyfrdwy, six miles to the north-west of Felin Lyn, which had previously been a fulling mill.

It is presumed that Chirk/Ruthin Estates initiated the installation of a water-driven saw at Felin Lyn but apart from the fact that in 1867 the Mill was listed as a 'Corn Mill and Saw Mill', we have no details. Mrs Jones (FL) said no sawing was done from the time her father took over the Mill in 1900 and she felt the period c1840 to about 1880 was the most likely.

Another question to be asked is who ran the sawmill? It is improbable a cornmiller would also be a sawmiller because of conflicting time demands and differing expertise. It is likely the facility was sub-let to some person who operated it on a part-time basis. A partial clue

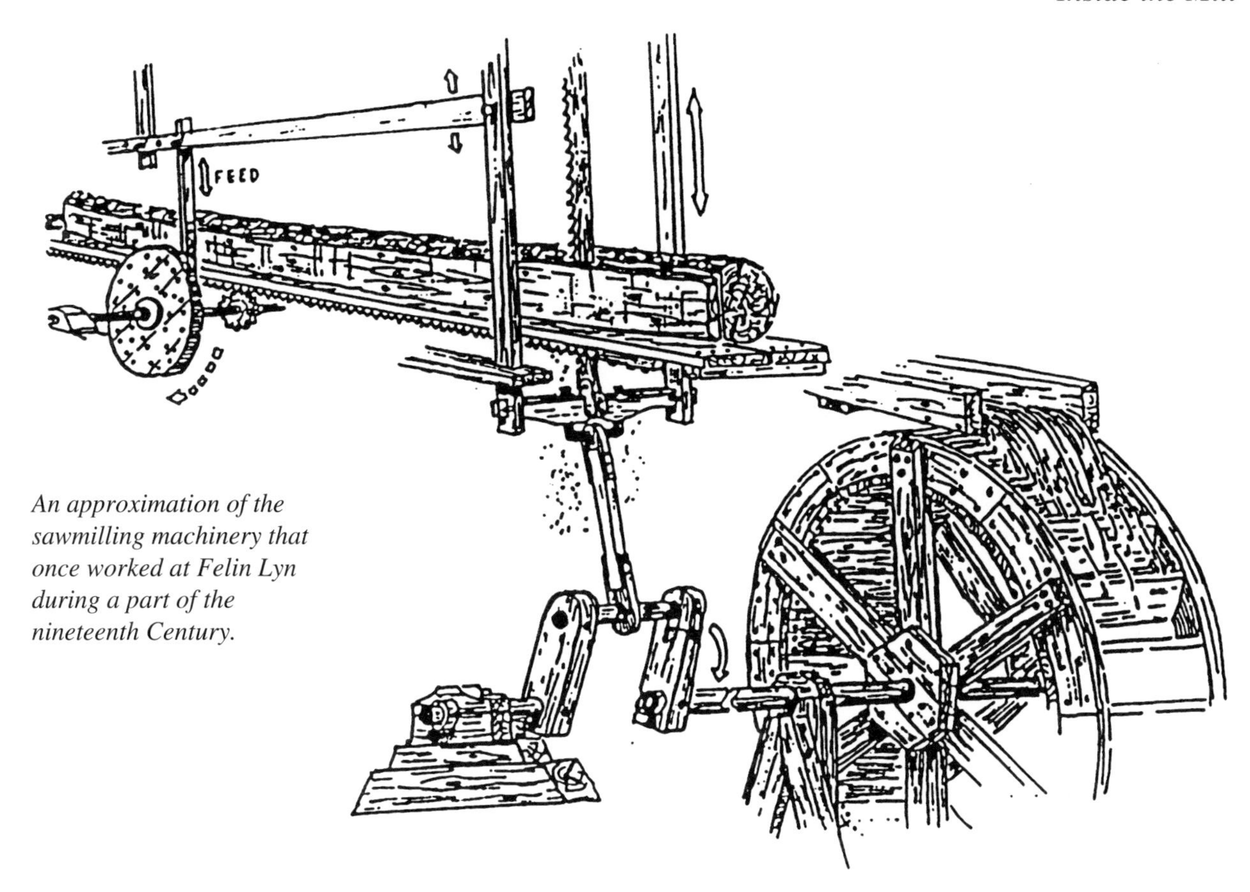

An approximation of the sawmilling machinery that once worked at Felin Lyn during a part of the nineteenth Century.

as to who one of these sawmill operators might have been is the family of miller Evan Evans (1815-cl880s) who had three brothers, one was a builder and another a carpenter and joiner.

Mrs Jones (FL) said: *"The barn had a higher level where the hay was kept and the turnips chopped, and my father told me there used to be an 'office' on the right hand side of the door where his uncles, one a builder and the other a joiner, kept their accounts and paid their employees on a Saturday."* It would certainly make sense for three brothers – miller, builder and joiner – to use Felin Lyn as a base for their activities and for the latter two to power-saw wood there. The birth dates of these two men suggest they could not have been involved in the business much before the mid-late 1860s, so we have to regard them as one of the last to operate the sawmill before it ceased to function.

First thoughts might suggest there was insufficient power to run a cornmill and a sawmill simultaneously or, if there was adequate power, that the revolutions-per-minute for the two operations was incompatible. However it seems this was not the case, for the late George O. Heald, whose father ran Pentrefoelas Mill in western Denbighshire between 1920 and 1949 says this: *"When we were grinding with two sets of stones, I have seen the large saw-bench connected and wood being sawn. Many people brought wood in to be sawn into planks, as our saw was the largest in the locality. This saw was capable of making planks, tongue and groove, and cogs."* The mention of cogs is of especial interest as it shows that the making of replacement cogs for the cornmill had been partly mechanised.

The timber-sawing machinery at Felin Lyn was located in the open on the east side of the waterwheel and consisted of a carriage to hold the log, and a vertical reciprocating saw set in a timber guiding frame. The carriage assembly consisted of two parts, one being the trackway that supported the carriage and the other the carriage or cradle that held the log firmly in position whilst it was being cut. The trackway had to be twice the length of the log to be cut, and since the site at Felin Lyn was constricted, it would appear the maximum log length that could be handled would not exceed ten or twelve feet. The carriage was moved forward at a uniform speed against the saw blade by means of a ratchet device powered by gearing, the whole being driven by a power shaft which in turn was driven by the waterwheel.

Saws were made of iron and consisted of a vertical blade about six feet long and six inches wide with teeth set at about one inch apart. The blade rode in a greased hardwood frame and was attached to a crank by a long pitman rod, which was connected through gearing to the axle of the waterwheel. Usually, the blade worked at the rate of 50-100 strokes per minute in which the down stroke did the cutting; the rate of advance would be about one foot per minute. During the working day about 75% of the time would be in sawing and the residue would be spent in carriage return, log set-up, and moving product, slab and sawdust. Using a single blade, it was possible to produce about 40-50 lineal feet per hour, or at least four times faster than sawing manually.

Trees that were felled within the Ceiriog would have been oak, ash and elm for utilitarian purposes and birch and alder for firelogs. Trees were normally felled in the winter for several reasons. Sap was at its lowest, surplus farm labour was available at year's ebb, and the ground was hard enough to allow removal of heavy trunks. The sawn timber was then naturally air-dried for 12 months or more before being made into an article such as a gatepost, coffin, part of a cart, or rafters.

Felin Lyn's sawmill would have been a great improvement over hand sawing but to modern eyes would have produced a crude finish. The vertical saws tended to wobble and so produced not the smoothest of finishes and were wasteful of wood because of the thick saw incision. Most of these problems were overcome by the invention of the circular saw which appears to have been independently developed in Holland and the United States at the birth of the nineteenth century. These saws appeared in Britain around the middle of the last century but did not become widespread until the introduction of steam-power, because circular saws need much higher running speeds to be effective.

There being exceptions to any generalisation, it is interesting to note that a surviving and operable Welsh water-driven flour and sawmill uses a 4-foot circular saw operating at 1,200 rpm. This mill, Felin Geri, near Newcastle Emlyn in Dyfed, had its timber-sawing machinery built by the Cardigan Iron Foundry in 1882. The 1882 date suggests the reciprocating saw at Felin Lyn was becoming outmoded and that this and another telling factor caused timber sawing to be abandoned there. The other factor is that it is more desirable to bring a power plant to a sawmill which needs an open and flat site, than to bring logs to the physically inconvenient layout of a watermill. Such a power plant became available by the 1850s, it being a portable steam engine. (Note 4.15)

Milling Process

No attempt will be made to describe the milling process in technical detail, as it is identical to all watermills whether they be in Turkey, Finland or Wales, and is well explained in numerous publications issued in the last quarter century. Rather, emphasis will be placed on some of the differences to be found in an 'upland' mill when operating in the days of Toll milling, as typified by Felin Lyn.

Oats were the cereal that distinguished the 'upland' from the 'lowland' mill. As previously described, the oats were taken to Felin Lyn's kiln for drying and were then bagged and taken inside the mill proper.

The first process the oat kernels were subjected to was called hulling, or husking, or shelling. The last term had various corruptions, such as sheiling, shealing or shilling. The soft Anglesey stones were used to hull the oats, and were so set that the stones knocked off the now brittle hulls or husks but did not bruise the grain itself. This stone setting would have had about a 0.2 inch gap between the millstones.

After falling from the stones, the hulls and the grain – now termed groats – dropped into an oatmeal machine. This machine was called a 'shiliwr' in Welsh, for shilio/silio/sillo means to hull grain in Welsh, and was driven from the pit-wheel by means of an auxiliary drive. The machine was simplicity itself for it consisted of an agitating sieve and a fan. Dust particles fell through the sieve, the husks were blown into a holding box or directly into the millrace, and the groats because of their weight were collected in a trough or in a sack. The groats were then taken up to the first floor again for the next pass through the millstones.

Grinding groats produced oatmeal which was satisfactory for many of the cooking recipes requiring oatmeal, and for animal feed. However if pinhead oatmeal (oat flour) was required, this could be obtained by bolting a quantity of the meal but there was little demand for this product.

Turning to barley, there was virtually no demand in the late eighteenth century and the nineteenth century for barley flour because it had been supplanted by wheaten flour. Much of the barley was bruised for animal feed except for a goodly quantity set aside as future malt for brewing beer. Like oats, it was ground on the 'soft' stones into a coarse meal and it is estimated that a third of Felin Lyn's annual processing tonnage was in this product.

Sometimes British farmers grew oats and barley

together in a field because they found that cohabitation of the two cereals produced enhanced yields as compared to growing them separately. The crop was threshed and milled as a mixture and was used as animal feed. In Wales this grain mixture was called 'siprys' and at one time may have been processed at Felin Lyn.

Finally there was wheat and it was treated identically in both upland and lowland mills. Since wheat was solely a human food and humans wished to eat it only in fine powder form, it followed that all wheat had to be converted to flour.

First, the wheat was passed through the grain cleaner to remove field dirt and extraneous seed. Next, and unlike oats and barley, it was ground on the hard French burrs which were closely set. The result was wheatmeal which is the product of milling before any dressing has taken place.

Dressing, bolting and sieving, which all mean the same thing, was a process of extraction and resulted in obtaining two commodities. They were flour and offal; the latter consisting of sharps, middlings and bran.

Watermills, such as Felin Lyn, in the last century were capable of extracting 60% flour from wheatmeal, the residual 40% consisting of bran (15%) and middlings and sharps (25%). The latter were pieces of the starchy interior of the kernel that had resisted the work of the millstones and these together with the bran were sold as quality animal feed.

As to terminology, wheatmeal was called 'wholemeal' in the sense that nothing had been removed. Once it was dressed and some constituents of the kernel were partially or wholly removed – such as the bran – it became brown flour which ranged in colour from brown to near white. 'White flour' had all the offals removed.

The millstones were enclosed in round wooden tubs to confine the escaping products and the dust, so it was never possible to view the grinding process. The upper surface of the fixed bottom stone was flat but the face of the upper revolving stone had a slight concavity around its eye or centre. This caused the grains to move to the periphery as they were split, crushed and finally ground. If the stones were well dressed and working properly, giving the right sort of output for their size, the meal was not heated as it issued from the chute. This was an important aspect as heated meal had poorer keeping qualities in storage.

The millstones had to be balanced perfectly, both statically and dynamically, for if the stones touched during grinding the cutting edges of the stones could be ruined. Worse still, was the possibility that a spark might cause an explosion, since flour dust was everywhere and being of organic matter was flammable. This could lead to an uncontrollable fire which was a major destroyer of watermills. For example, King's Mill at Chester was burnt down four times in a 110-year period, in 1789, 1819, 1847 and 1895.

The author recollects a now lost typed letter, dated c1910-1914, from the Oswestry Fire Brigade to his grandfather, the then owner of Felin Lyn. It concerned payment for services rendered but gave no details. It could not have related to a fire at the Mill since Oswestry is nine miles away. By the time a fire-engine had been summoned by telegraph from Pontfadog Post Office and had travelled to the premises, Felin Lyn would have been gutted. The most plausible explanation is that hay stored in the barn was generating heat, a fairly common occurrence on farms. Hay stored in a building or rick was safe up to about 170°F but close to 200°F it would burst into flame.

The critical moment in trying to remove the threat came when the heated hay was cut out and suddenly found a plentiful supply of oxygen and the mass took fire. The barn lay less than 20 feet away from the mill so the danger to the latter was very real.

The miller had a device, called tentering gear, which allowed him to make fine adjustments to the gap between a pair of millstones. The art of milling was the continual juggling of this gap and the pace of the waterwheel to achieve just the right results. Different cereals have differing hardnesses, and frequently any one cereal will show variations in hardness caused by location, seed type and husbandry. This meant the miller had to be watchful all the time, and take immediate corrective action if meal or flour coming off the stones was unsatisfactory.

It is a legitimate question to ask what time was needed at Felin Lyn for the various milling operations just described. Nothing is known about these milling rates at Felin Lyn and so the author has had to rely upon a haphazard collection of productivity figures and inferences from other British mills to form an idea of what they might have been.

Three matters affecting output should be mentioned: they are stone diameter, continuous milling periods, and product loss. It is obvious that a larger diameter millstone will grind more grain than a smaller one, so it is to be remembered that Felin Lyn's stones were of 55-57 inches diameter – somewhat larger than the British norm of 48 or 54 inches.

In a Toll mill, a miller would often process parcels belonging to four or six customers in any given day, so it was rare to run the mill continuously for more than two or three hours. Because of this, milling rates have been computed for minutes and hours, but not full days.

Lastly, in all milling work, there was (and is) some product loss. This varied from practically nothing when making coarse animal feed to almost 40% when producing fine oat flour. The balance was not actually lost, it was the dross resulting from the operation and always found a use as animal feed. With all the technical improvements of this century, only 68-72% of wheat grain is converted today to saleable flour.

Probable production rates at Felin Lyn are given in the Table below and should be accurate to within 10%.

Table 11
Grinding rates and dressing results

Cereal	*Meal grinding rates*			*Dressing results*		
	Ground to:	*Minute*	*Hour*	*Use*	*Resultant*	
Oats or Barley	Coarse meal	7.5 to 9.5lb	450 to 570lb	Animal & human food	Not dressed, 100% intact No loss.	
Wheaten flour	Fine meal	6lb	360lb	Human food only	70% as flour	Residue as animal feed
Oaten flour					60% as flour	

Based on using one pair millstones of 56 inch diameter.

Using these production rates, two examples of milling performance are worth quoting. The first concerns a sack of wheaten flour, which by the mid-nineteenth century had been standardised to weigh 280lb. To fill a sack of this weight required $6^{1}/_{2}$ bushels of wheat, or 395lb of grain, and needed just over an hour of milling time on the French burr stones to process it.

The other example examines daily and yearly production tonnages. The notion of a day containing a fixed number of working hours is foreign to the countryman, but let it be assumed in this example that a working day has eight hours and that there are two hundred milling days in a year, also that only one pair of stones was in use at any given moment. On this basis the mill could coarse-grind $1^{1}/_{2}$ to 2 tons of grain, or produce $1^{1}/_{4}$ tons of fine flour, per day, which gives a theoretical annual output of 300-400 and 250 tons, respectively. In practice this kind of momentum could not be sustained for a whole variety of reasons, but the figures do demonstrate that the Mill was capable of processing the annual tonnages calculated in Chapter 2.

This may be a suitable point to make mention of the humble but indispensable sack, which was the standard container for all grains on farms, at mills, and with customers. Sacks have been preferred over the centuries to solid containers, such as earthenware crocks and wooden lidded boxes, on two counts. First, they were much more wieldy for handling and carrying and, secondly, they let the corn breathe. Grain continues to take in oxygen and give off heat after harvesting and a sack conveniently allowed this respiration to continue. Wicker hampers would have performed the same function but were far less supple as containers.

The sack was a strong and rugged container as it had to carry weights of up to 300lbs. and stand much use and abuse. It came in two different weaves, one that was coarse for carrying whole kernels and the other of very fine weave to contain flours.

Prior to the middle of the last century, kernel sacks were made of hemp that was grown and harvested in Britain. Hemp was also used to make coarse work clothes and all kinds of rope. In the same period, flour sacks were made of linen which comes from flax which is another British-grown fibrous plant.

Because these sacks were hand woven and hand assembled, they were regarded much as we might regard household linens, and each farmer held himself, or his servants, accountable for each sack. A miller had a limited quantity of sacks which he used for internal processing in the mill and to contain his own personal property of grains and flours but these he would not permit to leave his mill. It was up to the farmer to provide the necessary number of kernel and flour sacks when transporting his own cereals. If a miller found an unmarked sack, it was normal practice to appropriate it by stencilling it with his name and/or the mill's name. As mentioned earlier, Felin Lyn's stencil plate survived on the premises into the 1950s.

Jute, another fibrous plant but grown in India, began to supersede hemp in the period 1820-80 for the simple reason that it was cheaper though not as strong. In due course the industry of mechanically woven sacking was established at Dundee, Scotland. The day of the mass-produced and standardised grain sack had arrived. When laid flat it measured about 52-54 inches in length and about 26-28 inches in width, and would hold 3-5 bushels of corn. Because bushel weights varied according to the type of grain, it was possible – for example – to fill an identical sack and have 168lbs of oats, 224 lbs of barley or 252lbs of wheat.

The cloth used to make flour sacks also changed at this time, linen being superseded by cotton and for the same reason – cheapness. The cotton came from India, Egypt or the United States and was woven in Lancashire.

Only when mass production made sacks commonplace and cheap was there less rigid concern about ownership and control at a country mill. Larger 'factory' mills and corn merchants charged a refundable deposit on all sacks leaving their premises.

The new style cotton flour sacks held 280lbs (20 stone) which seems a very unwieldy size. It required two men to lift such a sack on to the back of the carrier, who could then stagger with it for a short distance. The flour in the sack was capable of making 90 to 100 loaves, each of 4lb. size. In due course the sack content was halved to 140lb. to make it a practical load to carry. Later still, flour sacks for the retail trade were further reduced in size but this does not concern the story of Felin Lyn.

Notwithstanding the sizes and weights just mentioned, it is the recollection of most people who have handled grain sacks on farms or in mills that the weights were often quite excessive for an ordinary man. Weights mentioned often range between 175 and 240 lbs and frequently at two hundredweight (224 lbs). The Glyn Valley Tramway invoices of 1882 showed that the Tramway employees and the miller of Felin Lyn were lifting sacks of 224, 240 and 250lbs. Nowadays things have changed for the better for regulations now prohibit a lone employee from lifting more than 25 kilograms (55 lbs). Dr G. M. Davies, who lived at Chirk in his youth and who has given much valuable advice on the agricultural aspects of this history, says: *"The sacks I saw as a boy were certainly large two hundredweight ones – guaranteed to induce a hernia. Indeed my farmer-grandfather had an operation for one in 1932 in Chirk Cottage Hospital, which was then regarded locally as quite a surgical feat!"*

Finally, a word about how the trade of country milling physically affected the miller. The poet and the novelist seem often to use the adjectives 'dusty' and 'jolly' when describing a miller. There is much truth about the first adjective but the second may be questioned – as will be seen.

The white dust that settled on the miller was his trademark, the sign of his calling, and was universally recognised as such. This dust was so fine it could not be seen in the air except when a beam of sunlight caught it, and that did not often happen at Felin Lyn as the building faced north and there were no windows on the south face. This dust settled imperceptibly on every surface within the mill, giving it a permanent white mantle. It also coated the lungs of the miller as he worked and frequently older millers suffered from chronic congestion of the lungs, having worked a lifetime in an invisible dust laden atmosphere that was plain to see only when the particles came to rest. This dust was an irritant to the lung, in the same way that inhaled tobacco smoke is to a heavy cigarette smoker, and used to be called 'millers' lung'. Nowadays it would be considered a form of pneumoconiosis. It is thought the last miller of Felin Lyn died from some chronic respiratory ailment.

One nineteenth century writer observed of an English miller: *"His wan appearance may have been partly due to the inroads of a lung disease, which comes to millers from constantly inhaling flour dust. His cheeks grew hollow and his wasted hands displayed the blue veins of the miller's coat-of-arms-for he set his own stones."*

The second occupational ailment that affected many millers, and obviously the older men more so, was back strain caused by continuous heavy lifting. Felin Lyn, like most small country mills, had mechanical means to lift sacks in one fixed vertical path internally, but unloading and loading outside the mill was wholly manual, unaided by any appliance except the humble sack barrow. There were also some unavoidable manual lifts within the mill that could not be handled by the hoist. As just discussed, some of the sack weights were quite excessive and little wonder harm was done to the human frame.

There was a third way in which a miller's body was affected but was minor in comparison to coated lungs and strained backs; it affected the teeth. An upland miller constantly cracked oat kernels between his incisor teeth to test their hardness and flavour after kilning and before milling. This habit eventually wore the teeth into half moons and this in turn could lead to broken teeth and the problems that accompany them.

So there were definite occupational hazards and if contracted they did not make for a 'jolly' miller. A miller also acquired a physical characteristic through his work but it was not an ailment, it was miller's thumb. This was a distinctive flattened thumb caused by the constant rubbing of meal between thumb and fingers. Every time a parcel of grain was ground, the miller commenced the work by tentering the millstones and sampling the meal. This was done by 'thumbing' and the process was repeated until the out-pouring meal was to his satisfaction. In 1873 there appeared a novel called the 'Miller's Thumb' and in it the author has the miller's wife say to her little boy: *"Sift un, Janny, sift un, thee's a miller's lad and thee must have a miller's thumb."*

Seasonal And Weekly Routines

When Felin Lyn was a Toll mill the routines would be affected by two rhythms, one seasonal and the other weekly. The miller's activities very closely paralleled those of his principal customers, the neighbouring farmers.

If their grain crops were good, he was busy; if their crops were poor, he had time on his hands.

The seasons dictated to farmer and miller alike their work loads, but there was a difference. The farmer was most busy from spring to autumn, whilst the miller was most busy from late autumn to late spring.

Stocks of grain from the previous year's harvest would be at a low level by the end of a summer, especially if the previous harvest had been a poor one. In fact a crisis always occurred when there were two or more bad harvests in succession as happened, for example, in the years 1782-83 and 1816-19. As a result, everyone living in the territory of Felin Lyn was anticipating the new harvest and waiting eagerly to replenish flour stocks. From the day the newly harvested grain was sent to Felin Lyn, the miller's work would be long and arduous until there was a perceptible slackening in mid to late spring.

The system of processing the grain was the same throughout Britain, irrespective of location or altitude. At harvestime, each farmer stored sheaves of corn, with the heads still attached to the stalks, in a rick or barn. Once a month or so during the following year, the farmer withdrew a quantity of sheaves and threshed them with hand flails. The grain heads fell off and the straw was fed to the animals or used as litter for them. What remained was swept up and winnowed on a windy day, thus removing the chaff. The residue, principally grain, was bagged and in due course was taken to Felin Lyn. Custom dictated that no farmer could take more than one day's grinding to the mill, and at the beginning of the milling season this was restricted still further as everyone wanted a fast turn at the mill. At the time of the 'new' corn, the miller would process six or more farmers' parcels in a long day. Wheaten flour goes rancid after about two months because of the fat contained in the embryo or new seed, so this partly determined the frequency of visits to a mill by a farmer.

As a result, the miller saw each of his farmer customers several times a year and he was for ever grinding small 'parcels' of corn belonging to each of them. The miller had to grind these parcels in strict rotation of delivery and had to keep them separate. No one wanted someone else's corn and some farmers had preferences as to how their grain was to be milled.

Each parcel was measured by volume in bushels or was weighed in pounds so that owner and miller could mutually agree on the toll payment. These measurements were recorded in a mill ledger, and this particular activity explains to some extent why a miller was considered a literate man – more in figures than words – in his own small community.

How many hours a day did a miller work in his busy season, the winter? For the eighteenth and nineteenth centuries such information is hard to come by. We have to remember that all countrymen worked long, not always intensive but steady, hours and leisure was an unknown word.

It was quite normal for an industrial worker to labour for 10 - $10^1/_2$ hours per day for six days of the week in the mid-nineteenth century, and it was not until 1872 that a nine-hour day was achieved by some workers. It was only in 1919 that a 47-hour work week came to be, and a weekend of two whole days did not arrive until 1949.

It is thought the millers of Felin Lyn did work quite long hours at times, both in the Toll and Trade periods. This is based upon random comments at other mills.

The diary of a miller working a Thames-side country trading mill in the 1860s at Pangbourne shows that he frequently worked a twelve hour day or more. Typical entries read; *"9.0am to 9.0pm; 7.45am to 7.30pm; 8.30am to 9.0pm"*. Less typical entries read: *"9.0am to 1.15am; started 8.0am, worked the water all night grinding wheat."* (Note 4.16)

The miller of Mangerton Mill, near Bridport in Dorset, said in 1925 that he *"... ground barley and bruised oats for animal feed, often working 24 hours at a stretch."* In the following decade, J. Pritchard recollects events in the upland village of Michaelchurch Escley in the Brecon Beacons in the late 1930s. He says: *"...the miller would grind corn well into the night on occasions. The din of the mill and its need to continual attention made conversation nigh impossible within the dim and dusty interior, so at intervals the miller would pop out for a breath of fresh air and a burst of banter with his fellow villagers"*.

The late George Heald said that his father's mill (Pentrefoelas in south-west Denbighshire) at the busy period of autumn and winter might be running from 7.00am until about 11.00pm. During World War II on certain days the mill worked a full 24 hours and at other times was seldom stopped for a tea break and only for a sparse lunch that was eaten on the spot. So one can easily imagine that in any mill, in mid-winter, work often started and stopped in the darkness.

Mrs Jones (FL) also provided a clue about working hours after World War I. *"I recollect that the mill ground every day but that was due to grinding Indian corn (maize). The busiest years were up to 1935 when my father's health broke down. Most times the mill only worked during daylight hours but I have known it to work late when there was a demand for Indian meal."*

On the other hand one can also visualise a slackening of the pace in the summer, giving the miller a chance to do all those jobs that accumulate through lack of time. Such things as making wooden cogs, cleaning out the waterwheel pit and the tail race, and tackling alterations. It has to be remembered that the miller at Felin Lyn was also a smallholder, and had to take care of his animals, and carry out such seasonal tasks as manuring, hay-making and hedge-trimming. Hay was the Mill's only farm crop and it was cut and cured in the last two weeks of June.

The author as a child can remember the annual manuring of the mill meadow because his home overlooked the field. The well rotted manure, consisting of cow, pig and horse dung, was taken to the field by cart and off-loaded in small amounts in hillocks at about ten pace intervals. From these hillocks it was forked by hand evenly over the grass.

There was a period in July or August – dictated by the weather – when any long-term maintenance was carried out. Grinding was at a low ebb because most of last year's harvest had already been ground and the water supply was poor or non-existent because of summer drought. This was just the time to make major repairs or replacements to the mill machinery and for the landlord to inspect and make good any damage to the weir.

As to weekly routines, in this century the mill was worked on five days except at the beginning of the new harvest milling season when it was probably six days. The two days not worked at Felin Lyn would be the Sabbath, and market day. At most times the market selected would be at Oswestry and held on a Wednesday.

When the mill converted from a Toll mill to a Trading mill at the end of the nineteenth century, the tempo changed. The work became more even-paced throughout the year because it was no longer related to local harvests and local demands.

In addition to these seasonal and weekly routines, there would be the tribulations experienced in running any business in any century. There would be arguments with customers over late deliveries, milling quality, and charges. With helpers there would be misunderstood instructions, mistakes and unforeseen problems. Finally, with the equipment itself there would be breakages and mishaps.

Maintenance and repairs to machinery were a constant preoccupation. Dressing one millstone took about three days, replacing a bedstone took almost a week, whilst replacement of parts of the transmission might take two to three weeks. The installation of a new waterwheel, a rare occurrence, could absorb a month.

An attempt has been made to estimate how many days in a year were available for milling at Felin Lyn. As with so many details connected with this Mill, it rests on an imaginative guess. Non-productive weeks in the year might be:

2 weeks	–	millstone dressing
1 week	–	millrace problems & cleaning
2 weeks	–	machinery repairs and breakdowns
4 weeks	–	lack of water (summer drought & winter ice)
1 week	–	aggregate of religious holidays (before advent of public holidays).
2 weeks	–	smallholder work scattered throughout year
2 weeks	–	contingency, e.g. sickness, helping neighbours/relatives

Total of 14 weeks when mill not working

This leaves 38 weeks in the year for milling. Assuming the mill was worked five days each week, then 190 days in the year were available for milling. It has been estimated earlier in the book that Felin Lyn processed 240 tons of grain in an average Tolling year. If this tonnage was milled in 190 working days, then the mill had to process $1^1/_3$ tons daily which the previous Section showed was entirely possible. As already discussed earlier, it is likely that the daily tonnage in the winter would exceed the annual daily average, reaching perhaps $1^1/_2$ tons or $1^3/_4$ tons, whilst in the summer there would be a corresponding drop. These tonnages relate to the time when Felin Lyn was a Toll mill and there is a suggestion that if a mill, in its final days, was milling only maize it could add 50% to its daily through-put tonnage.

Another routine – never ending – was the control of vermin in the form of rats and mice. Farms and mills are considered by these creatures to be bulging food warehouses and are especially attractive when cold weather sets in and their field supplies dry up. As a consequence dogs and cats always earned their keep at a mill when they worked to keep the resident rats and mice to the minimum. (Note 4.17)

Renovation and Upgrading

Sometime in or about the 1870s, the whole complex at Felin Lyn appears to have been subjected to renovations and upgrading. Whether this was done as a planned single project or piecemeal, and when, are not easy to answer with certainty. This Section has been placed at the end of the chapter so that readers have been presented with all possible clues before considering the matter and possibly coming to a conclusion.

It is a pity that Sherlock Holmes was not able to poke around Felin Lyn at the turn of this century because no doubt he would have provided us with crisp answers; "Elementary, my dear Watson", but we are left to grope in the 1990s.

The clues to this work are varied. For material things they include: yellow bricks, new flooring, kitchen range, farm buildings, and replacement Anglesey millstones. And for dates: boom times of 1868-73, opening of horse tramway up the Ceiriog in 1873, world economic downturn in 1873, surge of imported wheat commencing in 1875, proof that Felin Lyn was a Trading mill by 1881.

In 1873 a horse tramway was built from the Shropshire Union canal at Gledrid (south of Chirk), to Glynceiriog; it was managed and operated by the canal company as one of its feeders. Close to the canal-side terminus of this tramway was the Trehowell Coal, Brick and Fireclay Co. (1868-85), which sent some of its products into Dyffryn Ceiriog. These included yellow bricks that carried no maker's name. It is known that the importation of these bricks commenced in the same year the tramway was opened because the smithy and attached house at Llwynmawr is made of them and usefully carries a date plaque of 1873.

At Felin Lyn these yellow bricks were used to build a four sided sloping hopper within a recently disused kiln and to embellish archways in the mill itself and the various farm buildings. This practice of adding yellow brick adornments to stone buildings was quite typical of the period and the region.

The 1980s examination of the inside of the mill itself showed the principal floor had been replaced with machined tongue and grove boards, unlike the attic floor above which was of cruder construction. The depth of the 'soft' bedstones, examined in 1981, also suggest they could have been installed in the 1870-85 period.

Within the millhouse there was an iron range which had been patented in 1869 which implies a later installation date. There was also a metal bakeoven in the scullery, a room not part of the original Mill buildings. All this suggests the domestic aspects of the Mill were improved by the provision of a scullery and iron appliances.

In the millyard it is possible that the cowhouse and piggery were also built as part of these improvements, as they have yellow brick arches, and one face of the piggery is built entirely of yellow brick. Mrs Jones (FL) made no mention of any building additions in her childhood, so the assumption is that all the farm buildings had been erected prior to 1900.

All these clues make it clear that Felin Lyn was improved in various ways within a period likely to have ranged between 1873 and 1881. There is a sense of purpose and planning about the changes, inferring they were executed as a single project and not in fragments. As evidenced in Chapter 3, owner John Jones had the wealth and business sense to make all these improvements possible.

Timing and the landlord's motivation within the suggested time frame are less clearcut and two scenarios are offered. The first is enhancement and the second is counter-attack.

The period 1868-73 was a prosperous one for all in Britain and the rest of the industrial world. There were encouraging profits for businessmen and farmers and improved wages and living conditions for workers. One of the local manifestations of this economic buoyancy was the penetration of the Ceiriog by a new form of transport in 1873.

It would make sense for a landlord in such prosperous times to improve a property that was so essential to the local community, for it was still a Toll mill. By this time Felin Lyn was 75-100 years old and needed a refit and the living quarters had to be modernised to attract a competent miller and a discriminating wife. That is one possible explanation.

The other possibility is that the landlord did nothing during this 'crest-of-the-wave' period but was frightened into action by the national grain adversities of the late 1870s. None of us are very good at spotting trends that seem to erupt from nowhere; its like the picnic on a bright sunny day with the ominous small black cloud in the distance which is unnoticed, until suddenly everybody gets drenched. This happened to the world in 1873-5 with a sudden and unforeseen financial downturn caused by industrial over-production, which was not overcome until the mid-1890s. Added to this general woe was a specific one for those engaged in corn – farmers, millers and dealers. As already mentioned several times, overseas wheat flooded into Britain in ever increasing amounts from 1875 onwards and quite disrupted the grain mechanics and markets that had been the very fabric of the land for centuries. (Note 4.18)

Sometime between 1875 and 1880 it must have suddenly become apparent to all that the country mill was becoming a liability and no longer an asset. A thinking landlord, backed by a progressive miller tenant, might well see that salvation lay in turning Felin Lyn into a Trading mill. We know from the recently discovered Glyn Valley Tramway invoices that this had taken place by 1881.

Both outlines just presented are persuasive and it is left to the reader to make the choice, for the author is unable to make up his mind.

NOTES

4.1 **Craig-yr-oryn Quarry, Glyn Traian Parish.** A map of 'North Wales' published in 1824 by J. & A. Walker of London and Liverpool happens to mark this quarry. The map has a scale of about 0.4" to 1 mile and on average shows one place-name for every square mile. Craig-yr-oryn is listed as 'slate quarey' (sic) but curiously no other quarry is shown on the entire map, such as Llanberis slate or Llanymynych limestone. Even with such faults of omission, it does suggest that Craig-yr-oryn had a certain importance in the first quarter of the 19th century.
A Glyn Valley Tramway invoice of January 1881 lists 10 iron wagons and 52 rails for this quarry. See also *"Gazeteer of Welsh Slate Industry"*, Alun Richards, Llanrwst, Gwasg Carreg Gwalch, 1991, 239pp; 5 line entry re quarry on p.200.

4.2 **Virtue of Wood Fuel when Baking Bread.** In the author's home town in western Canada, the results of an interview with a veteran baker appeared in 7th May 1988 issue of the *'Kamloops Daily News'*. Mesato Shoyama, then aged 64, said his father, then he, had operated the bakery at the same location since 1928. Until 20 years ago all the bread was baked in a wood fired stove but now an electric oven is used. Shoyama said "...bread tastes much better if it is wood cooked but it is slower and is extra work"

4.3 **Miller's Candlestick.** See footnote on p.20 of source quoted in Note 2.7.

4.4 **Countryside Sanitation.** All this may sound primitive by 1990s standards but was the norm for the day in country dwellings. The author is reminded of the fact that his parents retired to a cottage in the Radnorshire hills in the 1950s and they had neither running water nor electricity for the ten years that they lived in it.

4.5 **Ancient Method of Removing Husk.** The use of heat to remove the husk of cereals stretches way back into history. The practice was well known 3000 years ago in Israel and is described in Verse 15, Chapter 2 of the Book of Ruth in the Old Testament of the Bible. Ears of barley were held in a fire until the husk was burnt away and this was known as 'parched' corn. This method was practised until comparatively recent times (examples quoted 1695, 1793, 1831) in the Hebrides. A woman would uproot oats, not using a sickle, and would set the ears a-fire with a splinter of burning wood. The instant the husk was burnt, she beat off the grain with a stick and so obtained 'instant' groats.
This method was called 'graddan' from 'grad', the Gaelic word for quick, and from this we can see the connection with the Welsh word 'gradell' for a cooking griddle. Another Gaelic method was to thresh the oats with a stick, winnow it, and then put the grains with husks attached in a pot over the peat fire. All the time the grains were stirred with a wooden spoon to prevent them burning and the husks became 'parched' and brittle. After cooling the grains were rubbed or rolled and the husks fell away.

4.6 **Booklet:** *"Drying Kilns attached to British Corn Mills"*. Jones, D. H. & Major, J. K.; Netherlands, International Molinological Society, 1973, 7pp.

4.7 **Clogs.** Book *"Wild Wales"* by George Borrow. See Chapter 21; 1850s period.

4.8 **Kiln Tiles.** See 13 page article *'Drying Kiln Clay Tiles'* by Barry Job in Occasional Journal No 13 of Midland Wind and Water Mills Group (Staffs. Salop. Worcs. & Warwickshire), 1994.

4. 9 **Article:** *"Water-powered Cornmills of England, Wales and Isle of Man"*. Jones, D. H., Denmark, Trans. of 2nd International Symposium on Molinology held 1969 & pub. 1971. p. 303 to 354. Detailed review of mill machinery showing regional & altitude differences.

4.10 **Foundries and Watermills – Distance Apart**. Some examples of distance separating a watermill from the foundry that supplied some/all of its metal machinery.

Watermill Site	Machinery	Foundry	Distance
King's Mill, Wrexham, Denbighshire	Launder 1829	Bersham, nr Wrexham	2 miles
Pentre Mill, Loggerheads, 3m. S.W. Mold, Denb'shire	Waterwheel & launder	R. & W. Jones, Ruabon	12 miles
Ffoelas Mill, Pentrefoelas, Denbighshire	Machinery	Llanrwst	8 miles
Bacheldre Mill, 8m E. of , Newtown, Montgom'shire	Waterwheel	J. Morris, Welshpool	11 miles
Lower or New Mill, Rhayader, Radnorshire	Waterwheel 1901	J. Mills & Co, Llanidloes	12 miles
Wagnall Mill, 2m S. of Presteigne, Radnorshire	Waterwheel, 1870	T&W Thomas Leominster	13 miles
Felin Geri, Cwm Cou Cardiganshire	Castings	Cardigan	9 miles
Four watermills in Cheshire	Castings 1850-1900	Four different foundries	Not exceeding 10 miles

4.11 **Booklet:** *"French Millstones; Notes on the Millstone Industry at La Ferte-sous- Jouarre"*, Owen Ward, Holland, International Molinological Society, 1993, 75pp. Detailed & interesting account of burr manufacture, with 34 illustrations.

4.12 **Liverpool French Burr Importers & Dealers**: In 1824 there were six such firms and the two with long life were: (a) Kay & Hilton, Fleet St., 1814-cl900; (b) variously Cotton & Davies/Edward Davies & Son/Davies & Sneade, 1817-cl900. Burr stones from these two firms have been noted in North Wales,

Lancashire, Cheshire, Shropshire, Staffs, Worcestershire, Radnorshire and Pembrokeshire.

4.13 **Quarrying Millstones in Anglesey, North Wales**. The method of extraction at Ynys Quarry, Brynteg, Tynygongl, Isle of Anglesey, is of interest. A yard-and-a-half circle was drawn with one edge of the circle touching the exposed vertical face of the rock mass. This was then worked by hand with chisel and heavy hammer to a depth of 18 inches. Next a hole of chisel size was made in the centre of the circle to the same depth. Now the exposed rock mass was attached on its side face at a point 18" from the top and a horizontal slit was worked for a short distance. A heavy iron bar was driven into the centre hole and four men would pull and vibrate it until a rough and total fracture took place at the 18 inch depth level. The crudely shaped stone was then taken to a dressing shed, where it was shaped into a perfect circle. All this work was done entirely by hand till the day the quarry ceased to be worked.
See also a useful article *"Millstone Making in Anglesey"* by Dr G. Tucker, 8pp., Journal No. 1. Midland Wind & Water Mills Group. Birmingham. 1980.

4.14 **Transporting Millstones by Sea**. See p.17 of *"Melin No. 8"* (1992), Journal of Welsh Mills Society. Article quotes a specific sea delivery of millstones from Benllech Sands (adjacent Red Wharf Bay), Anglesey to Aberayon, Cardiganshire, in 1818. Four 50" diameter stones costing £26-2-6 were carried by a 30 ton sloop for £5-0-0. Landing expenses and harbour fees cost another 15/-. Such coasting vessels would sail into a sandy bay at high tide and then beach themselves. At low tide they would load or unload cargo over the side, using a derrick that could lift one-and-a-half tons.

4.15 **Timber Sawing by Water Power**. (i) Example in Wales of a joint commilling & sawmilling operation is: Felin Geri, Cwm Cou, nr Newcastle Emlyn, Cardiganshire. (ii) Best known description of sawing by water-power is contained in 'Sawmill' chapter of book *"Mills of Canada"*, Carol Priamo; Toronto, Macgraw-Hill Ryerson, 1976, 192pp. The practice was widespread in North America but, by comparison, much less in Britain. (iii) See p.46-50 of book *"Archaeology of Montgomeryshire Canal"* by Stephen Hughes, Aberystwyth, Royal Commission on Historical Monuments in Wales, 1981. Provides detail of Welshpool sawmill owned and operated by Powis Castle Estate; has fine schematic drawing of building, equipment and waterwheel.

4.16 **Booklet:** *"Robert Stone, Miller of Pangbourne"*. International Molinological Soc., 1980, 46pp. Extracts of his diary between 1869 & 1882. A rare glimpse into daily routines of a mill.

4.17 **10th Century Welsh Laws about Cats**. These were to be protected animals because they safeguarded grain supplies. A kitten was to be valued at 1d and a mouser at 2d (high prices for the times). Anyone killing a cat was to be fined its worth in grain. These were part of the laws of Howel Dda (the good), 890s-950, regional Welsh prince and in later life 'king of the Kymry'. Well-known in Welsh history as the first man who merged and rationalised Welsh regional laws into a national code and had it written down. Earliest surviving Welsh version is contained in *"Black Book of Chirk"*, written c1205.

4.18 **Booklet:** *"Stephen Lewin and the Poole Foundry"*, (by R.Wear & E. Lees, Industrial Rly Soc., 1978, 101pp) is the detailed history of a Dorset agricultural and steam engine business that operated in 1870s and early '80s. It shows machinery prices reached their peak in 1873 and went into decline from 1875 onwards; see pages 26-32. Agricultural wages in the Borderland also confirm the trend. Weekly rates for farm labourers were: 11/- @1870; 14/3 @1872; 13/- @1882; 14/- @1898.

Chapter 5

*s*iprys *a*nd *m*aslin

*o*r *m*iscellany

The chapter title consists of a Welsh word and an English word and both mean a mixture of growing grain crops. *Siprys* is a mixture of oats and barley and its English equivalent was *dredge* or *drage*. *Maslin* implied a mix of two or more grains but most commonly was thought of as wheat and rye – bread corns. There is no reference or remembrance of siprys growing in the Parish of Glyn Traian but it was sown occasionally at the top end of the Ceiriog as late as the mid 1930s. The purpose of introducing these words is to explain that the content of this chapter is a mixture. The topics within the chapter are not interconnected, but they do have a common thread running through them – Felin Lyn.

In 1984 a highly dramatic confirmation of the ancient use of maslin literally surfaced. Some peat cutters working in a bog at Lindow, Cheshire, (45 miles north-east of former Felin Lyn) came across a body and knowing it was a murder case, called the police. It turned out to be a murder case of sorts, being the ritual killing of a 25-year-old Celtic man 2,000 years ago. The body was so well-preserved that some skin and hair remained and it was possible to analyse the contents of the stomach. This disclosed the victim had just eaten some rough bread made from wheat and barley and possibly rye. (Note 5.1)

Farming The Gwryd

Not giving a mention to farming, and to cereal farming specifically, in a book of this kind is akin to making no reference to religion when discussing church architecture. So this section has been included to redress the balance – however slight.

To make the subject more personal and small scale, one piece of the territory of Felin Lyn has been selected and will be described and examined in some detail.

The small side valley of the Gwryd (pronounced 'goorid') has been chosen because it is a definable and recognisable piece of land and because Felin Lyn lies at one corner of it. This feature of definition was also apparent to early Welsh or Norman administrators, for the Township of Nantgwryd had identical boundaries.

This subsidiary valley runs north-south and is at right-angles to the principal valley of the Ceiriog. It is $1^1/_2$ miles long and is $^1/_3$ of a mile wide at its base, and opens out to a width of a mile when gaining the hill crests. The area covered is about 650 acres, which equalled about one-sixth of the territory of Felin Lyn.

The floor of this little side-valley is at 450 feet altitude and rises to 1,400 feet at the hill summit that carries no name; this hill-top is the watershed or divide between the Dee and Severn river systems in this area. It is drained by the Nant Gwryd, a brook of $^3/_4$ mile length which rises at a spring at the 1,000 feet level and empties into the Afon Ceiriog close to Felin Lyn. As previously explained, Nant Gwryd was diverted into the mill headrace and only excess waters were permitted to escape directly to the river.

No weather records have been kept for this side valley but it is thought that rainfall is about 40 inches a year and falls on at least 200 days (55%). Sunshine probably amounts to about 1,300 hours in a year, peaking in July.

The Gwryd has been farmed for at least 600 years, for in AD 1391 *'villa de Nant Goryt'* was listed as the principal farm in the Township of Nanygwryd. This 'villa' is now known as Nantgwryd-uchaf, and the farmhouse has a medieval look about it and is reputed to have been rebuilt in stone (from wood) in the sixteenth or seventeenth century. The manner in which the land was, and is, farmed provides a good example of what was common throughout the uplands of Wales in preceding centuries, with origins reaching back into the mists of Celtic herding practices. The system was to establish a farm in some sheltered position on the lower slopes where the soil was workable and the harshness of winter was softened. Such farms were often located at the 500-600 feet altitude and were called 'hendre', literally the 'old place'. Round about the farmstead, fields were carved out of the landscape and enclosed. In the better half of the year, traditionally from May Day to All Saints Day (1st May to 1st November), the animals would be taken up the hillsides with attendant herders to graze the waste or no-man's-land. For the convenience of the herders, temporary summer camps were built called 'hafotai' (singular 'hafod') and such were frequently found at the 900-1200 feet level; they were so named after 'haf', the Welsh word for summer. The technical word for this farming method is transhumance. (Note 5.2)

This system is practised today in the cattle country of British Columbia, Canada, at all the larger ranches, in an area close to where the author resides. In winter the cattle are penned close to the ranches which are at 1,000-2,000 feet altitude and are fed hay. After calving in the spring, the cattle are driven to wilderness areas which may be at about the same or much higher elevations. Here they graze at complete liberty in the 'wastes' until late autumn when early snows and the cowboy round-up return them to the home ranch, the herds much swollen with yearlings. It is a logical way to use undeveloped land for pastoral purposes.

There is no place-name in the Gwryd with 'hendre' or 'hafod' incorporated in it, nor for that matter in the Parish of Glyn Traian. The nearest 'hafod' place-name lies $1^1/_2$

Cilnant. *This was a typical farm within the Parish of Glyn Traian and the 'territory' of Felin Lyn. Situated exactly one lane miles S.S.E. of the Mill at 800 feet above sea level. Became uninhabited in 1987 and is being rebuilt after falling into ruin. Drawn in its original state by a local inhabitant who has contributed much to this history.*
Mr. Dewi Jones, Llwynmawr.

miles to the west of Felin Lyn, up valley, and is on the northern slopes of the Ceiriog at 950 feet altitude. Interestingly enough for this history the placename indicates its activity, for it is called 'Hafod-yr-haidd' or 'barley summer place'. Other 'hafotai' in the Ceiriog appear at the 850-1,000 feet level and this suggests that bush and woodland gave way naturally to herbage at these altitudes.

It is fairly certain that the system of 'hendre' and 'hafod' was practised in the Gwryd from ancient times, and persists in muted form to this day. The population explosion in Britain in the seventeenth and eighteenth centuries caused most of the 'hafotai' to be converted into year-round farms, with such farms seeking some lower altitude fields to offset their exposed situations. Meantime the long established 'hendrefi' (plural of 'hendre') had now to compete with the upstarts for communal grazing and some tillage of the no-man's-lands. A nineteenth century development was the enclosure of some of the wastes of the Gwryd and their conversion to private property. However, even in 1958 Denbighshire still had 42,000 acres of waste or common land, much of it on the Berwyn mountains.

When Felin Lyn ceased to grind corn full-time in 1936 the land usage pattern in the Gwryd showed all the signs of ancient practice. All the larger farms – those over 60 acres – had land in roughly equal proportions at two different locations and altitudes. The former 'hendrefi' had bottom lands and top lands, and the former 'hafotai' had higher lands and top lands.

The Tithe Commissioners' survey of 1839 showed the Gwryd had just over a hundred fields and enclosures and some open land, most of it private. Each of the fields carried a name and ranged in size from one to five acres, with the average at $3^1/_2$ acres. However when these fields were used for tillage they tended to be larger, ranging from three to five acres and having an average of four acres.

The 1851 census showed 12 farmsteads in the Gwryd which ranged in size from 25-110 acres, with both the average and median size at 50 acres. If their locations are plotted by altitude in bands of 100 feet steps from 400-1,199 feet, there is one farm in every 100 feet step except for two each in the 600-699 feet and 700-799 feet steps and three in the 800-899 feet step; this might suggest that the

Gwryd 'hafods' were at the 600-900 feet level. (Note 5.3)

The land was used in the normal Welsh fashion with sheep and fattening cattle on the hill tops and sides, and hay, cereals and roots grown in limited quantities in favoured spots, usually close to the farmstead. A typical Welsh farm of 50 acres in 1850 possessed the following animals: two draught horses, one or two foals, 6-8 milking cows, two heifers, 6-8 yearling cattle, two sows, 5-7 store pigs, 10-15 hens, two or three pairs of ducks, one pair of geese, and 50-70 sheep on the mountain. Naturally, it is not known if this is typical of the Gwryd but it does provide a good insight into what might have been seen.

Needless to say such an 'off the beaten track' area has had very little written about it, but once again John Hughes (Dol) has come to the rescue. In this extract from his memoirs, written in Welsh, he says: *"For two or three years, I helped my uncle Humphrey of Brithdir (farm 1¼ miles S.E of Mill) to collect tithes with horse and cart, or sledge, on the slopes of Llangwryd, Penllwyn, Caemor, Tynyfron, and Talygarth and carried or dragged it to the tithe barn in Llwynmawr, where there were two byres and a room for fattening cattle. I used in the winter to chop straw and turnips to make mash for fattening cattle. I should say that my father collected tithes from distant places. It was a great help to him with a large family to support and he did this until the introduction of the Commutation of Tithes Act of 1836."* We believe he was aged about 15-17 years of age when doing this work and it would have happened in the latter part of the 1810s. (Note 5.4)

The Llwynmawr tithe barn was sited close to the cross lanes at that hamlet and close to the edge of Nant Gwryd 'vale'. Hughes says that later the barn was put up for sale by the Church of England. His brother purchased and converted it into houses and made the 'acre of tithe' into gardens – then promptly sold the lot; nineteenth century developers!

Turning to the specialised aspect of cereal farming, nothing is known about it in the Gwryd in earlier centuries. It is assumed oats were the dominant cereal, followed by barley and perhaps also rye. Wheat was probably introduced in the late eighteenth century, for that was the time when Felin Lyn was built and equipped to grind this 'hard' grain.

The soil was tilled with a single furrow plough, until tractors were introduced in World War II, and up to the 1700s would have been pulled by oxen. These animals were castrated bulls trained for haulage and in former times each farmer owned a pair and took part in communal ploughing. The plough needed 4, 6, 8, or even 12 oxen to pull it, depending whether the land was new unbroken or

long-time cultivated.

The eighteenth century saw the general introduction of horses as haulage beasts, being both faster and more versatile. An oxen team took most of a day to plough an acre but with horses this output could be doubled. (Note 5.5)

It is not known when oxen ceased to be used as draught animals in the Gwryd but was probably in the period 1775-1820 and was preceded by a certain restructuring of the farms. An ox is a grazer and will work with a supplement of hay, but a horse needs oats when in draught. This meant some of the smaller farm holdings were consolidated into their neighbour's so that more oats could be grown for these new fangled pulling horses.

Oats and barley were invariably spring sown, usually in early April. There is a Welsh saying which local farmers adhered to when weather permitted them to sow oats, their most important cereal crop. In Welsh it is *"Tridiau aderyn du a dau lygad Ebrill"*, which translated literally means *"The three days of the blackbird and two eyes of April."* This is a reference to the last three days of March and first two days of April, so that March 29th became the target date in the Gwryd to sow oats.

All farms of over 25 acres, and perhaps smaller ones also, grew oats, irrespective of their altitude in the Gwryd. Size and altitude determined if barley and wheat were grown, and usually if a farm exceeded 60-70 acres and conditions were favourable all three cereals were grown.

Ten percent of the previous year's harvest was set aside as seed grain and was sown at the rate of two to four bushels per acre depending upon type of grain, soil and time of year. The day before the seed was sown it was pickled as a disease prevention measure. Originally strong brine and sheep dung were used but was later superseded by a weak solution of copper sulphate.

Wheat could either be sown in the autumn, about 20th October, or in the spring at about the same time as the oats. Barley was invariably sown last as it matures at a faster rate than oats or wheat.

The actual sowing was done by broadcasting the seed by hand, which looks an easy task, but in fact requires considerable experience to ensure an even spread. Far more seed was required than with present day methods, for loss by various causes was the norm. Another country saying was, *"Sow four grains in a row; one for the pigeon, one for the crow, one to rot, and one to grow."* Even in 1930 only 70% of sown corn seed reached maturity.

An alternative and superior method of planting was to make small holes in the ploughed land with a dibber, insert the seed in the hole, and then rake over. This was a very laborious method and took a family team about two days to plant an acre of corn; it was not normally practised unless seed was very scarce.

Crop rotation was applied by either ensuring the same cereal was not grown in the same field at less than a three or four year interval or by using different fields in successive years. A typical rotation could be: oats, barley, roots, wheat, clover.

As the crop grew and matured the farmer's constant concern was weeds and pests. The weeds were the good old Biblical 'tares' and could be dealt with when the corn was short enough to be undamaged by trampling feet, but at a later stage the farmer just had to watch them grow amongst his corn. As for pests, their depredations ebbed and flowed from one year to the next.

Above ground the principal enemy were fungi which invaded the cereal flowers so that when these became fruit they were blackened and unwholesome. This was known as smut, and the cleaning machine at Felin Lyn was used to remove them; in some mills there was a specialised machine called a smutter to do the job. Other perils to growth were airborne insects that caused stalks and leaves to turn a reddish hue or 'rust', and earth-bound ones that attacked the root system, such as eelworms.

More visible predators included rabbits, crows and field mice who attacked grain crops at varying stages of growth. Field mice are one of Britain's smallest mammals and with great agility will climb a corn stalk, nip off the whole of the head or ear and then eat the lot on the ground at leisure. All growing cereals are affected by these hazards to varying degrees.

As to harvesting, all three grains were usually reaped from the end of August to the end of September. It is significant that the Welsh word 'medi' with a capital 'M' means 'September' and with a small 'm' means 'to reap'. Barley and wheat were allowed to get completely ripe but oats were cut when there was still a little green left in the stalk.

We know a sickle (toothed edge) or a reaping hook (plain edge) was used in the Gwryd up to the beginning of the nineteenth century, for this was the universal reaping tool throughout the world at that time. The reaper grasped a bunch of straw in his left hand and then sliced through it with his sickle, finally placing the bunch of cut straw behind him in a neat pile. The work went slowly and only about a quarter to a third of an acre could be cut per day by one reaper, but it was work that could be done by men or women working as a family team.

Then in mid-nineteenth century there was a change from sickle to scythe to increase productivity. Previously a scythe had been used only to cut grass and bracken but now it was used to cut corn. With it a reaper could cut two acres of oats or one acre of barley or wheat per day. Using a scythe was very arduous work and could be done only by men well-versed in its use. The many centuries' use of the sickle was ended only because of scarcity of farm labour created by the industrial revolution of the nineteenth century, which enticed people away from the land with prospects of better paying jobs. Specifically in the Ceiriog, the woollen mills at Glynceiriog were recruiting women, teenagers and some men, the slate mines just beyond that village were hiring men and boys, whilst the collieries and the railway at Chirk had need of men and teenage boys.

After the corn was sickled or scythed, women and children followed, binding the cut straw into sheaves of about 10-12 inch diameter at the binding point. These sheaves were then stood upright and assembled into clumps of four, six or eight which made a stook, or to use the older words 'shock' or 'shook' (all related to shaking).

The drying of the grain whilst it was still attached to the straw was all important and this was achieved by letting it stand stooked on the field till the moisture in the grain had fallen below 18-20%, and ideally to 15% or a trifle lower. Above 22% the grain on the straw could sprout or go mouldy when in store. Wheat could be dried in 7-10 days in ideal conditions but with bad weather all three cereals might take up to six weeks to be harvested. With oats there was a rule of thumb that said it must be stooked for three Sundays (i.e. 15 days) at least and this was known as 'churching'.

A local resident remembers her father being very sensitive to signs that might indicate a weather change, such as the posture of a flowerhead, animal behaviour, sky patterns, or how sounds (e.g., locomotive whistle) travelled and from what quarter. On one occasion her father said, *"We're going to carry oats all night because there is a moon to light us and rain is on the way"*; his forecast proved correct. A case of 'Shine on Harvest Moon'.

As can be seen, weather was the all-important factor in corn harvesting, so the hours were long and hard in the fields when days were dry and sunny, starting from the time when the dew was off the ground to dusk. An hour long dinner break in the middle of the day, with good food and beer supplied by the farmer's wife, was the only relaxation. A Pontfadog correspondent said; *"My mother made a herb beer at harvest time but not from barley and it could be quite potent when left out in the sun. Perhaps she made this kind of beer because she was intimidated by her mother-in-law who was a temperance activist. Some farmers would club together and buy a keg of cider."* Cider became popular on Welsh farms in the latter half of the nineteenth century. The herb beer was possibly a brew of nettle tops and dandelion leaves.

When the corn was considered dry enough for storage it was transported by two-wheeled carts and sledges to the farmstead. The barn was filled first and then the residue was built into ricks. These ricks were built on a base of mushroom-shaped straddle-stones and tree branches which ensured the rick was ventilated and vermin resistant. The sheaves were built into a rectangular or circular pile with their butts always facing outwards and were sloped at the top to make a pitched roof; this was then thatched with wheat straw to make the whole waterproof.

No one farm in the Gwryd celebrated the end of these harvesting tasks but when the whole community had completed the work, there was genuine heartfelt thanks to God and personal satisfaction in knowing that grain for man and beast was available for another twelve months. The end of the harvesting was marked by harvest thanksgiving services held in all the chapels in the area (the custom is still maintained) which consisted of a prayer meeting in the afternoon and a sermon in the evening, held on some weekday between the middle and end of October. Each service was, and is, attended by people of all denominations with a 'full house' at each service.

As in England there were several harvest hymns that were sung all over Wales. The Welsh equivalent of the hymn "We plough the fields and scatter the good seed on the ground" could be:

Ti o Dduw folianwn
Am Dy ddonilau rhad
Mawr yw 'dofal tynner
Drosom dirion Dad.
Llawn yw'r ddaear eto
O'th drugaredd lân
Llawn yw'r calon innau
A diolchgar gân.

Ni sy'n trin y meysydd
Ni sy'n hau yr had
Tithau sy'n rhoi cynnydd
Yn Dy gariad rhad
Doniau Dy ragluniaeth
Inni'n gyson ddaw
Storfa'r grëadigaeth
Yw d'agored law.

It cannot be too strongly emphasised how everyone reacted to a harvest. A good harvest meant plenty of staple food on the table for the coming year, and if you were a farmer with excess to sell, then there was extra cash in the pocket. Conversely, a poor harvest meant a belt tightening at meal times which got progressively worse as the year wore on. This particularly affected cottagers and landless residents who had to buy their wheaten flour and rolled oats and found the price per peck or bushel kept creeping up until the next harvest.

Nowadays we are so far removed from the basic agricultural existence of our forebears, that it is difficult to imagine how fundamental to survival were the seasons and their changes. We no longer meet cyclic changes of the year instinctively, organically or spiritually. We simply go to the refrigerator or alter the heating thermostat and the countryside is thought of in terms of scenery or a place of respite from urban stresses.

At the beginning of the research for this book, the late Mrs Elizabeth Humphreys, a native of the area, remarked to the author that 1879 was the year of a terribly bad harvest. This had come down to her from her grandparents. Later investigation showed that it was the worst harvest of the century in Britain. With the passing of Mrs Humphreys, so disappeared this local folk memory when harvests were of universal significance – for better or for worse. (Note 5.6 and Appendix XII)

For the non-farmer, harvest performance was of much less importance after about 1880 because the newly emerging country store provided an alternative food service.

However the farming community continued to rely on the harvests for their cereal foods for the next 50 years but in dwindling fashion. It was a matter of faith and tradition that you ate what you grew. Mrs Margaret Lewis, aged 93 in 1995, provides truth of this.

She has a recollection, which from weather records is deduced to be 1909, when she was aged six. At that time she lived at Tyn-y-fron farm, near Llwynmawr, in a family of eight siblings. She says: *"It was a particularly wet summer and the corn was blighted. My mother's bread would not rise and I could eat only the crusts, so bad did it taste."*

Once the farmer had brought in his corn harvest, his work was far from done. It should also be stressed that he had harvested two products from his cereal plants and both were vital to his livelihood, namely straw and grain.

In rough and ready terms one acre of cereal plants, irrespective of type, supplied one to one-and-a-half tons of straw and between three-quarters and one ton of grain. The farmer used all his oat straw and maybe some of his barley straw to feed his stock in the lean winter and early spring months. That was why oats were cut on the green side, so as to give better quality feed, since not all of the nutrients had moved into the head. Wheat straw was useless as feed and so was used as bedding for livestock and in due course became the binder in manure. Bracken, which grew relentlessly in the Gwryd, was used for the same purpose, since no animal will eat it for it is poisonous and produces a form of fatal leukemia. If any thatching of ricks or root clamps had to be done, wheat straw was used.

The farmer used his stored sheaves in two ways. Part of the oat crop was fed to horses and cattle at the rate of one sheaf per animal per day in the lean parts of the year. The stock would eat the straw and the grain still attached to the head.

For the remainder of his corn crop, the farmer withdrew at monthly intervals quantities of all the grain he had grown and – keeping them separate – he would hand thresh the sheaves on his barn floor and then winnow the result.

Threshing was done on the hard earth floor of the barn, using wooden flails, sometimes in the hands of one man but more often in pairs. The flailing caused the ripe ears to part from the straw and producing 10-14 bushels of grain was considered a good day's work by a pair of men. At a rate of 30-40 blows or strikes a minute, the work was very strenuous and monotonous, and it was customary to pay a bonus of one-twentieth of the grain thrashed collectively to the threshers. The last known instance of a flail being used in Dyffryn Ceiriog was in the mid 1930s by Dafydd Jones, Blaenrhiwlas Isa, two miles east of Llanarmon. In the Gwryd its use had died out about a three-quarters of a century earlier.

The next operation was winnowing, which consisted of throwing the threshing debris, less the raked-up long straw, into the air on a windy day. The best and heaviest grains fell closer to the winnower, the average-sized grains a little further away, whilst the poorly formed and diseased grains, chaff and weed seed, were carried still further away. It took about an hour for one person to winnow a bushel of grain, so the process was a slow one. The best and heaviest grains were usually set aside as next year's seed, and after this the remaining grain was stored.

Before storing the grain or taking it to the Mill, there was one further operation of removing the awns, found on barley ears and sometimes on now forgotten forms of wheat and oats. This was done with a hand-held tool called a hummeller which was a square metal grid iron fitted with a 3 foot handle. The heap of grain was repeatedly stomped on with the hummeller until the awns broke off.

Before the early 1800s the grain was stored in the farmhouse itself which clearly indicates the value placed on the commodity. The general introduction of wheeled carts and implements in Denbighshire in the nineteenth century led to the construction of cartsheds to house them and it became the practice to build a granary above the cartshed. Here the corn was stored loose or in sacks in reasonably vermin-proof surroundings with good air circulation, until it was time to take it to Felin Lyn for processing. This allowed the grain to continue to breathe and lose moisture. In the years of a plentiful harvest in the last century, perhaps the excess was sent to Oswestry for sale at the Corn Exchange.

The first farming operation to be mechanised on a widespread scale in Britain was that of threshing and winnowing. This was because it was a very demanding manual task and it had the same relationship to agriculture as fulling had to woollen manufacture – both heavy jobs calling out for mechanisation.

The early mobile threshing machines gave a definite increase in productivity and encompassed the three jobs of threshing, winnowing and hummelling. A good flailer could produce two or three sacks of grain a day, but a threshing team of twelve men could bag some seventy sacks in the same period, giving a rate of six sacks per man, per day. Furthermore, the mechanically threshed grain was much cleaner.

The mechanisation of these cereal farming operations in the Gwryd was strangely uneven. It appears that steam-driven mechanical threshing was introduced in 1850-60, mechanised cutting of grain in the 1920s, mechanical binding in 1939, and tractor haulage in 1942.

The late Thomas E. Davies (1902-86) of Llwynmawr said his grandfather (born 1843) remembered threshing being done by flail when he, the grandfather, was ten years of age. At that time the forbear was a boy servant on a farm at Tregeiriog, further up the Ceiriog, and his master purchased a horse-drawn steam-driven threshing machine in about 1855-57. For an upland area of Wales this has to be considered an early appearance of steam power, for the first portable steam engine in Britain – pulled by two horses – was publicly demonstrated in 1841.

One of the grandfather's jobs as a youngster was to follow the machine when touring the farms in the Ceiriog including the Gwryd, until he was twenty years of age; presumably he was the coal-and-water boy for the engine and doer of all the menial jobs. Later, say about 1875, two men from Llwynmawr acquired a similar but larger machine, again horse drawn and steam driven. It is quite possible that the only daughter of Evan Evans (1815-c1880s), miller of Felin Lyn, married one of these men who were William Jones and John Thomas. The late Thomas Davies, our informant on these details, was himself hired occasionally when a boy of twelve, as a water-boy on such an engine and found it hard work; the engine consumed 12 cwt of coal per day.

An undated photograph survives, which shows this latter portable engine (4-8hp rating) driving a thresher at Brithdir, a farm at 800 feet altitude, within the territory of Felin Lyn, and on the edge of the Gwryd. The photo was probably taken sometime within the period 1880-1905. After World War I the worn-out portable was replaced by a traction engine which together with thresher and chaff-cutter visited farms about twice a year.

Dr. (Agri.) G.M. Davies, whose uncle farmed at Pontfadog in the early part of this century, usefully adds that the portable engine and threshing box were hauled separately by two or four horses depending upon the gradients to be encountered, and that it was the responsibility of the farmer hiring the set to provide the horses.

At the turn of the century one contractor was charging 2¾d for threshing one bushel of wheat and 2¼d for one bushel of oats or barley, in England. The price charged in the Ceiriog is not known.

The rest of the cereal harvesting continued to be hand done in the Gwryd for several decades. In 1900 one-fifth of Britain's grain crop was still harvested entirely by hand. This one-fifth would obviously include small hill farms where machinery was both inappropriate and unaffordable, and in the Gwryd all harvesting (except threshing) continued to be entirely hand done until the mid 1920s. Even after that date mechanisation was minimal.

A horse-drawn reaper (which cuts corn and deposits loose bundles on ground) was seen in Chirk in the 1880s and a mechanical binder (which cuts corn and binds a sheaf with string) was certainly in use there in 1918. But in Dyffryn Ceiriog the pace was slower and in the territory of Felin Lyn there were only two mechanical 'contraptions' by 1920. They were horse-drawn hay mowing machines, one each at the farms of Crogen Wladys and Ty'n-y-graig, but none in the Gwryd. Such machines might have been manufactured by Thomas Corbett's Ironworks at Shrewsbury, which was the largest agricultural machinery firm in the West Midlands during its life span from the 1870s to the 1930s.

Sometime in the mid-1920s one of the farmers of the Gwryd purchased a horse-drawn mowing machine which he used not only to cut hay but also corn. This example was quickly followed by others, including the miller of Felin Lyn but his was used only for hay mowing. For cutting the corn, the mower was fitted with a cradle attachment. The job required two men, one to manage the horse and the other to pull neat bundles of corn off the cradle with a big fork. Each bundle was then tied at the waist with straw to make it into a sheaf.

In at least one respect manual reaping held its own, namely when dealing with oats. Oats have a weaker straw than wheat or barley and are prone to 'lodging', which means that they get flattened in parts by wind and rain. This unfavourable condition could be better handled by scythe or sickle than a mechanical reaper. (Note 5.7.)

It was only after the demise of Felin Lyn as a cornmill that a horse-drawn binder was seen at work in the Gwryd in 1939, and a tractor in 1942. This latter machine was owned by the Denbighshire War Agricultural Committee and came to plough the uplands above the 1,000 feet level for cereals.

A glimpse of farming life in the 1920s was kindly provided by the late Tom Roberts (1906-87) who used to farm the Bonc and whose farmhouse lay a quarter mile south of Llwynmawr. This farm is just beyond the area of the Gwryd but is typical and illustrative of the farms in the neighbourhood.

Bonc Farm had 100 acres, of which 50 acres were grouped about the farmstead at the 600 feet altitude and the other fifty acres were rough pasture at the 1,000 feet level. Between World Wars I and II the high ground was not ploughed and was used to graze sheep and young cattle. Tom Roberts would plough 12-14 acres each year of the 'hendre' farm, rotating the crops in the following order: oats, wheat, roots, barley mixed with grass, pasture. He would grow 5 acres of oats, 2-4 acres of wheat, 2 acres of barley, and 3 acres of roots. The roots were mainly turnips, mangolds, and potatoes. His average oat yield was 18 hundredweight (2,016 lbs), or 33½ bushels, per acre. A 'Farmers Diary' for 1908 gave current average yields per acre in Wales (specifically) as: oats 33bu.; barley 29bu.;

These harvesting scenes were taken about 1920 at Penllwyn, which is a farm at about 700 feet elevation and 3/4 mile south of Felin Lyn. The crop is oats and the sheaves appear to be hand-tied with straw. Photographs of such scenes in the locality are very rare.

Mrs. Mair Jones, Pontfadog.

wheat 24bu. This suggests Tom was achieving the Welsh harvest average for oats.

Roberts took all his corn to be ground at Felin Lyn until the mid-1930s, when he purchased an oil engine to crush his oats and barley for animal feed. The wheat that he grew was used for home breadmaking. He and Mr Dewi Jones were able also to collect data on cereal growing during the 1920s in the neighbourhood and this is presented in statistical form as Note 5.8.

Seven farms, ranging in size from 32-160 acres, are reviewed, and all of them grew some kind of grain. Their growing altitudes ranged from 600-1,100 feet. The acreage devoted to cereal growing ranged from 8%-24% and it is interesting to note the circumstances attending these two extremes.

The farm that had 8% of its acreage in cereals was Pwll-hir at 32 acres; this is the highest habitation in the Gwryd, standing at 1,150 feet altitude. This farm grew 2-3 acres of oats and fed them unthreshed and in sheaf to its cattle. At the other end of the scale was Plas-onn farm, which devoted 24% of its 62 acres to grain; this farm lies adjacent to Pwll-hir at 1,100 feet altitude. It had 15-18 acres of arable land each year, consisting of 50% oats, 30% barley, 10% wheat, and 10% roots. Oats and wheat were sown at the end of March and barley at the end of April and harvesting of all three was done from the end of August to mid-late September – weather permitting.

Mrs Margaret Lewis, who has already contributed other information, was born and brought-up (period 1904 to 1927) at Ty'n-y-fron on the western edge of the Mill's territory. She says the farm had 75 acres and each year about 20 acres were under the plough. Of the acreage devoted to cereals, about four-fifths was in oats and one-fifth in wheat; no barley was grown. These details of farming in the Gwryd will place the purpose and operations of Felin Lyn in clearer perspective, and it may be helpful to remember that the Gwryd comprised one-eighth of the territory of Felin Lyn and that its most distant farm was exactly two (lane) miles from the Mill.

It must also be remembered that cereal growing has always been a minor affair in Welsh farming. A 1933 survey of Welsh farming receipts showed that for each £1 earned, nearly 10s. came from the sale of cattle and dairy products, about 4s. from sheep and wool, and only ls. from sale of crops, of which grain contributed 8d. A Welsh farmer was, and is, primarily a pastoralist.

One must conclude this sketch of cereal farming in the

Gwryd by pointing out that all the work was done within a bond of neighbourliness and co-operation. This had not come originally from some innate goodness but was born of necessity. In medieval times and before, it was essential to pool resources to ox-plough land and harvest corn, and to a lesser degree the need was still there. One man would borrow another's horse when his own went lame, a second would lend an implement, and a third would help out with seed corn. Such deeds were not gifts but were repaid in labour or kind. Members of the community who had no land were also a part of this community spirit, for a load of manure for a cottager's garden would be repaid with labour at harvest time. Such attitudes and actions, of course, were not the prerogative of the Gwryd but were a part of the fabric of rural life and are worth emphasising. Interdependence was the keyword.

Legal Documents

In historical research, needless to say, title deeds of properties have considerable value. Alas, the title deeds of Felin Lyn are missing. Title to property is transferred by conveyancing which in Britain is carried out under two systems, namely registered and unregistered lands. Until recently most of Britain was covered by the unregistered system which meant that property ownership went unrecorded by any official body. With registered lands, owners and changes of ownership must be registered publicly and it is only in recent years that Clwyd County has become an area of compulsory registration with transactions now being publicly recorded. As a result there is no government department holding past ownership details of what used to be Felin Lyn.

Title deeds of property are normally held by the owner, or an agent such as a solicitor or a bank. In the case of Felin Lyn, the deeds were in the hands of a firm of solicitors in Chester in 1963 and were then passed to the new owner who subsequently disappeared. No one knows where he lodged them so only time will tell whether they will ever surface again. Once deeds of unregistered land go astray there is very little that can be done about their disappearance.

However all is not lost, because by good fortune the author was handed down through his family the copies of two Conveyances dated 1931 and 1962. These contain all the essential legal facts about Felin Lyn.

The original of the 1931 Conveyance appears to be of parchment and its four pages are held together with ribbon bindings. It is written in ink in copperplate hand and transfers the property from Sir Alfred T. Davies, KBE, CB, DL, (1861-1949) and Lady Mary Davies to their son Thomas Llewelyn Davies, and is dated 10th July 1931.

Most of the document consists of legal jargon typical of any property deed. The two parts that might interest a mill historian are quoted in full below.

"The messuage or dwelling house and Corn and Timber Sawing Mill (together known as Glyn Mill) and the messuage or dwelling house erected within recent years on a portion of the site of such premises and known as 'Glandwr' with the Garden and Land adjoining the same and containing in all Five acres three roods and twenty poles or there-abouts be the same a little more or less all of which are hereinafter referred to as 'the said Mill' and 'Glandwr' situate at Pontfadog in the Townships of Crogen Iddon and Hafvelygynfor [Author: this is taken to mean 'Hafodgynfawr'] *or one of them in the Parish of Glyn Traian (formerly the Parish of Llangollen) in the County of Denbigh, together with all Rights of Way light drainage water and other rights and easements (if any) hitherto enjoyed in connection with the said Mill and Glandwr."* All this without any punctuation as is so typical of legal documents.

The second quote is of especial interest as it appears to have been copied from earlier deeds. *"Reserving to the Owner during his life on giving the Tenant Fourteen days previous notice in writing to enter upon the said Mill on six consecutive week or working days in every year for the purpose of grinding corn."* No doubt all miller tenants blanched at the idea of an unskilled owner coming in and operating the mill equipment.

This provision comes as less of a surprise when read in conjunction with a clause in a contemporary English lease. This reads: *"To provide one team of horses two days in each year for the landlord's use, if required, and also two loads of good winter straw and to deliver same without allowance."* These appear to be vestigial rights of the medieval lord-of-the-manor.

The 1962 Conveyance is a much more prosaic document, being typewritten. It transfers the property from Thomas Llewelyn Davies (1892-1978) to John Richard Thompson Smith of Wrexham and is dated 20th July 1962. Only one quote is appropriate to the subject of this book.

"In pursuance of the said agreement and in consideration of the sum of £1600 on or before the execution hereof paid by the Purchaser to the Vendor the Vendor as Beneficial Owner hereby Conveys unto the Purchaser All That dwellinghouse and mill and the out-buildings and appurtenances thereto belonging situate at Pontfadog in the Parish of Glyn Traian in the County of Denbigh and known as Glyn Mill Pontfadog aforesaid

together with the four fields or parcels of land held therewith containing in the whole 6.401 acres or thereabouts."

The differences in acreages of the property over the years cannot be reconciled. If the components of the property shown on the 1912 Ordnance Survey map are totalled they come to 6.6 acres. This compares with 5.9 acres in the 1931 conveyance and 6.4 acres of the 1962 sale; if anything, the 1962 acreage should be slightly smaller, since Glandwr cottage and its garden were excluded from the sale. Perhaps our touching faith in the exactness of recorded legal land measurements is a little misplaced.

Local Markets

Prior to the coming of the railways and the depopulation of the countryside, markets and fairs were the most important meeting places for trading necessities, hiring labour, and socialising, that the country dweller had. Markets met weekly needs, whilst the local fairs often specialised in some commodity and were held at frequencies of one to five times a year.

Before the middle of the nineteenth century, the nearest trading place for the miller and his wife at Felin Lyn was the fair at Llansantffraid Glynceiriog (two miles up valley) which was held four times a year on 14th February, 1st May, 1st August, and 1st November. The nearest weekly market was four miles away northwards over the mountain top at Llangollen which was held on a Saturday, plus fairs on 17th March, 31st May, 21st August and 22 November. However the way was steep and, though suitable for foot or horseback, was difficult for a laden two-wheeled cart.

George Borrow visited the Llangollen Fair on 21st August 1854 and noted that it mainly involved pig sales with local buyers and a lesser activity with small Welsh cattle going to English buyers. He also saw a few horses and ponies but no sales. Borrow said the pigs arrived in two-wheeled carts with stout cord netting drawn over them to prevent escapes. The pigs, which he described as small, would have been about five months old and went for 18/- to 25/- each. (*Wild Wales*, Chapter 22.)

The most accessible (no severe gradients), more distant, and larger market was in England at Oswestry, Shropshire, nine miles to the south-east. The market was held twice weekly on Wednesdays and Saturdays and continues with much vitality to this day.

Precisely why Oswestry's dominance as a market town has lasted undiminished for over 700 years is unclear. It is an English town that serves the Welsh hinterland in a wide arc to the west, but that is an insufficient explanation in itself because other English border towns that served as market centres in medieval times have shrivelled. The prime function of today's thriving market is the sale of livestock every Wednesday.

It is not a bilingual town but rather a place where English and Welsh are spoken side by side, not interchangeably, but in a completely natural atmosphere.

Oswestry was a trading post between the two nations when, on the orders of Edward I, it was made into a walled town, complete with castle, in about 1280-1300. It was the intention of the English king to make the place into a secure base for his intended conquest of Wales. The perimeter wall was about a mile long and was pierced by four guarded gates. But over the centuries the military significance of Oswestry faded, the walls were broken down, and the gateways became a convenient place to levy tolls on goods entering or leaving the town.

From the mid-1600s an open space close to the demolished castle was used as a market place for corn at Oswestry and in about 1849 a large building was erected which accommodated a Corn Exchange and a Cheese and Butter Market, and beside it a Horse Market was created. If there was any dealing to be done in corn, there is no doubt that the millers of Felin Lyn considered Oswestry to be the focal market. (Note 5.9.)

The town grew apace in the latter part of the last century, mainly as a result of the arrival of the railway and the decision by Cambrian Railways to establish its headquarters and works there. In 1851 its population was 4,800 and by 1911 had reached exactly 10,000.

It cannot be too strongly emphasised how important the weekly visit to market meant to country people. It fed the mind just as much as it fed and clothed the body and satisfied a very basic need of humanity. There was the practical side of buying essentials – and frivolities too – not to be found in a person's own parish. It gave the farmer, in this case the miller, intelligence about price trends in the sale and purchase of animals and grain.

The millers of Felin Lyn had slaughter pigs for sale at different times of the year and they were much concerned about anticipating the periods of best prices. A walk around the market with eyes and ears alert, and conversations with acquaintances and strangers alike, would help the miller to make a decision – hopefully profitable. Even if the pig was not sold at Oswestry, the knowledge gained was useful when selling ex-mill. In the days of Toll-milling, the miller was less concerned about corn prices because he received a share of the grain being milled, irrespective of its current value. Nevertheless,

Oswestry Market would provide him with up-to-date prices for locally grown grains.

The other important aspect of a market was social. Everyone yearns for company, and news, and gossip, especially when these things are curtailed or denied. Imagine the period prior to the middle of the last century at isolated farmhouse and cottage where a postal service was virtually non-existent, a newspaper an expensive rarity and illiteracy widespread. One can then understand how market day was looked forward to with pleasurable anticipation.

Turning to this century at about the time of World War I, Mrs Jones (FL) provided a delightful aside concerning some of the times when her parents went to Oswestry market in their horse and trap. She says all three children were left at Felin Lyn and were allowed to 'run' it. She says: *"I must make it clear that this only related to Indian corn. That was easy as the big hopper in the old kiln would be filled with maize which came down to the middle room to be ground and then as meal to the ground floor. When the lower bin was full, we stopped the mill. We did not fill and weigh sacks and such, nor did we grind wheat, oats or barley."*

Contemporary References to Felin Lyn

For such a very ordinary mill as Felin Lyn, we are fortunate to have two written references to it, both made in the twilight of the Mill's existence. The sources and information are as follows:

E. Mitford Abraham, Ulverston, Lancs (1883-1959)
This man was an enthusiastic amateur historian of British wind and water mills in the 1920s and 1930s, when such people were a rarity. He travelled the length of northern England taking notes and photographs and fortunately for posterity all these are held by John Rylands Library of Manchester University. He made no attempt to cover Wales and in his notes there are only ten references to Welsh watermills. By good fortune, three of them refer to mills on the Afon Ceiriog and going in a downstream direction are Tregeiriog, Felin Newydd (just below Glynceiriog), and Felin Lyn. If this is not luck enough, the entry for Felin Lyn is twice as long as the next longest entry. Speculation as to how this arose is made elsewhere in this chapter. The entry was recorded in two parts dated 1936 and 1943.

"PONTFADOG, near Chirk, 1937: The last of the Ceiriog river cornmills. Three pairs of stones (one French), flour bolter and wheat cleaner. Owned by son of Sir A. T. Davies, whose house is above in wood on left. Not worked since June 1936. Mr Evans (tenant and miller) died last year. Mrs Evans worked it last winter. New tenant has pigs and takes over in March (1937) and is under agreement to work mill as there are still half a dozen farmers who want to have their corn ground there.

October 1943: Dam opposite Frondeg (Dolywern) blown up by dynamite early this month. Worked last winter, but it is now intended to sell all iron for scrap. Wheel in bad condition and cogs in one pinion wheel broken. One view taken in snow Xmas 1932." [The 'house above in wood' is Brynhyfryd, the childhood home of the author.]

Mrs Jones (FL) was sceptical about the Mill being worked after 1936. She said: *"The man to whom my mother sublet it, did not do any grinding. He was not at the mill long. After he left I think three other tenants came, but whether they ever ground I cannot say. I never went near Felin Lyn from the day my mother left. I cannot imagine my mother ever milling local wheat; I don't think she ever did any grinding at all."*

William Davies, Glynceiriog, Denbighshire. (1906-73)
We are indebted to this local inhabitant and local historian for the only review of watermills in Dyffryn Ceiriog. It is a comprehensive and detailed history and probably took several years to compile. It appeared as a series of seven newspaper articles between 16 April and 28 May 1941 in the local newspaper Border Counties Advertiser, published at Oswestry, Shropshire. The articles totalled about 8,500 words. The entry for Felin Lyn is regrettably short but does contain the only reference to grinding charges. One must be careful not to assume that the period referred to in the quote below and the publication year are necessarily the same; in fact there is likely to be a 5-8 year gap.

"FELIN LYN. With the exception of the mill at Chirk[†] *this is the only mill in the Ceiriog Valley still in use for corn grinding. Its millrace runs from a point some two or three hundred yards below Dolywern bridge and runs through the lands of numerous owners, who use its waters at appropriate times for irrigation purposes. Part of the waters of Nant Gwryd are also used to supplement the water of the Ceiriog for power purposes. The charge for millering (sic) at this mill was, I understand, 5d per 100lbs of grain. Nowadays the present proprietor charges, I understand, a toll of 10lbs of the grain out of each and every 100lbs of grain ground."*

([†]) See Appendix V. Chirk Mill ceased to be a watermill in its original condition c1914-20.

Breadmaking at Llwynmawr and Pontfadog

Breadmaking at its crudest consists of adding water to some kind of flour, whether the flour be made of acorns, rice, sorghum, peas, or whatever, and baking the resulting 'paste'. It has been practiced by man for at least 7,000 years and today is still his most widely used food. So the central and continuing importance of bread is plain to see.

Breads in the world, past and present, are divided into two categories; flat, unleavened breads or risen leavened breads. Both have co-existed for hundreds of years but probably the majority of the world's population today eat flat unleavened bread, cooked daily. This bread has a solid dense composition because it is not diffused with air and is usually baked in a thinnish layer to make it more palatable. Examples of extremely thin flat breads are chapatty of India and tortilla of Mexico.

Leavened breads are those which are aerated and as a consequence the bread is produced as a risen loaf, in marked contrast to the flat breads. Such breads are made from grain containing gluten which is a plant protein, with wheat – especially North American – having the best gluten content. When wheaten flour is mixed with water and the dough is kneaded, the gluten forms an elastic network of little pockets which are capable of trapping air or gas. This is the foundation of risen bread.

At first, women used the air induced in the kneading process, and the moisture in the dough converted to steam during baking, to create the rising. But this does not make for a satisfactory loaf, especially when the bread grain has low gluten content, as is the case with barley or rye; oats has virtually none.

So a leavening agent was introduced which caused fermentation and the production of carbon dioxide gas, which got trapped in the gluten web. This agent was yeast which is a microscopic and unicellular plant which has a fast-moving life-cycle when placed in the dough. Another agent introduced in this century, but no improvement over yeast, is the chemical sodium bicarbonate. These agents produce an expansive dough which creates a risen loaf, now considered the bread 'norm' for Britain.

This somewhat lengthy explanation about breads has been felt necessary, so as to put the making of bread in the Ceiriog and in the neighbourhood of Felin Lyn into proper context. (Note 5.10.)

Prior to the building of the flourmill of Felin Lyn of this story, it is most probable the housewives of the district baked both flatbreads and risen breads. The flatbread was extremely thin – almost transparent – and had the diameter

of a dinner plate and was made of oatmeal. It was baked on a circular iron plate called a 'gradell' in Welsh. In more recent years a confusion has arisen about the shape and constituents of this flat-bread, which in Welsh is called 'bara ceirch' (bara means bread and ceirch is oats). Modern Welsh oatcakes have the shape and consistency of scones and are sometimes misnamed 'bara ceirch' but they cannot be classified as flatbread.

Precisely what the weakly rising loaf was made of, we do not know, as no written evidence survives. It was probably made of barley meal only, or a mixture of barley and rye meals. Such a loaf was cut and served in wedges. On special occasions perhaps the housewife purchased a small amount of wheaten flour at Chirk or Oswestry and added this to the meal she was using.

Barley and rye have poor levels of gluten and so do not make for good risen loaves. As a result these loaves rose only about three inches and were probably 9-12 inches in diameter. Our present day round-and-flat cake and the way in which we serve it in wedges is a survival of the earlier barley and/or rye loaf. This bread was nutritious but dense and unappetising and was made more acceptable by covering the wedges with butter, dripping, jam or the like. It grew stale very quickly and was baked daily or every other day. (Note 5.11)

Then came the construction of the flourmill at Felin Lyn which had the capability of producing wheaten flour as well as oat and barley meal. Perhaps a reminder should be added here that the gluten content of oats is poor and so has never been used to make risen breads; in times of scarcity oatmeal may have been added to barleymeal as a supplement.

Wheaten bread was well known for many hundreds of years in south-east England because that was the prime area for growing the crop, but in many places in Britain very little if any wheat was planted until the nineteenth century.

It has been estimated that in 1750 only half the population of Britain ate wheaten bread, the other half relying on risen breads of rye and/or barley, flat oatmeal bread and/or oatmeal cakes. By 1825 it is believed that only a quarter of the British population did not eat wheaten bread, and that this was due mainly to climatic conditions in areas where wheat was not a viable crop.

As discussed earlier, it is thought that Chirk Castle Estates introduced the growing of wheat on its uplands to the west of the Castle in the last quarter of the eighteenth century. The home farm of Chirk Castle had grown wheat for several centuries (specific reference in 1330 to *'proceeds of wheat to Michaelmas time, £20-15-0'* and it is presumed the mill of the castle, called Castlemill and lying 700 yards to the south, was equipped with a pair of hardstones to grind the wheat. In the immediate area this would make it unique amongst mills as all the others would be grist mills capable only of grinding the soft grains of oats, barley or rye, into meal.

At this juncture there has to be a 'chicken or egg' speculation. Was Felin Lyn built with hard stones in anticipation of the local introduction of the new crop – wheat – or was it meeting a newly created demand? We shall never know the answer but undoubtedly the facility would have encouraged more local farners to grow wheat. This development would have encouraged the housewife to make bread with wheaten flour and possibly the use of yeast as a leavening agent. Very soon a wheaten risen loaf was being eaten in ordinary households in the land about Felin Lyn.

It is presumed this baking was done in the time honoured way. A clean place was swept on the hot hearth-stone, the dough was placed on it, and then covered with a metal hood which in turn had hot ashes heaped all around it; this hood was usually an old discarded cauldron. The baking would take about an hour.

The next change in breadmaking at Felin Lyn and in the neighbourhood occurred not in the composition of the bread but in the cooking apparatus involved. This probably took place between 1870 and 1890 and was the direct result of developments in urban kitchens, and the building of the Glyn Valley Tramway,

The Industrial Revolution of the early nineteenth century caused a considerable exodus of people from the country to towns and cities. Immediately, these people encountered problems with fuel for cooking and warmth, for no longer was it possible to go foraging for firewood on a daily basis. The substitute fuel was coal but coal does not burn well on a hearth because it needs a raised fire basket with a good flow of air around it.

So fire baskets suspended above the hearth came into being and these evolved into the iron cooking range. These were first widely advertised at the Great Exhibition held in London in 1851. At first the cast iron range was an urban innovation in those places where coal was in plentiful supply, but within fifty years its use had become general in town and country.

The housewife had now to adapt her baking methods to this new piece of equipment. Instead of baking the bread on the hearth she now put the dough in a holding tin and baked it in the oven, which was placed to one side of the fire basket or grate.

When Felin Lyn was renovated, c1873-80, not only were the buildings and milling equipment upgraded but attention was also given to the needs of the miller's wife. A cast-iron kitchen range was installed on top of the old hearth and a cast-iron bake oven was installed in the scullery. Both these pieces of cooking equipment and the way in which they were used have already been described in Chapter 4.

Gleanings of dead wood or split thin logs were used to fire the bake oven, which was used once, possibly twice a week, but the range was coal-fired. Buying coal for Felin Lyn in 1800 would have been an expensive and awkward business but by 1900 it was easy and relatively cheap. Chirk was on the southern tip of the North Wales coal field and from the 1870s coal was mined there in great quantities in modern deep pits. The creation of the Glyn Valley Tramway resulted in cheap coal being readily available in the district and by 1910 the Tramway was hauling 3,000 tons of coal annually up-valley, giving a coal consumption of about 4 or 5 tons per household. To get this coal, the miller would take his two-wheeled cart to the tramway siding at Dolywern and offload a ton at a time from one of the small railway wagons.

Prior to the arrival of iron ranges at Llwynmawr and Pontfadog, the miller's wife and all the other housewives in the district, baked bread on their hearths using wheaten flour that had been ground at Felin Lyn. The side-by-side introduction of imported flour and kitchen ranges produced changes in household victualling, cooking, and diet.

At first, housewives would continue to use the flour of Felin Lyn, but slowly there would have been a switch by non-farming residents to buying imported flour from the local store as a matter of convenience and because it was cheaper. So began the erosion of the dependence on Felin Lyn to supply the flour for all the bread baked in the area.

The late Tom Davies (1902-86), who for over 50 years kept the general store and post office at Llwynmawr, confirmed that a bakery operated at the store from 1877-1913. This opening date of 1877 has great significance for it means that home baking was commencing its wane and further emphasises that Felin Lyn was no longer the vital link in the local human food chain. The wheaten flour for Llwynmawr bakery was delivered in a four-wheeled wagon drawn by shire horses and came from Chirk Mill.

In 1916 a new bakery was established in the neighbourhood by a Mr R.W. Ellis, behind the combined store and post office at Pontfadog. This bakery was originally equipped with an oven that was fired outside with 3-foot logs split lengthways in half, but the oven itself was accessed from within the building. About five years later the building was enlarged and a newer type of oven installed with Ellis receiving his flour from Llangollen Mill, which at that period had a 3-pair stone capacity and a fair business in flour. This Pontfadog bakery closed in about 1950. It was from this bakery that the author's family got their bread when living at Brynhyfryd, above Felin Lyn, and the author well remembers being sent occasionally to the bakery to get a loaf when supplies had run out; such a loaf was often warm, had a wonderful smell, and an enticing crust that usually got picked at before reaching home.

R. WILLIAM ELLIS,

Grocer, Baker and Provision Merchant,
Corn and Flour Dealer,

POST OFFICE,

PONTFADOG.

TRY OUR

NOTED WELSH BREAD.

This advertisement appeared in a 40-page booklet titled "The Ceiriog Valley, Visitor's Guide". Undated, but circa 1934.

There are exceptions in every trend and the late Tom Roberts (1906-87), who farmed the Bonc, Llwynmawr, had this to say: *"In the 1920s we grew some two to four acres of wheat each year and some of it after grinding at Felin Lyn was used for our own bread making. We had to mix it with equal proportions of bought flour, otherwise the bottom of the loaf would spread to almost twice its original dough size at its base."* It is obvious that the bought flour was North American with its high gluten content.

The late Mrs Elizabeth Humphreys echoed this practice by saying that her mother at Caecoed farm in the 1920s would obtain dark brown flour (wholemeal) from Felin Lyn. This she would mix with white bleached commercial flour to produce a not-too-darkish loaf which was home-baked. For the same time period another correspondent said the home-baked loaves were made with grey coloured flour and each loaf lasted about three days; this would contrast with the store-bought loaf that would disappear in one meal.

From this short history of local home baked breads, it becomes apparent that this art practised over the home hearth for more than two thousand years in the Ceiriog, took only 25-50 years to die out completely.

This is also an appropriate place to mention the consumption of cereals at meals. Families in the nineteenth century in the Ceiriog ate four meals during the day: breakfast, dinner at noon, tea in the late afternoon, and supper. Bread and butter and oatmeal cake figured prominently at breakfast and tea-time, whilst porridge or broth or bread and cheese was a typical supper dish. Dinner was the principal meal of the day and was the only one which contained meat – and then not always. It usually consisted of 'cawl' (broth containing oatmeal and meat) or bacon and potatoes, and bread was always provided.

From this it can be seen that bread was eaten at three, sometimes all, meals each day and oatmeal appeared in various guises in at least two of the meals. Another favourite food was 'sucan' which has the consistency of blancmange. It is made by soaking oatmeal in water till it becomes sour, draining off the meal, and then boiling the residual solution.

Mention should also be made of barley water, still sold commercially, which is made from an infusion of barley. It is a refreshing drink, has mild curative powers and was widely used in the past, going back to the times of Hippocrates who prescribed it. Mrs Jones (FL) mentioned that it was sometimes served at the Mill in her childhood.

The only pre-twentieth century record of a meal served locally, known to the author, comes from the memoirs of John Hughes (Dol) who said his grandmother at Dolywern served occasional Sunday dinners to chapel folk. It consisted of mutton broth, mutton with oatmeal in it, white bread (a significant detail as it was made from wheat) and beer; presumably this would be in the 1820s.

How people ate in the middle of the nineteenth century in Dyffryn Ceiriog we do not know by direct quote. However there is a Privy Council report of 1863 which describes the diet of the 'peasantry' in Wales and says North Walians ate as well as *"...those of the same class in the best agricultural districts in England"*.

The report defines breadstuffs as bread, flour, oatmeal, peas and rice, and had this to say specifically about North

Wales. In all cases (sample of households) wheaten bread was eaten and when made at home it was sometimes baked in loaves, otherwise in flatcakes over the open fire; *"...the former was more common when there was an oven and was generally preferred since the latter was apt to drive off the gas made in fermentation and render the cakes sad"*.

Oatmeal was used in 60% of the households and in the majority of cases was used to make broth, sucan and budram. Barley was formerly used more, though in some cases bread was still being made from a mixture of rye and barley. Rice and peas were eaten by 60% and 8%, respectively, of the sampled households. In all, the total breadstuffs consumed was rated as 'very large' at 14¾lbs per adult weekly in North Wales; this compared to a consumption rate of 14lbs for the whole of Wales.

Turning to more recent times, Mrs Jones (FL) remembered well the meals served by her mother at Felin Lyn in the first 20 years of this century. Breakfast consisted of porridge and nearly always a boiled egg. Midday dinner usually had meat in it, with a roast joint on Sunday and its cold remains on Monday, followed on other days by such things as ham, stews or rabbit pie. Such dishes would always be accompanied by potatoes, and garden vegetables when in season. This was followed by such desserts as fruit pies, jam tarts, rice pudding, custards and bread & butter pudding. An occasional treat was trout when the millrace was being emptied and cleaned out. Trout had been considered since medieval times as one of the miller's perks and it is no coincidence that the restaurant dish of *'truites a la meuniere'* translates as 'trout (cooked by) the miller's wife', since in French a miller is a *'meunier'*. A fuzzy photo of the 1920s shows Emlyn, the miller's son at Felin Lyn, holding a clutch of trout in each hand, thus attesting to this practice.

Tea time saw bread and butter, cheese, lettuce and the like. Suppers always seemed tasty and Mrs Jones remembered in particular the pork sausages on Wednesday evenings purchased that day by her parents on their shopping trip to Oswestry. It is worth observing that the bulk of this food was home grown, caught or processed. Out of the individual foods mentioned, only the joint of meat (when not pork), the rice, large fruits and the pork sausages, did not emanate from the smallholding.

Missing Mill Ledgers

The ledger or account book of a mill is a very important source document, for by the nature of things it is likely to be the only day-by-day record of the activities of that mill. In a sense it is akin to the log-book of a ship.

An old mill and an old ship stand mute but from their structures much of their functions can be deduced. In the case of a ship, one can see what it was designed for, such as coasting or ferrying. But it needs the examination of an old log-book to fill in such details as specific cargoes, precise tonnages, ports of call, loading/running/idle times, speed, weather and unusual incidents.

In the same way a mill ledger discloses customers, sales, types and quantities of grain being processed each day, tolls or prices being charged for milling and for sale of processed products, and so on. From such raw data a fairly accurate assessment can be made of the mill's territory, monthly and seasonal patterns of activity, pricing structure, and maybe even a rough idea of profitability.

In Chapter 1 it was indicated that one, or possibly two, early mill ledgers had survived to at least the closure of full-time milling at Felin Lyn in 1936. It is obvious what a valuable contribution these books would make if they could be tracked down.

Though the ledgers have not been found at time of publication, the reader is likely to be interested in the byways that have been followed in searching for it or them. The late Mrs Jones (FL) explained how one of these ledgers left Felin Lyn.

"Before my mother quit the Mill in 1936, a man from the Lake District, who was very keen on watermills, came to see her. He had a sister, Miss Mary Abraham, living in Dolywern. The man asked my mother if there were any old ledgers and knowing of the ones in the attic, she gave them to him. He was delighted with this gift and wrote to my mother thanking her again". If the ledgers have not been destroyed, which is unlikely, it is possible they can be located and studied.

Miss Mary Abraham was a friend of the author's parents and lived at Dolywern, not a mile away from Felin Lyn, for over 40 years and died in 1975. By one of those odd coincidences, not infrequent in the writing of this book, the author last talked to Miss Abraham in 1974 when he was visiting Britain; it was a phone call made from Glandwr, adjacent to Felin Lyn. In retrospect what a missed opportunity this was because both Miss Abraham, and Miss Parry of Glandwr, could have provided many interesting details concerning Mitford Abraham or Felin Lyn, but at that date the thought of writing a history was non-existent.

Mr J. Kenneth Major, who has had a lifetime interest in British wind and watermills, read a draft of this chapter and immediately came to the conclusion that the person referred to was the late E. Mitford Abraham (1883-1959), then of Ulverston, Lancashire, and a pioneering mill enthusiast. Abraham has been mentioned earlier in this chapter under the heading 'Contemporary References to Felin Lyn'.

Mr Major said the mill archives of Mitford Abraham had been deposited with Manchester University and an inquiry to the University disclosed the happy news that there was a reference to Felin Lyn in the 'Abraham Collection'. However the Collection contains no original manuscript material, such as millers' notebooks or ledgers, so the trail appeared to have petered out at this point.

On hearing of this development, Mrs Jones (FL) searched through her family papers and was rewarded by discovering a letter written by Mitford Abraham in July 1937, from Caydale Cottage, Rake Head, Ulverston, Lancashire. It is addressed to her mother, Mrs Jane Evans, and the relevant part of the letter reads:

"I have cleaned the red account book and am having it rebound. There are some entries I don't understand. What does 'scribbling' oats mean? We use the word 'shelling' oats for oatmeal, but I did not know oatmeal was made at your mill. Did your husband keep a separate book for flour sold, for there are very few entries; surely plenty of flour was ground and sold in the 1880s up till 1900. I hope to see you again and will no doubt have more questions to ask you."

With this letter he sent two photo prints of Felin Lyn, showing Mrs Evans standing behind a wall and in front of the mill door. These photos were taken in November 1936 but regrettably are of such indifferent quality that they are not suitable for reproduction.

Mitford Abraham was conscious of the historical worth of the ledger and took the trouble to have it rebound, so it is likely it has been deposited with or donated to some institution. However it is not held by the Lancashire Records Office, Manchester University, or the National Library of Wales, so only a patient and comprehensive inquiry is likely to track down this account book.

The next development in this story was that the author noticed the ten Welsh mills recorded by Abraham were situated in a line drawn between Chester and Dyffryn Ceiriog, suggestive of some specific reason for coming to the Ceiriog, such as fishing or a visit to relatives or friends. It became obvious that the details relating to Felin Lyn were more numerous than those of other mills and pointed to a local knowledge. For example, Abraham can name the house that overlooks the weir of Felin Lyn, a matter of little significance when someone is merely passing through a place. Local enquiries established that Mitford Abraham or a relative did indeed have some connection with this house, which is called Fron-deg.

Further enquiries enabled contact to be made with the daughter of the late Mitford Abraham, a Mrs Margaret Fell James, who lives in Cumbria, and who kindly filled in the details. Sad to say, she has no idea of the whereabouts of the missing ledger.

Mrs James explained that her paternal grandfather was a Liverpool manufacturing chemist who married twice, having Mitford Abraham by his first wife and Mary Abraham (of Dolywern) by his second wife. Her grandfather rented Fron-deg as a holiday home some time in the period 1890-1910, and so Mitford and Mary came to know the Ceiriog well, as children and as adults. Mitford mentions Fron-deg in a 1906 diary when aged 23. He also spent his honeymoon there, so the house with its view of Felin Lyn's weir held memories for him.

The Queen Hotel (1909-1961), Dolywern, which stood 300 yards from Fron-deg, stated in one of its brochures that the hotel water has been analysed by Messrs Clay & *Abraham*, Analytical Chemists, Liverpool, who pronounced it *"very pure water"*. This is confirmation of a connection between the elder Abraham and the locality.

Mitford Abraham continued to visit Dyffryn Ceiriog intermittently throughout his life, especially after his half-sister, Mary, decided to make her home at Dolywern. His notes about Felin Lyn's weir and the Mill itself, written in October 1943, were made as a result of one of these visits.

Mrs James searched her own private papers to see if she could find any trace of, or reference to, the missing red covered mill ledger but found nothing. However, happily and miraculously, she came across a family (as opposed to an archival) photo taken at Christmas time, 1927, of Felin Lyn, by her father. It shows a snowy scene of the tree-lined headrace just behind the Mill and was taken in the field that belongs to Llangwryd-isaf.

So by one of those strange coincidences in life, the weir of Felin Lyn may have been the spark that ignited Mitford Abraham's life-long interest and concern in wind and water mills, which in his time were beginning to decay and disappear. Only since his death has his work of recording become known and appreciated. Correspondingly, by a twist of fate our knowledge of Felin Lyn has been increased by Abraham's diligence as a mill observer and recorder.

It is to be hoped that the luck encountered this far in trying to locate the mill ledger will hold out, and that the publicity brought about by the publication of this book will cause it to surface. The author feels strongly that the ledger has not been destroyed but is held by some individual or institution.

When it does appear it will either confirm or confound

some of the assumptions, based upon generalisations, taken in this book. For that we shall be grateful, for we shall have got closer to reality, an elusive aspect of the web of history.

Neighbouring Watermills

It is useful to locate and describe the watermills immediately adjacent to Felin Lyn to assess their impact one upon the other. In attempting to determine the type of waterwheel used in these two mills, it has been found that the river gradient in the vicinity is a fairly even 1 in 100. The head of water available at the site of a mill determines the type of waterwheel to be installed and since the types have varying mechanical efficiencies, it is helpful to speculate on the type of wheel used in these two mills. Undershot, breast-shot, and overshot waterwheels are estimated to have efficiencies of 25%, 55% and 65% respectively, when using the same waterflow. It will be seen that Felin Lyn was equipped with a wheel type that had the superior efficiency.

Mill 'A'

This was a corn mill situated one mile upstream at the hamlet of Dolywern. Since about 1840 it was known as 'Glan-y-wern' (alder bank). Prior to 1800 it was called 'Felin Uchaf' (upper mill) which suggests that some time prior to the nineteenth century there was a sister mill about a quarter of a mile downstream.

The first mill was a stone-built single storeyed building in the shape of an 'L', with one arm housing the mill and house and the other arm the stable, cowshed and barn; it was reputedly built in the 1600s. About 1795 a great flood carried the weir away, and since Chirk Castle Estates was then in Chancery (re joint female heirs), no repairs could be effected and the mill fell into disuse and then ruin; in 1819 it was pulled down.

All of the above information has been provided by John Hughes (Dol), for he was born near the mill in 1802 and his grandfather Thomas Hughes (1739-1803), was miller there. The adjacent sketch was drawn by John Hughes and has been abstracted from one of his notebooks.

The weir was refashioned at its former location in 1836 and in 1837 a new three-storeyed mill was built into the adjacent steep bank, so as to take advantage of grain delivery from a lane abutting the top floor. The waterwheel was fitted to the south side of this new building and was fed by the reconditioned 1,200 foot long millrace which provided an 8-10 foot head of water.

A pleasing millhouse was built close by with the millrace running behind it. In later years this house had a rearward extension added and the millrace was carried through it in a large diameter pipe.

At a still later date a lofty single storey addition was built onto the mill on the flat ground between it and the river, and in so doing a peculiar modification was made. The waterwheel fitted originally to the south wall was repositioned on the east side of the new addition which made for water supply problems. This was solved by building a slate trough through the building to deliver water to the outside wheel; it can still be seen.

The waterwheel still exists in situ and is of cast iron of unidentified origin. It has a 10-foot diameter, 34-inch width, 34 buckets, and is carried on a 14-inch diameter wooden axle. The axle projects into the mill for about 4 feet to a further bearing and mounted on the axle is a 2-

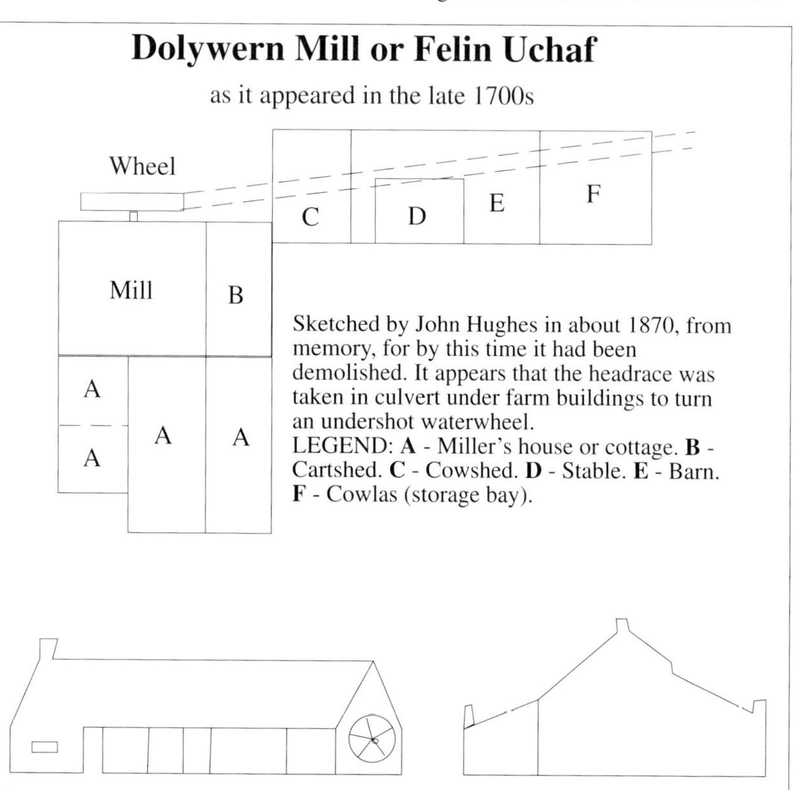

Dolywern Mill or Felin Uchaf

as it appeared in the late 1700s

Sketched by John Hughes in about 1870, from memory, for by this time it had been demolished. It appears that the headrace was taken in culvert under farm buildings to turn an undershot waterwheel.
LEGEND: **A** - Miller's house or cottage. **B** - Cartshed. **C** - Cowshed. **D** - Stable. **E** - Barn. **F** - Cowlas (storage bay).

foot diameter wooden driving wheel of 10-inch width. It evidently drove machinery on the ground floor of the original mill which stood about 8 feet above the floor of the newer building.

Two monolithic millstones have been incorporated as features in a paved path on the present property; they are both of 38-inch diameter but it is not known if they are from the mill or were imported for effect. There is also the memory of a highly practical but rarely mentioned item in milling histories, a horse drinking trough. It was sited in the millyard and was fed from the tailrace.

Curiously, the history of Glan-y-wern Mill is the reverse of the norm in that more is known about its early life than its later life. After 1837 some speculation is needed to fill in the gaps. At some point it was converted from a cornmill to a maltings and it is believed this took place between 1855 and 1880, resulting in alterations and additions.

Malting calls for a 'growing' floor, kiln, and light bruising of the grain and all these facilities were to hand. Most likely these changes were engineered by John Hughes, publican and master brewer of Llwynmawr Inn, for his wife's family had or did own the mill. Perhaps he became its tenant or owner.

It is said malting work ceased in about 1916. This has a ring of truth about it because scarcity of labour in World War I would cause malting and brewing to be concentrated at larger facilities, in this case Wrexham.

Mr Patrick MacIver, now retired and of Hove, Sussex, has childhood recollections of Glan-y-wern Mill. He writes: *"My father moved our family to Dolywern in 1923 and though we lived in the millhouse, the old malt mill (which came with the property) was paradise for us children. The mill buildings had been stripped of equipment before our occupation and the top floor became our huge playroom, whilst the middle floor was converted into a self-contained flat as an overflow from our house; in the lower floor were stores and a potting shed. We preserved the millwheel and enjoyed showing visitors how it still revolved on its flintstone bearings."*

Local opinion has it that Glan-y-wern's weir was also a victim of the great flood of 1941 and that thereafter the millrace carried no water. From then on the waterwheel did not turn – even for visitors.

Mill 'B'

Nothing is known about this mill prior to the nineteenth century, not even its name. It is shown on a 1 inch (approx.) map of 1793 but not on one of 1808. This may or may not have significance as it could merely be a surveyor's or draughtsman's omission. Since it lay close to Ty'n-ddol farm and was a fulling mill, it will be identified here as *'Pandy Ty'n-ddol'*. Its existence and location are shown on the 1838 Tithe Survey where it is simply marked 'Mill'; by this time it was most likely in decay. It was sited nearly one mile downstream from Felin Lyn and lay close to the river on the south bank opposite the farm of Ty'n-ddol; to add to the obscurity this farm was called Talygarth Ucha on the 1838 Tithe map. The mill lay in the Township of Talygarth and it is significant that the whole of this township lay on the north side of the Afon Ceiriog except for about five fields which lay on the other side of the river and held the mill and its race. Its headrace was 700 feet long, giving a 5 foot to 7 foot head of water suggesting the use of an undershot or breastshot wheel.

J.W.D. Davies in his 1941 review of Ceiriog mills supplies the only known details about its working days. Mr Davies says it was a fulling mill or ' pandy ' prior to 1800. It was purchased about 1803 by a young Yorkshire woollen manufacturer, John Mason, who was the first person to mechanise flannel making in the Ceiriog. Mason converted the fulling mill to a flannel mill where probably only the weaving was done. It is known that he imported several workers with mechanical weaving skills from the Welshpool-Newtown-Llanidloes area. By c1815 the mill was proving too small for Mason and so he moved to the newly built Lower flannel mill in Glynceiriog in 1818-20. (See Item 14 in Appendix V and Note 5.12)

The only other reference to this mill comes from the notebooks of John Hughes (Dol) who lived at Dolywern as a boy. He says he attended makeshift private schools in the neighbourhood which sprang into life only so long as a master and some kind of meeting place were available. He mentions that a part-time schoolmaster found a *"...schoolroom in the old Pandy opposite Tan-y-garth on the other side of the river at the foot of Stryt Ddu. It was a very cold place and the old house and barn had long passed their usefulness."* No date is attached to this reference but it has to be between 1808 and 1819.

All buildings had been demolished by the turn of this century, but for a time the weir and race were maintained as a meadow irrigation system and are shown on a large scale Ordnance Survey map that was field-surveyed in 1872 and published in 1899.

Competition Assessment

From this review it is obvious that Felin Lyn had no fear of competition in a downstream direction, as the next cornmill was at Chirk four miles away. Upstream there does not appear to have been much durable competition either, for it seems that Glan-y-wern mill operated only as a cornmill from 1837 to its conversion as a maltings cl855-cl880; a competitive period of 20 years minimum and 45 years maximum. In rural economic terms of the last century, it would appear that Felin Lyn was left in peace to serve its territory.

Welsh Remembrances

It is rare for any obscure building and its inhabitants to have anything written about them and luckily Felin Lyn was an exception. The two remembrances that follow were written in Welsh, the mother tongue and conversational language of the two writers.

The first piece appeared in a booklet in Welsh entitled 'Atgofion o Bowys' (Memories of Powys), edited by David Ll. Jones and Elizabeth A. Williams, and was published by the Powys Eisteddfod Committee in 1976; the quotation appears on page 12 of the booklet. It was written by a lady who lived all her life at Pandy Bach farm (not far from Felin Lyn) and who died in 1982 aged 92.

"Roedd mwy o droi a hau yd nag sydd heddiw a lle pwysig i'r ffermwyr oedd y Felin Lyn, Pontfadog. Gresyn ei gweld heddiw yn mynd a'i phen iddi. Gymaint prysurdeb a welodd gynt! Edward Evans oedd y melinydd am lawer o flynyddoedd a'i dad o'i flaen yntau; cymeriad gwyllt heb flewyn ar ei dafod. Byddai'n addo malu'r yd erbyn amser arbennig ac yn aml yn methu a chyflawni ei addewid, llawer siwrne ofer a gaed o'r herwydd. Ni chodai arian am ei waith yn malu, ond cymryd toll o'r yd. Gweithiai'n galed a diflino, a disgwyliau i eraill wneud yr un modd. Deuai wagen i fyny o'r Waun a thri o geffylau yn ei thynnu. Dyna oedd golygfa gwerth ei gweld ! Heidiai'r plant i'w gweld, onid dyna ddileit pob hogyn ysgol, ac onid uchelgais pob bachgen oedd bod yn berchen ar wedd o geffylau hardd tebyg i'r rhain a'r addurniadau pres ar y gers yn sgleinio?

"Datlwythid y pynau blawd ger trofa Pandy Bach a chariai Edward Evans hwy ar ei gefn i'r Felin. Mae'n dawel iawn yno bellach a dim ond atgo a erys ohono'n gweiddi nerth ei ben ac yn gweithio'n eger i falu'r yd i'w gwsmeriaid."

The English translation is as follows:

"There used to be more ploughing and sowing than there is today. Felin Lyn, Pontfadog, was an important place for farmers. How sad it is to see it almost derelict. How busy it used to be! Edward Evans was the miller for many years as was his father before him.

"He was a wild character who did not mince words. He would promise to grind corn by a certain time, and would often fail, causing many a wasted journey. No charge was made for grinding but a toll of corn was kept by the miller. He worked tirelessly and expected others to work in a similar fashion.

"A wagon drawn by three horses came from Chirk and was certainly a sight to behold. Children gathered from far and near, each one cherishing a dream that one day he would be the owner of a trio of sleek horses displaying much shiny harness brass.

"The flour sacks were unloaded near Pandy Bach and Edward Evans carried them on his back across the river to the mill. Silence reigns in Felin Lyn now and all that remains are memories of Edward Evans, his raucous voice and his diligence as a miller."

(Comment: The penultimate paragraph refers to a period prior to c1914 when Chirk Mill is known to have made 'wholesale' deliveries by miller's wagon up the Ceiriog valley. In the last paragraph it is thought that the words 'flour sacks' should not be taken literally. They probably refer to sacks of incoming grain, principally maize, that were delivered by the Glyn Valley Tramway and off-loaded at Pandy Bach.)

The second remembrance comes from the late Tom Roberts, a retired farmer, who was aged 79 when he composed it in 1985. His family came to the Bonc (farm), which lies close to the village of Llwynmawr, in 1911. His father, and then he himself, farmed the Bonc until 1970; sad to say the farm and buildings are falling into disrepair, for no-one lives there now, though the land is still farmed. What is of especial interest is that Tom Roberts was the last surviving farm-customer of Felin Lyn and knew Felin Lyn well from 1918 (when he finished school) to 1936 (when the last full-time miller died). This is what he had to say:

"Atgofion am Felin Lyn

Rhedai'r ffos ddwr i yrru'r felin drwy rai o'm caeau i. Yr oedd pob ffermwr yn gyfrifol am lanhau'r ffos a ai drwy ei dir. Ar ol llufogydd deuai llawer o gerrig a llaid i lenwi'r ffos, weithiau i fyny i naw modfedd, i droedfedd o ddwfn. Yr oedd Ned y melinydd i fod i'n rhybuddio ddiwrnod ymlaen llaw, a ni y ffermwyr oedd i fod i gau'r dorau, ond un buan oedd Ned ac yn aml iawn wedi cau y llif ddorau ei hyn rhyw ddwy awr cyn i ni gyrraed, ac wedi dal, a chasglu dwy i dair pwcedaid o bysgod fel yr ai'r dwr i lawr. Byddem yn glanhau'r ffos gan daflu'r sbwriel ar y cae. Yr oedd y melinydd i ofalu am ddigon o gwrw i'r ffermwyr oedd yn gwneud y gwaith hyn. Yr oedd yn rhaid i

Ned wneud aml i siwrnau yn ol a blaen i dafarn Llwynmawr i ddiwallu syched y glanhawyr. Nid yn aml caem gyfle i gael trofa ar Ned!

"Yr oedd gennym ni yn y Bonc rhyw gan acer o dir, hanner ar y gwaelodion a hanner ar y mynydd. O'r tir hyn byddem yn troi tua deg acer, dwy i dair acer ar gyfer gwenith a'r gweddill yn haidd a ceirch. Deuai'r peiriant dyrnu acw ddwy waith y flwyddyn. Peiriant ager yn y dyddiau cynnar ond gyda thractor yn y blynyddoedd diwethaf. Byddem yn dyrnu y rhan fwyaf ddechreu Rhagfyr er mwyn cael blawd y flwyddyn nesaf, ac eto mis Mawrth i gael had at y cynheuaf nesaf. Byddem yn dyrnu deirgwaith adeg rhyfel.

"Cadwyd y gwenith a'r haidd mewn sachau yn yr ysgubor ond yr oedd y ceirch yn bentwr ar y llawr. Dipyn o waith oedd cadw'r llygod i ffwrdd ond yr oedd digon o gathod o gwmpas. Daliai'r sachau tua cant a hanner i ddau gant o bwysau. Yr oedd rhai sachau gyda pum rhes goch o'u hamgylch yn dal dros ddau gant o bwysau.

"Byddem yn mynd a grawn i'r Felin Lyn bob rhyw ddwy i dair wythnos. Aem a sachaid o wenith a rhyw bedwar i bum sachaid o haidd a ceirch. Dim ond dwywaith y flwyddyn aem a sachaid o wenith. Ni oedd yn gyfrifol am y sachau, yr oedd yn rhaid cael tair sach ar gyfer y gwenith am ei fod yn cael ei falu i dair gradd sef: y blawd, y bran, a'r 'thirds' i'r moch. Byddem yn bacio'r drol a'r ceffyl at ddrws y felin a llusgo'r sachau i mewn i'r felin, yna deuai cadwyn i lawr drwy'r nenfwd uwchben, clymwyd hon am enau'r sach aed a hi i fynnu i'r llawr uwchben i'w falu. Hyd y gwn nid oedd neb yn ei bwyso wrth ddod i mewn.

"Deuem yn ol i ymofyn y blawd wedi ei falu mewn rhyw ddau neu dri diwrnod. Disgyna'r blawd drwy wahanol bibellau o'r llawr uwchben i gafn mawr oedd wedi ei rannu i wahanol flodiau. Yna byddai'r melinydd yn ei gafnu i sachau a'i bwyso, a ninnau'n codi'r sachau trymion i'r drol. Nid wyf yn cofio'r gost am falu ond cadwai'r melinydd gyfran am ei waith. Byddem yn aml yn prynu 'Indian corn' a 'India mel' ganddo i besgi'r anifeiliaid a deuai'r 'bill' mewn rhyw fis. Byddem weithiau'n mynd a chrymanau ac arfau eraill i'w hogi ar y maen, yn enwedig adeg torri gwrychoedd."

The English translation reads: *"The millrace ran through some of my fields and it was the responsibility of each farmer to keep clean his section of the race. After sudden rainstorms tons of gravel and muck filled the race, often up to 9-12" deep. Ned, the miller, was supposed to warn each farmer the previous day of this operation and as one farmer had a key to the weir sluice gate, it was this farmer's responsibility to shut the gate. But Ned was very crafty and very often closed the sluice gate about an hour or so before the farmers arrived, thus enabling him to fill two or three buckets with trout caught in the residue; we sometimes got a portion of the catch.*

"We cleaned the millrace with shovels, depositing the spoil on the fields. However, it was part of the bargain that the miller was responsible for adequate beer for the farmers during the operation. The farmers, seeing this as the one and only opportunity to get something out of Ned, took advantage of the situation and he had to make several journeys to Llwynmawr pub to cater for their thirst!

"We at Bonc farmed about a hundred acres, half was near the valley, the other half being mountain. We ploughed about ten acres per year (other than war years), two to three acres for wheat and the remainder for barley and oats. The threshing machine visited us twice a year (three times yearly during World War II) and was done by steam power in earlier days and tractor after that war. The bulk of the threshing was done in late November to early December for meal for the animals, and again in March to obtain spring sowing seed. The threshed wheat and barley was kept in sacks, as a rule, but oats when dry were heaped loose on the granary floor. It was difficult to keep rats and mice away but there was an abundance of cats about. The sacks held about one-and-a-half to two hundredweight [some 168 to 224lbs of corn] *but there were certain sacks about which we called '5 row' on account of them having five rows or bands in red on them, which held over two hundredweight.*

"We visited Felin Lyn at intervals of two or three weeks. We would take, by horse and cart, four or five sacks of barley and oats; we took wheat only once or twice a year. The farmer was responsible for the supply of sacks. It was necessary to have three sacks for wheat grinding, as it was milled into flour, bran, and thirds for the pigs, and entered the three bags from separate chutes. On arrival at the mill, the cart was reversed to the door of the ground floor where the sacks were pulled down and dragged into the mill, where a chain and hook appeared through a trap door in the ceiling. The chain was tied around the neck of the sack and winched to the floor above for grinding.

"We would collect the milled corn in a day or two. The flour returned through different chutes from the first floor into a large divided trough on the ground floor. The miller would scoop the meal into sacks and weigh them. The farmer lifted the heavy sacks, generally unaided, on to his cart. I do not remember the cost of the work but the miller kept a portion as well as making a charge; I used also to buy bags of Indian corn [maize] *or maize meal. The bill*

[invoice] *would arrive at the farm in about a month.*

"I often took tools, such as billhooks and axes, to the mill for sharpening on a water-powered grindstone that was set up in the barn, particularly at hedge cutting times."

Evolution of Types of Ceiriog Watermills

Unless someone has a specialist interest in watermills, most people regard surviving watermills – whether active or derelict – as old and 'quaint'. In point of fact, and Felin Lyn was a typical example, virtually all existing mills are those in the final stage of development. European watermills evolved in three basic steps or stages and Felin Lyn was at Stage III.

The Ceiriog has a long history of watermilling and water-powered machinery and, thanks to Chirk Castle documents, has a better recorded history of the subject than many areas of Britain. But having said that, these records are sketchy and contain little technical detail. What is about to be described is largely speculative, but is bolstered by fact obtained locally or at national level.

Agriculture came early to the Ceiriog for the simple reason that the naturally open uplands provided ready made farmlands. Celtic families had established themselves at the head of the valley and along the upland spines by 2000BC or earlier. Such settlement would have been sparse with probably less than two persons per square mile. On the moorlands these peoples practised pastoral farming, as is attested to by existing Welsh names of the lands at the valley-head. In the same period the lower end of the Ceiriog, where it meets the Shropshire plains, was heavily wooded and probably attracted only the nomadic hunter.

The Romans built a 50-acre wooden legionary fortress for offensive operations near Chirk in the middle of the first century AD. Between then and the time the Mercian king, Offa, built his dyke c.796 AD to delineate the Welsh border, it is probable that small scale arable farming commenced in the lower reaches of the Ceiriog. The creation of the Dyke with its territorial boundaries would have encouraged stability in the area and so led to more settlement and the creation of small farms hacked out of the woodlands and bush. In this reconstruction of events, the building of Offa's Dyke and the technical possibility of watermills appearing in the Ceiriog, coincide.

The Stage I of watermill development is called Horizontal or Ungeared and frequently in northern Europe, the 'Norse'. It was of simple design, consisting of a short vertical shaft to which at its lower end were attached between 10 and 25 flat wooden 'turbine-like' paddles or blades. The top end of the shaft was rigidly attached to an upper millstone, which was probably of about 30 inch diameter. Water was fed to the paddles by means of a wood or stone spout, causing the one assembly of paddles, shaft, and upper millstone to revolve at 70-100 rpm. The whole arrangement relied upon the water having high velocity and small volume, typically a mountain stream after rain, and was intended to work only on an intermittent basis. The meal so produced was of indifferent quality by Felin Lyn standards and was probably ground at a rate of some 10lbs per hour. This was a considerable improvement over the hand quern which ground at 2lbs per hour and with manual labour involved.

The emerging consensus of mill historians is that the Horizontal mill was invented in the mountain regions of western Asia in the century or two before Christ and that its use spread along the principal trade routes – eastward and overland to China, and westwards around the Mediterranean basin and then carried beyond by trading ships.

The machine needs a fast falling small stream to turn its 'turbine' by impact and could be seen in all the hilly parts of Europe at one time but was slowly superseded by more powerful designs of mills. A few such mills still exist in Europe which virtually makes them museum pieces. However, Horizontal mills are still in daily use in many parts of Asia, for example there are about 50,000 of them in Nepal. (Note 5.13.)

The mill itself was no more than a small shed spanning a stream and the last one to work on the mainland of Britain was at Kinlochbervie in the western Highlands of Scotland which ceased working in 1864. The Horizontal mill survived to the beginning of this century in the Hebrides, Orkneys and Shetlands, and western Ireland. It is said that the last one in the British Isles expired in the mid 1940s at Fillaguile, Co. Galway. The British Government has preserved an example at Dounby, Orkney, where the mill is a stone shed with a floor area of 82 square feet. Such mills were intended to provide a service to between one and a half-dozen households and were subject to intermittent use through lack of rain.

The author has a theory that the Horizontal or Stage I mill was introduced to the Welsh Celts, who lived in the Ceiriog area, by Irish Celts. The notion is that it was Irish Christian missionaries who brought with them the know-how of this 'machine'.

It is worthwhile taking a little space to explore this possibility. Imagine the year 400AD when the Roman

This is the only known surviving view of Felin Lyn's weir taken during its working life. It is from a postcard published by Frith & Co., Reigate, Surrey, sometime in the period 1905-14. The postcard caption reads: "The Weir, Dolywern, near Llwynmawr". To the right is the primitive fish ladder whilst to the left is the intake of the millrace, obscured by trees. In the background lies the then hamlet of Llwynmawr.

Mrs Blodwen Mather, Dolywern.

legions had all but pulled out of Britain, leaving a vacuum for the next 500 years over much of Europe which the history books call the 'Dark Ages'. On the edge of Europe was a land untouched by Roman occupation, so that when Roman authority collapsed elsewhere it was unaffected by the event. This was Ireland.

The consequence was that Ireland, peopled by Celts, experienced a golden age between the fifth and eighth centuries and became the Christian spiritual and educational leader of western Europe. Christianity took root in heathen Ireland in the early years of the fifth century and the first bishop was appointed in 431AD.

Almost immediately these Irish Celts were sending Christian missionaries to their Celtic brothers in western Scotland, Cumbria, Wales, the West Country, and Brittany, and it is most probable that practical ideas accompanied spiritual ideas. It is worth noting that the vernacular literature of these Irish Celts, written in the seventh century, is the oldest written literature in Europe after Greek and Latin. (Note 5.14)

This flowering of a benign civilisation came to a sudden and sickening halt when the Vikings raided and plundered its land rich in cattle, ornaments and expertise of all kinds; this began in the early 800s AD.

Evidence of Irish Celtic influence in the Ceiriog is embedded in existing place names, like fossils in a rock. The first word of the village name, *Llanarmon* Dyffryn Ceiriog, means *'church of Garmon'* (or Germanus) and honours an early Celtic missionary. Garmon (c410-c475 AD) was born a Breton but was trained by St Patrick in Ireland and was then sent to Wales to spread the new faith and stayed there for some 20 years, before being appointed Bishop of (Isle of) Man.

Llanarmon Dyffryn Ceiriog was a point on Garmon's missionary tour of Wales and here he established a 'cell' and probably converted some of the local heathens to Christianity. Since almost the whole population of Britain was heathen at this time in history, it is well worth highlighting this local episode.

Another village name, *Llansantffraid* Glyn Ceiriog,

honours another Irish Celtic saint but this time the clue lies in the part-name 'ffraid' for Llan-sant-ffraid means *'church of Saint Bride'*. This lady (c455- 523 AD) is also known as Brigid, Brigit or Bridget and comes across the centuries as a woman of forceful personality in a circle of male Celtic Christian leaders. In this early church all missionaries and teachers of distinction were called 'saints'.

Bride's father was an Irish pagan prince and her mother a slave in his household. It is believed Bride received a Christian upbringing and in the course of time she became abbess of Kildare. Bride can be considered to be one of the founding leaders of the Celtic Church. Her influence spread far and wide after her death and she is still venerated in parts of Alsace, Flanders and Portugal. Londoners will recollect her name through the well known City church of St Bride's in Fleet Street. (Note 5.15.)

Since Bride was brought up to herd cattle, milk cows and make butter, she retained a life-long interest in such matters and is variously described as the patron saint of farmers, blacksmiths, students, artists and healers.

A third place name having an Irish association is a pre-historic site called 'Tomen-y-Gwyddel', which is situated on the northern flank hills between Llanarmon and Glynceiriog at 1,500 feet altitude. This name translates as *'mound* (or possibly *'tomb'*) *of the Irish'*.

Because of its topography, Dyffryn Ceiriog is to this day subject to east-west influences and it is the author's theory that it was subjected to Irish Celtic Christian influences whilst that land was in its ascendancy. It is thought that Garmon had established a Christian cell at Llanarmon by the year 450AD and it would appear that missionaries of Saint Bride settled in the Ceiriog before or after her death.

It is probable that this positive Irish influence was felt from the fifth century to the beginning of the ninth century when it shrivelled because the Irish were fighting for their very existence against the Vikings. In its place came a counter-influence from the east. At first it would be an influx of fellow British Celts from the lands of England to-be who would not accept the domination of the invaders from the Continent. Later, the influence probably became hostile in character when the Anglo-Saxon invaders finally reached the borders of the upland country in the mid-eighth century and so isolated the British into Celtic pockets of what have become known as Cornwall, Wales and Cumbria. The British Celts in the Wales pocket eventually became a nation and now are the only ones to retain their native language in widespread natural day-to-day usage.

The inhabitants of the Ceiriog knew exactly where they stood when the Mercian king, Offa, built his Dyke in the late 700s at the lip of the Welsh uplands and told them to stay on their side of the Dyke, though he said they could make peaceful visits across the line. As remarked earlier, Felin Lyn was two miles on the Welsh side of Offa's Dyke.

The Irish influence was motivated by a burning desire to establish Christianity in the land of the pagan Welsh Celts, but with it came expertise and guidance in practical matters connected with farming, household work and crafts as well as encouragement in artistic and cultural activities. It is not too far-fetched to suggest these Irish Celtic missionaries also brought with them the knowledge of a machine which did away with the laborious and time consuming chore of hand grinding corn with a quern. (Note 5.16.)

It is known Stage I mills were in use in Ireland before the seventh century and legend has it that such a mill was introduced three centuries earlier by King Cormac macAirt who hired a skilled man *'from over the wide water'*. Further, various saints of the Celtic Church have been traditionally credited with the foundation of watermills. None of this sounds implausible when placed beside the feat of the Irish Saint Brendon (c.490-c570) who is said to have sailed a leather boat to North America and back. A 1970s reproduction of the voyage in a reconstructed leather boat proved it was feasible.

The suggestion is that the Stage I mills were introduced to the upper reaches of the Ceiriog sometime between the years 400AD and 1000AD and most likely in the period 500-800AD. Often called a Norse mill, it will in this context be referred to as an 'Irish' mill.

Countering this hypothesis is the formidable fact that no remnants of any horizontal mill have ever been found anywhere in Wales. However, the flimsy structure and the simple mechanism - all made of wood except for the millstones – do not lend themselves to preservation over a few or several centuries. An equally telling argument can be used in rebuttal. The Horizontal mill was used by the inhabitants of all the hilly countries in Europe from Turkey to the Faroe Islands, so why would the Welsh be the one nation to shun its use?

The Stage I mill had much to commend itself to small, impoverished and pioneering communities, and in fact was re-adopted and modified by the pioneers who settled the eastern parts of North America. It was simple to construct and maintain and was inexpensive. Its only disadvantage lay in its intermittent operation, for it was powered by a mountain stream that was effective only after adequate rainfall.

J. W. Davies in his 1941 history of Ceiriog watermills mentions a '*probable old mill, below Nant Rhyd-Wilym*'. This is at the very head of the Ceiriog valley and is close to the last occupied house and farm, Swch-cae-rhiw. His description continues: *"The remains of an old watercourse can still be seen and the ruins at its far end prove that either a mill of some importance existed here or that the occupants of the building had knowledge of water power and its use long before recorded history"*. The very name of the adjacent farm, Swch-cae-rhiw (plough share-field-slope) suggests that some arable farming was carried out here at an altitude of 1,100 feet. It is presumed that this mill, in its final evolution, would have been a Stage II type (explained following pages) but its precursor was most likely to have been an Irish mill in view of its classic setting.

Another probable site of a Stage I mill is at the farm of Sarphle, which lies three-quarters of a mile west of Llanarmon. This farm is situated on the lower slopes of the valley at 975 feet altitude and had a waterwheel of some type until about 1870 – itself a significant date in the history of British milling. The farm does not lie beside the Ceiriog, which itself is a small river at this point, but is on the Nant Sarphle, a mile-and-a-half long tributary. A hoard of five hundred Roman coins dated between 42 and 226AD were found on this farm in 1918 and materially added to the British Museum collection: thus it is clear that the site has had connections with human settlement for a long time. No doubt this farm mill finished its working life using a small diameter conventional vertical wheel, but almost certainly it started out as an Irish mill.

It is also of significance that, of the five watermills in operation in 1800 in Dyffryn Ceiriog upstream of Glynceiriog, four of them were sited on tributaries of the Afon Ceiriog, itself a very modest river in its higher reaches.

In the course of time, Stage I mills were supplanted by Stage II mills in more populated areas, simply because Stage I mills have very limited grinding capacities. When Stage II mills appeared in Britain is open to debate, but the period 1000-1300AD seems reasonable. The Domesday survey of 1086 lists over 160 mills in Shropshire but nothing is known about their 'Stage' category.

Stage II mills had been designed by the Romans and they variously used water, animals, and slaves to drive them. In essence the Stage II mill is the mill with which we are familiar. It had a vertical waterwheel and an entirely new concept of gearing but still drove only one pair of millstones, which were probably of about 3-foot diameter.

Less than a hundred years after Chirk Castle was built we have a good description of a Stage II mill being built at Chirk. The description is in Latin and is dated 1391-93. It commences: *"Predicti nativi de villis de Pennclawdd, Dyntrayn, Glynn et Llangollen excepta Pengwern, quorum nomina superius infra tenura gavellarum expressantur, facient unum molendinum domimni apud Chirk, tam infra quam extra..."*

The translation reads in full:

"The aforesaid villeins in the townships of Penclawdd, Dinbrain, Glyn and Llangollen (except Pengwern) shall construct a mill for the lord at Chirk, both the inside work and the outside work in all things relating to carpentry, except the outside wheel. And prepare the great timbers and carry the timbers and the millstone to the said mill and thatch the mill with straw and set its walls with laths." (Source: "Extent of Chirkland")

This mill would have been a small building and looking at it, without seeing the waterwheel, one could easily mistake it for a cowshed or small barn. Inside, the machinery was quite uncomplicated. Above the single pair of millstones was a hopper which could hold a sack of grain, and below the stones was a bin to receive the meal. The millstones themselves were probably quarried within a ten mile radius. The meal was not closely ground so little flour was produced. No sifting or bolting of any kind took place at the mill, and if flour was needed it was done at home by women using kitchen sieves.

The earliest recorded mention of a mill anywhere on the Ceiriog is at Llanarmon Dyffryn Ceiriog in 1329. Today this is the last village up the valley. In 1332 there is documentary evidence of there being five watermills and one fulling mill on the Afon Ceiriog, but they are unnamed. In another list of 1391 four mills are specifically listed; going downstream they are Glynfawr, Crogen (now Castlemill), Chirk and Brynkinallt. With the possible exception of Llanarmon, these would all be Stage II mills.

It is also known that when the Lordship of Chirk was acquired by FitzAlan in 1322 there were 14 grist mills on the property, but of course the Lordship covered other lands apart from the Ceiriog.

These Stage II mills altered little in the four to seven hundred years of their existence. Only the housing changed from wood to stone walls in the fifteenth to seventeenth centuries, and in some cases the miller moved to his place of work with his cottage tacked onto the end of the mill itself.

A sketch of a Stage II Ceiriog mill just prior to its eclipse by a Stage III mill has fortunately been preserved. It is of the mill at Dolywern and has been described and illustrated earlier in this chapter. The sketch shows the typical one storey structure of a Stage II mill, with farm outbuildings attached.

It is even possible to speculate about the Stage II mill that preceded the Felin Lyn of this story. We know there was a predecessor because a book published in 1697 lists 'Velinlyn' as being 200 yards above 'Pont Fadog', and 'our' Felin Lyn was built in the late part of the 1700s. But there is no way of knowing when this Stage II mill was built; it could be anywhere between 1400 and 1600AD.

However we have clues as to its location and size. We start off with the concept that when a replacement building, road, or bridge is built, it is usually constructed to one side of the old facility so that life and trade are not interrupted in the transition period. It would appear to have happened in this case because the 1839 Tithe Commission map depicts a building immediately west of Felin Lyn. It is shown as a stubby looking 'U' with the arms of the 'U' facing west, and on the plan its length occupies one-tenth of an inch. The plan of this building has been magnified many times and an attempt has been made to scale it and to relate its position to Felin Lyn. This approach is not scientific and is a little unfair to the 1839 cartographer as he was quite unable to show precise building measurements with the scale at his disposal. It is found that the base of the 'U' measures 24 feet long by 11 feet wide and it is presumed this was the principal part of the structure. The two wings were each about 10 feet square and may well have been lean-to sheds and perhaps additions to the original building. The principal oblong building appears to have stood about where the cottage of Glyndwr now stands, which was built on the site of old ruins in the early part of this century. Glyndwr's foundations measure about 32 feet by 11 feet.

Unorthodox though the method of obtaining these measurements may be, it does show us that a Stage II mill was quite a small structure and in its simplest form probably consisted of one room 12-15 feet square. This predecessor of Felin Lyn would be of one storey construction and may have been made of wood or stone or a combination of both. The roof would have been of thatch or turves, for slates were not common in Denbighshire until the first half of the nineteenth century.

The waterwheel was probably placed on the unencumbered or east wall of the building, as repeated in its successor. Another obliging confirmatory detail is that if the old tailrace was extended backwards in a straight line, it would hit the north-east corner of the medieval building, as anticipated.

All this suggests that the 200yd section of the headrace nearest Felin Lyn antedated this Stage III mill and was cut for the predecessor Stage II mill and solely used the waters of Nant Gwryd. This would mean it could be run on demand for much of six months of the year, but for the other six months it could be used only intermittently and in the height of the summer not at all. So much for the forerunner of Felin Lyn.

The mill of Chirk Castle, at the hamlet called Castlemill, was also a typical Stage II mill and somewhat similar to Dolywern, in that it was a long, low, stone building, or 'long house', containing a series of rooms which housed people, animals, fodder, and the mill-room. The grinding capacity of a Stage II mill is not precisely known, but it is possible it could have produced well-ground meal at the rate of between 100 and 170lbs per hour with a 3-foot diameter millstone.

The Stage III mill was a technical refinement of a Stage II mill and not a different concept, as was the case between Stage I and Stage II mills. It appeared between about 1725 and 1775, when all things mechanical in Europe were receiving surges of attention.

Its basic difference was that it had gearing which permitted two or more sets of millstones to be run concurrently or consecutively. A Stage II mill had only one pair of millstones, so the millwright had the choice of putting in hard stones to grind wheat or soft stones to grind coarse grains, such as oats and barley. In the uplands, the coarse grains dominated or excluded wheat and so almost all upland Stage II mills were fitted with a pair of soft stones. Such mills were called grist mills.

A Stage III mill had the decided advantage of grinding any type of grain and this soon affected the farmer's decision to grow some or more wheat and the housewife to bake her bread with wheat.

Inside a Stage III mill the stones themselves were usually of larger diameter (4 feet and more) and one pair of them was made of hard stones for wheat-milling and was usually imported from France. Another equally important innovation in these new mills was the installation of machinery to clean the grain before milling and to convert meal to flour. A Stage II mill merely ground grain to meal and any sifting was done elsewhere, at a house or farm in the country or in a bakery in a town. To emphasise their altered and improved functions, these Stage III mills called themselves 'Flour Mills', and this is how Felin Lyn was recorded on the large scale Ordnance Survey map.

Because of its better all-round efficiency, the Stage III mill was provided with more handling and storage space and the result was a two or three storey building. The bulk of these mills were built between 1750 and 1815, though a few were still being built as late as 1860. Felin Lyn is a most typical example of the style.

So we end this Section by repeating what was said at its beginning, that Felin Lyn was not 'old' but was a rural mill at the final stage of development of the corn grinding watermill.

Author's Recollections of Felin Lyn

From 1931 to 1939 I lived as a young boy at Brynhyfryd, a house one hundred yards up the Graig lane from Felin Lyn; consequently this mill lies buried deep in my subconscious. The following recollections are very marginal to the history of Felin Lyn and I am indulging myself by including them.

I attended Pontfadog Primary School from 1933 to 1936 and would pass Felin Lyn every day on my way to and from school, and there is no doubt that the ponderous and majestic movement of the waterwheel and the splash of water kindled this lifelong appreciation of water-driven machinery. My then teacher, Miss Sadie Parry, lived next to the Mill in the cottage 'Glandwr' for over 50 years till her death in 1979 aged 91.

I have no recollections of the interior of the Mill and it is highly likely that Mr Evans, the miller, kept all of us children out of the place because the unguarded transmission machinery was of great danger to a wandering child.

Curiously enough, other recollections relate to transport and show that the 'motor' was not the dominant local carrier prior to World War II. Two builders' men (firm of Phillips) came from Glynceiriog to do repairs to the structure of the Mill, and I can remember them bringing their equipment – tools, ladders, cement – on a two-wheeled hand cart. They obtained sharp sand from the river immediately below the nearby bridge.

Another memory, shared by a contemporary, is of the death of the miller, Ned Evans, in 1936. In those days two-wheeled horse drawn hearses were always used at funerals in the Ceiriog and were capable of negotiating lanes, sharp turns and steep hills. Contrary to custom, Mr Evans had asked that his own cart be used, drawn by his faithful old horse, 'Flower'. Respecting his wishes, the mill cart was washed and cleaned and this carried the coffin from Felin Lyn to the Baptist chapel graveyard at Glynceiriog. As was also the custom, the coffin was made by a local joiner, Daniel Edwards, at Herber, which is on the way to Chirk.

Then came a dormant period, presumably after the death of Mr Evans. In 1939, at the beginning of World War II, my parents moved to Hereford and my direct contact with Felin Lyn ceased. However the Mill must have made a lasting impression on me for the following event to have occurred.

I visited the Ceiriog in the summer of 1942, aged 14, and took some photos of my old home and two photos of Felin Lyn, which by some miracle of preservation I still have. One of the photos shows the front of the Mill and appears in this book, whilst the other is of the intact waterwheel but is of too poor a quality to be reproduced.

Those readers who lived at the time of World War II will appreciate the significance of this photo taking. At that time the war had been running for three years and it was not possible to buy rolls of film, cameras were forbidden in parts of Britain, and everywhere else taking snaps of anything but the most innocuous subject was frowned upon or not permitted. This meant I had hoarded a roll of film for some time and had deliberately planned to use one or two shots on the Mill. It obviously had some kind of priority and affection at that time.

There is little else to tell. The weir, breached in 1941, became an obstruction to water flow and the River Dee & Clwyd Catchment Board requested my father, as the owner, to remove it. A photo taken in May 1942 by my father shows the weir had given way at its west bank, leaving the bulk of the structure intact. I remember travelling with him to visit the weir at Dolywern, in 1943, and there we met a representative of Wragg Sawmills of Hereford who was anxious to purchase the large oak sills (say 10 inches × 10 inches and 20 feet long), so scarce was large timber at that stage of the war. The late Mitford Abraham's notes pinpoint the date of the final destruction of the weir as October 1943.

My next visit, to step inside Felin Lyn itself, was in 1977 whilst on vacation in Britain. Here I found the Mill abandoned and slowly disintegrating; a sad sight for one who knew it when it was still at work. It was at this time that the idea came to me to attempt to record its history, but it was not until 1980 that I bestirred myself to do so. I contemplated ten pages at the most and never realised it would involve many years of work. I was again inside the Mill in May 1981 but it never occurred to me that it had but a few months to stand, for in September of that year it was demolished with good reason and without warning.

As to compiling this book, my experience (which is now of 17 years duration) is probably typical of those many hundreds of people who are inspired to write a book, produce a manuscript, but never see it published. I started in 1980 with no clear idea of where I was going in a writing sense and it took six to eight years to complete the essence of what you are reading here. Then another two years was spent in a fruitless long range quest to find a publisher, first in Wales and later elsewhere in Britain.

No publisher was interested and it became very clear that I possessed a quite unrealistic ambition and had an unmarketable manuscript on my hands. Then suddenly there appeared a general publisher, on the verge of retirement, who was also a lifelong milling enthusiast. He occasionally published mill literature as his contribution to the cause and agreed to publish my work. Sadly he died of cancer in 1990 when the text had just been set to type and the project came to naught. There was no money to proceed and the typesetter has never been located, so making the galleys worthless.

Another attempt was made to interest publishers in the university and institutional field but with no more success than that encountered in the private sector in the 1980s. Again the manuscript, this time a set of galley proofs, was consigned to a bottom drawer. It has finally seen the light of day as a private publishing venture with a print run of 1,000 copies. In truth, no commercial publisher can afford to print such a title with such a short run and make a profit. The whole process is daunting!

Books written about a single building are scarce and are invariably limited to palaces, cathedrals and other majestic structures. It is understandable why publishers would balk at producing a book on a nondescript mill but I have developed a passion for this sliver of Welsh history and want to share it with others. That is how the book has reached your hands.

Country Beer

There is an ancient link between brewers and bakers, and therefore millers, because both trades use grains and then yeast for fermentation. In fact, the ancient Egyptians first made beer from fermented bread. This leads to the question of whether Felin Lyn, or for that matter any upland mill that possessed an oat kiln, assisted in any way with the making of country beer. Milling literature is strangely silent on the subject and Felin Lyn's few sources make no mention of it.

Beer is a generic term for an alcoholic drink that is obtained through the action of yeast on an infusion of malted cereals, the cereals being whatever is cheaply available in a region of the world, such as rice or maize. Beer has always been the staple alcoholic drink in Britain and for the last few centuries has been made from barley with a small amount of hops added as a flavouring agent.

The raw material of beer is malted barley. Malting is a process that artificially induces growth in the grain and then arrests it, and its purpose is to breed enzymes which in turn allow the starch in the cereal to be converted to sugars in the brewing stage. In the last century and before, the process took some 12-18 days depending upon seasonal outside temperatures and everything was done by hand; now the process is fully mechanised and the time cycle much reduced.

The barley was steeped in water for two days to start the germination process. The water was then drained away and the sodden barley was laid thinly over a slate or tile floor and turned at least once daily for 7-12 days. During this time the stem and rootlets thrust out of each barley-corn and were allowed to grow nearly as long as the kernel itself. At this point growth was stopped by placing the barley in a kiln to the depth of about 6" and here it was slowly dried for four days. The starting temperature was 90° and would eventually rise to about 120°F for light coloured beers and to about 140°F for the darker coloured ones. Higher temperatures were not tolerated as these killed the enzyme in the malt needed in the brewing.

After being allowed to cool, the malted barley was then bagged. Externally the malt looked little different from its original appearance for the grains were still intact, if a little wrinkled, but it had lost a quarter of its weight in the process. Making malt was considered a craft and was carried out by a maltster, who in the country probably worked at it only on a part-time basis.

The next operation after kilning was to lightly bruise the malt using 'soft' stones which allowed water to penetrate the starchy interior of the kernels but not to let them disintegrate.

It immediately strikes one that in the days of locally made beer and locally ground corn, in the uplands of Britain, a miller could readily supply two of the processes needed in the production of beer. He had an oat kiln that was never in continuous service and at any time he was fully capable of bruising grain; so why then could he not kiln barley malt in his oat kiln (that worked at similar temperatures) and subsequently bruise the finished product? If the local miller did not perform these tasks, then who did and with what equipment?

Only two references about the possible connection between upland mills and beer brewing are known to the author. The first reference comes from the booklet 'Drying Kilns' (Note 4.6). The authors say that on occasions a mill kiln might be used for malting and cases were known of malting floors attached to a mill, but were not necessarily physically adjacent to the kiln. The second reference refers to the bruising of malted barley and is given on page 51 of the book 'Scottish Country Miller, 1700-1900' (see

Bibliography). It is quoted in full:

"Before the tightening of the licensing laws, the ordinary country mills had been accustomed to grind small quantities of malt as casually as they ground oats or peas or bere (Scottish word for barley, also spelt *bear*). *Similarly, while home brewing was common, households often brought their malt to be ground at the mill where they bought their meal. In these circumstances malt had become by use and wont subject to tolls in the same way as other grains."*

One explanation for reticence on the subject may be because malt production was taxable until 1880 and so it was in the interest of the beer drinking countryman to say as little as possible about the whole matter. After 1880 an instrument was used in breweries to measure the alcoholic potential of the beer being made and tax was assessed on the beer itself, a system still in vogue today.

Beer, like corn milling, was a local country activity until the third quarter of the last century, when cheap and convenient rail transportation altered the whole supply complex in Britain. Prior to that time, beer was considered an extension of food; its raw materials were grown locally, and it was brewed and drunk locally. Its making was part of the kitchen duties and so it was usual for the women in cottage, house, farm and alehouse to brew the beer. This was certainly the situation in Dyffryn Ceiriog, as elsewhere in Britain, until about the 1880s, and then as with country corn milling an erosion set in, gentle at first and then dramatically quickening. (Note 5.17)

Local comment suggests home brewing died out during or just after World War I in Dyffryn Ceiriog due to labour shortages and the beginning of a different life style. Jane Edwards (1879-1967), wife of the last miller of Felin Lyn, traditionally brewed beer for the mill haymakers and did this till at least 1930; Gwladys, one of her daughters, had a childhood recollection of carrying this beer out to the workers in the field. Of the four local pubs, the last to brew its own beer was the one at Llwynmawr which ceased the practice in about 1930.

The erosion of countryside beer making was contemporaneous with that of country corn milling and home bread making, and was all part of a pattern. An efficient and pervasive railway system made it cheaper and time saving to create a product at some central point and then distribute it to consumers. Brewing clearly shows this trend; in 1870 there were 32,682 brewing licenses in Britain, in 1910 there were 5,164 and now there are 78 companies operating 131 large breweries. Today the nearest brewery to the Ceiriog is Wrexham Lager which was built, significantly, in 1882, and is now owned by Ind Coope.

With so little evidence available, what assessment can be made of Felin Lyn's role in the making of local beer? It is most likely it kilned and bruised malt for some or all of the pubs in the Parish, and sold malt to local households. This would have continued until the kiln at Felin Lyn was made inoperative in the period c.1873-80 but after that it probably made no contribution to local beer brewing. At one time there were six pubs or beer houses within the Parish of Glyn Traian and all but one of them were within a mile of Felin Lyn. There used to be a legal distinction between a pub and a beer-house but over time this has become blurred. To the east of the Mill there were the *Butcher's Arms* (Graig) and the *Swan* (Pontfadog) and to the west there were *Llwynmawr Inn, Queen's Head, Star* (halfway between Dolywern and Glyn) and a pub in the former hamlet of Pentre Cilgwyn. The precise name of this last pub was 'The Plough'. It had a tailor's shop attached to it, was renamed *The Plough & Needle*, and was closed before 1875. (Note 5.18)

The '*Queen's Head*' was so named because it opened in 1837, the year that Queen Victoria came to the throne. In 1909 it was converted into a small temperance hotel that had three additions made to it within the next ten years and eventually had 18 bedrooms; in 1961 it became a Cheshire Home.

Without a doubt, Felin Lyn had more than its fair share of malting work in the years c1850 to c1865 when it and Llwynmawr Inn were run by the same person, the youthful John Hughes, already mentioned in Chapter 3.

All the references in the last century in the district to malting converge on Dolywern. In the 1851 Census a 72-year-old 'farmer and maltster' lived there: all publicans had a dual livelihood and in the case of Dolywern it was as a maltster. John Hughes (Dol) says a malthouse was built at Dolywern in 1850 and is reputed still to stand, now as a garage. He also said that some time after 1836 his father and uncle went into a joint venture at Dolywern to water meadows, *grind malt* and churn milk using small waterwheels – each one for a different purpose. The final reference concerns the former cornmill at Dolywern, Glan-y-wern, which was converted to a maltings in the period 1855-80 and worked as such until about 1916.

Mr Patrick MacIver lived in the former millhouse as a

child in the 1920s and though malting had ceased by then he has knowledge of how the malting operation was carried out. He says: *"Barley was delivered by cart to the top floor of the mill and man-handled into a big hopper. From there it was put into shallow iron cisterns and steeped in water for three to four whole days. After steeping, it passed through a chute to the floor below for processing, until it reached the lowest floor for grinding. The milled malt was carted to the brewery of Llwynmawr Inn, nearly half a mile away, while the cornings were sold as fodder for the dairy cattle. After World War I the big breweries were able to convince their customers that brand names were important and the little breweries disappeared."*

Some time between 1861 (when Felin Lyn was not occupied by a miller) and 1867 (when it was run by Evan Evans), John Hughes ceased to be a tenant of Felin Lyn. This meant he had to look elsewhere for malting facilities, and it would be natural for him to consider the ailing or unused mill at Dolywern, Glan-y-wern, as a potential malthouse, since his wife's family owned the premises. Presumably it would have all the facilities he needed plus almost unfettered time availability, in contrast to the situation at Felin Lyn where he would have had to fit in his malting work with the daily schedule of a country mill.

It is likely that at about this time John Hughes may have considered expanding his brewing work by selling beer to other pubs which eventually led to their acquisition by him or his successors. The Golden Pheasant Hotel, the former Llwynmawr pub, carries two date plaques of 1755 and 1877 and the latter suggests when additions and improvements were made. In the 1881 census John Hughes is listed as *'Public House & Brewer (Master)'*, aged 55.

Reverting to Felin Lyn, the nagging question is what was its contribution in quantitative terms to local beer making prior to 1875? An 1871 report showed that Britain had one pub for every 204 head of population and on this basis the parish of Glyn Traian with 975 persons would have had a theoretical 'allocation' of $4^3/_4$ pubs and in actuality had more. The precise question is how much locally grown barley was put aside for malting?

Statistics for the second half of the nineteenth century show that the per capita consumption of beer per year in Britain ranged between 27 and 31 gallons. Even today it is about 24 gallons. The statistics meant that every man, women and child drank half a pint of beer every day, though in reality the men drank $1^1/_2$ to 2 pints, the women infrequently and the children not at all. A conservative approach will be taken and it will be assumed that beer drinking in rural Ceiriog was lighter than that found in the urban and industrialised parts of Britain, and stood at 25 gallons per capita per annum.

Felin Lyn's territory contained an average of 537 persons and when these are multiplied by 25 gallons, we conclude that 13,425 gallons of beer were drunk annually by this particular community. It does seem a lot of beer!

Working backwards we have to ask ourselves how many pounds of malt produced one gallon of beer, and here we encounter a problem analogous to making tea, which is also a process of infusion. Either one can add several teaspoonsful of tea to the pot at the beginning, getting strong tea with the first cups and weaker tea as the pot gets topped up with hot water, or there can be consistency of strength by making fresh pots using small amounts of tea for each pot.

The same approach was used by home brewers and the favoured method seems to have been to use considerable amounts of malt so that the first infusion produced a strong beer, the second a weaker beer and the third and final rinsing a 'small' beer. A typical country recipe had one bushel of barley malt (36lbs), flavoured with a $^1/_2$ lb of hops, producing 14-18 gallons of beer. This equated to 2-$2^1/_2$ lbs of malt and a half-ounce of hops producing one gallon of beer. Two pounds of malt equals $2^1/_2$ lbs of barley.

Multiplying 13,425 gallons by $2^1/_2$lb gives a requirement of 33,562lbs of barley (or 15 tons) per annum. If one favoured a slightly stronger malt infusion, the barley needed for malting could climb to 20 tons. These requirements represented close to a fifth of the annual barley harvest in the territory of Felin Lyn in the last century. This estimate of 20 tons was incorporated in the calculations used in Chapter 2 to determine the annual tonnage of cereals processed by Felin Lyn.

Before writing this section, the author was daunted by the task because there seemed to be not one fact or clue to work upon. He was forced to persist because malt bruised in a mill has to form a part of the tonnage processed annually and this latter figure was crucial to an understanding of what made Felin Lyn tick. Slowly a picture emerged and has now been told, and it is hoped others will be stimulated to make further investigation about malt processing at country mills and publish their findings on this very neglected aspect of milling. The quantity of barley malt processed by Felin Lyn, as calculated in the paragraphs above, can be considered only as tentative and needs corroboration from other, as yet unknown, sources.

Adapt or Die

Putting aside the sentimental aspects of watermilling, it was obvious by the end of the last century that the water-driven cornmill was an obsolescent machine in Britain. Even if the arrival of cheap imported corn had not ensured its demise, it would have seen drastic changes. The shift of population away from country to town, the steam engine as a prime mover, and the creation of an efficient rail transportation system, brought about a new type of milling industry. Large mills were built in towns, adjacent to railway tracks, with machinery driven by steam. No longer was siting and power dictated by the location of a river or stream. A local example of this abrupt change was the construction in Wrexham in 1865 of a steam driven cornmill connected to railway sidings.

The second half of the last century saw drastic changes and the impact came from the large ports of Britain which received the overseas grain. For Felin Lyn, for North Wales, and for the north-west of England, the new methods of processing and distributing both grain and its products grew with staggering speed. Storage facilities for imported grain were first built at Liverpool in 1868 and had a capacity of 30,000 tons. This had risen to 217,000 tons by 1905 and made Liverpool the largest grain storage site in Europe. At the turn of this century Liverpool had established itself as the centre of bulk wheat sales and buyers would come from all parts of Britain to make bids. Other neighbouring ports also created storage and milling facilities; Birkenhead with 30,000 tons, Manchester with 80,000 tons and Ellesmere Port with 20,000 tons. Truly stupendous amounts when compared with a country mill's annual processing of 200-300 tons of grain.

On the south side of the Mersey, between Birkenhead and Runcorn, was an 'instant' town of the early nineteenth century. It was called Ellesmere Port and had been built in 1805 by the owners of the Shropshire Union Canal as the trade connector between tidewater and their canal system. Ellesmere Port did indeed connect with the small country town of Ellesmere in northern Shropshire, which lay 10 miles east of Felin Lyn.

Two grain warehouses were in existence at Ellesmere Port in 1882 and in 1899 another, but six-storey, warehouse was built. In 1905-06 three large flour mills (presumably steam driven) and a large grain elevator were added to the grain handling complex.

Virtually all the grain supplied to these Ellesmere Port mills was imported and came from Canada, the USA, Australia, and the Argentine. It was delivered to the steam driven mill factories in barges of 80-100 ton capacity from Liverpool, Birkenhead or Manchester, and after milling the flour was distributed, in barrels holding 196lbs, by the canal system. Narrow boats of 20 ton capacity would convey the flour to Chester, the industrial Midlands, and the Welsh border country as far south as Newtown.

Not all the cereal cargo was in flour. The best local example of incoming imported grain occurred at Maesbury in Shropshire, three miles south of Oswestry and nine miles south-east of Felin Lyn. Located at Maesbury was (and is) Peates Mill which has an interesting history of development. It was built in 1846 as a conventional corn watermill on the site of a former malt kiln but was dramatically modernised in 1890 when water power gave way to steam power and steel rollers replaced the millstones. From this date, or before, Peates Mill received its grain and coal fuel by canal, having a 200yd arm dug out to connect it with the Shropshire Union Canal. The bulk of the grain that it milled was imported wheat from Ellesmere Port and was sold locally, much of it in the neighbouring town of Oswestry. Even the miller of Felin Lyn occasionally purchased wheaten flour from Peates Mill after World War I.

At Ellesmere Port the loose grain was bagged in 2cwt. sacks (about $3^1/_2$ bushels) and loaded in a canal narrow boat for the 61-mile and circuitous journey to Maesbury, which involved the negotiation of 41 locks. At Maesbury Mill the sacks were hoisted out of the narrow boat and emptied into bulk storage, which by 1912 could hold 700 tons. The boats took a week to load, unload, and do the round trip of some 120 miles, which was a very good performance. A boat carried 20 tons of grain on each trip and the weekly fleet delivery was about 200 tons.

This water-borne grain supply system between Ellesmere Port and Maesbury started late in the last century and was carried by the Shropshire Union Canal Company in its own boats until 1921, when the Company gave up the carriage of goods as being uneconomic. Peates Mill decided to become its own carrier by purchasing eleven of the Company's narrow boats and worked them as grain carriers until 1932 when the method was abandoned because of poor upkeep of the canal – by now owned by the London, Midland and Scottish Railway. (Note 5.19)

In 1933 further modernisation took place at Peates Mill. Electricity replaced steam as the prime mover, storage capacity for grain was increased by 30,000 bushels, and five steam lorries replaced the canal boats; these steam lorries ran direct to grain silos at Birkenhead.

Peates Mill at Maesbury is still very much in business as corn merchants under the name A.&A. Peate Ltd and is still run by the Peate family. It handles about 150 tons of grain weekly, some of it acquired from a radius of 40 miles around the mill but the bulk is imported from Canada via the Mersey.

This is an interesting and rare example of a conventional water-driven cornmill, deep in the heart of the country, that has maintained its original purpose by switching to successive contemporary technologies of the trade. Aggressive management through the decades has ensured it is still in the business when all its neighbouring brothers and sisters, who clung to water power, have perished.

Modern Lifeless Bread

The new era of late Victorian milling did two things to wheat processing that had not been done in the preceding milling history of the world.

A succession of high speed steel rollers, powered first by steam and later by electricity, reduced the grain to a fine flour of a consistent quality. All traces of the bran, the outer skin of the kernel, were removed to ensure that the flour was white. Then the inner seed that produced a new plant, the germ, was also removed. This was done because the germ contained fat and when this was released into the flour, it turned the flour rancid after about two months. The germ also attracted rodents and insects who knew instinctively where the goodness lay. Naturally, this could not be tolerated under the newly emerging systems of a semi-standardised product and an elaborate distribution system involving factory mills, bakeries, grocery shops and housewives.

The very word 'flour' derives from the English 'flower' and the French 'fleur' and originally carried the connotation 'best of something', in this context the best of the meal. Under modern technology and merchandising white wheaten flour became the worst part of the cereal.

As a consequence of this refining all the nutritionally better parts of the wheat berry were removed and much of it given to animals, whilst the chalky, lifeless, residue was carefully preserved for the humans. This situation has now existed for close to a century in Britain and other highly industrialised countries, such as the United States.

The gross nutritional deficiencies of highly refined white wheaten flour were suspect and even pinpointed by a handful of people in the early nineteenth century but have never achieved widespread understanding to this day. A Frenchman carried out experiments and had this to say in the British medical journal, the Lancet of March 11th 1826: *"A dog, fed on fine white bread and water, both at discretion, does not live beyond the 50th day. A dog, fed on the coarse bread of the military, lives and keeps his health."*

Unfortunately for us all, the existence of vitamins was not known to the scientific world until just prior to World War I, and was not common knowledge until World War II. Vitamins are minute substances in food which are required to maintain normal health, and their absence can cause body imbalance and, in extremes, such diseases as rickets and scurvy.

In grains, the vitamins are contained in the skin (bran) and in the germ, and both of these parts were deliberately removed in the new milling process!

For nearly half a century vitamins have been put back as an additive but not quite in the composition that nature supplied. In the phraseology of the present-day milling industry this is known as 'enriched' flour but it should be more accurately called ' partial vitamin replacement' flour. Various exotic chemicals are now added routinely to flour, most of them to facilitate manufacture of bread rather than to extend shelf life.

At the turn of the century, the milling industry discovered that oxidising the flour, which improves its quality, could be instantly achieved by bleaching it with chlorine gas. This was very simply done by blowing small quantities of the gas into the chute that delivered the flour into sacks at the big milling factories. Bleaching by agents of chlorine continues to this day. A sad episode involving this chemical process occurred at Cobden Mills (a highly mechanised steel roller mill), Wrexham, in about 1923. The eleven-year-old son of the mill manager was in the plant one day and was killed by an escape of chlorine which he had accidentally discharged whilst playing with equipment.

Specialised museums are now plentiful in the world so it comes as no surprise to learn of a Bread Museum and Archives in Ulm, Germany, founded privately in 1955. This museum has some very unflattering things to say about modern white bread, calling it 'white death' and counter-productive to the digestive system and therefore unfit to eat.

The elimination of Felin Lyn and all the other stone mills in Britain was inevitable in the relentless march of civilisation, but it was a dietary aberration of a dimension which common man is only just beginning to comprehend. (Note 5.20)

However all is not lost. On the contrary, the awakening interest by the general public of industrialised countries about the effects of over-eating has caused a related interest in physical exercise and nutrition. The public's growing awareness about the need for good nutrition has in turn drawn attention to the emptiness of modern mass-produced bread, the 'staff-of-life' that has been emasculated. Momentum is developing to revert to the wholemeal loaf where nothing has been added or subtracted.

It may be unrealistic to attempt to turn the clock back by suggesting we all eat freshly-baked wholemeal bread, but consumers do have power if they act in concert. If buyers of wrapped bread examined their purchase before buying it and found it wanting in nutritional terms, all they have to do is to replace it on the shelf. Nowadays there are no end of nutritional alternatives and a major decline in sales of the wayward bread manufacturers would eventually force them nutritionally to upgrade their product.

Concluding on an optimistic note, if the present trend – set in the last 10-20 years – continues and strengthens, we shall all be eating noticeably better quality bread by the year 2000.

Melin Wynt (Windmill)

There is a suggestion that a windmill once worked on one of the hilltops in the Parish of Glyn Traian. It is in no way connected with the history of Felin Lyn but its possible existence was unearthed whilst writing this book and is so unexpected as to warrant mention.

It all started in an unlikely quarter – Welsh poetry. Dyffryn Ceiriog has produced its fair share of Welsh poets and two of them are known throughout Wales and beyond. They are Huw Morus (1622-1709) and John Hughes (1832-1887). The latter is better known in Wales by his bardic name 'Ceiriog' and is sometimes referred to as the Robbie Burns of Wales. All their works were naturally written in Welsh but have been subsequently translated and published in English.

When the draft of this history was being finalised, the author asked his friend, Dewi Jones of Llwynmawr, if he could find an appropriate few lines to be used as dedicatory verse at the front of the book, with the proviso that they had some reference to milling and were written by one of the Ceiriog poets. Dewi searched his two volumes of Morus and three volumes of Hughes and to his surprise found only one milling reference in all the poetry, but it was richly rewarding.

It was in a poem written by John Hughes with the title 'Pan na bo dwr bydd gwynt' or 'When there's no water there's wind'. The poem has three verses and the first verse is the most informative; it goes:

Roedd melin ddwr a melin wynt,	*A watermill and a windmill*
Yn malu yd y glyn;	*Ground the corn of the vale;*
Ar fin y mynydd safai un,	*One stood on the edge of the hill,*
A'r llall ar fin y llyn:	*And the other on the water's edge:*
Ac un melinydd oedd i'r ddwy	*One man was miller for both mills,*
'Nôl dull y bobol gynt;	*As in the days of old;*
A'r rheswm ydoedd, meddynt hwy –	*And the reason was, or so they say –*
Pan na bo dwr bydd gwynt.	*When there's no water there's wind.*

Callously stripping the poetry of its imagery to get at the hard facts, we have: two mills with one miller; situated in the 'glyn' (in this context defined as Ceiriog land between Offa's Dyke and Glynceiriog); windmill sited on edge of hill and used when the water supply poor.

Windmills are not usually associated with Wales for obvious reasons but some did exist and to date about 200 sites have been recorded. Most of them were sited along the coast line from Flintshire to Monmouthshire, with the greatest concentration on the Isle of Anglesey and almost all of them were within 15 miles of the sea. The nearest known windmill to Llwynmawr was eight miles to the north-east at Rhosllanerchrugg, which is three miles south of Wrexham. It is shown on a large scale estate map of the 'Honourable Frederick West', dated 1826, so presumably was still working at that date. An early type tram or plate-way passes within 200 yards of the windmill and is a sign of encroaching industry. If indeed there was a windmill on the hilltop south of Llwynmawr, then both it and the one at Rhosllanerchrugg were built by the same owner, Chirk Castle Estates.

No positive evidence, such as a Welsh field name incorporating the word 'windmill' or finding a stone circular foundation, has surfaced to support the idea of the existence of the windmill. At this stage it must be regarded as a pleasing story, but there are several facets that make it plausible, even probable.

W.H. Davies in his 1941 survey of Ceiriog watermills listed a mill that once existed close to a farm called Bryn Bugeilyn (hill of the little shepherd) which lay nearly two miles south-west of Felin Lyn. This farm was deserted some time after World War I and was torn down about 1947. It stood on the brow of the southern flank hills of Dyffryn Ceiriog at an altitude of 1,300 feet, looking northwards into the valley. Behind it to the south, the land flattens out and the local summit is reached 600 yards away at 1,470 feet. The prevailing wind comes from the south-west in winter and the west in summer and the lie and slope of the land make for a most satisfactory windmill site some 300 yards west of former Bryn Bugeilyn.

The old farm was incapable of using any water-powered device since the source of Nant Iorwerth (Edward's stream) lay close by; this $1^1/_2$ mile tributary of the Afon Ceiriog joined the mother stream at Dolywern after falling 850 feet. Davies could not take it upon himself to call the Bryn Bugeilyn site a windmill since the notion seemed so absurd. In effect, he lists it as a mill without a water supply. In 1983, Dewi Jones, who lives a mile from the supposed site, also mentioned that the place was traditionally associated with a mill.

After the discovery of the windmill poem, Dewi Jones visited the site of the old farm, Bryn Bugeilyn, and came across small pieces of kiln tile and the foundations of a detached kiln measuring 12 feet square. In earlier centuries oat kilns were built at the side of fields or at farms and it was a later development to have them built attached to a cornmill. For example, the author's earliest traceable forebears lived in the early 1700s at 'Tyn-yr-odyn' (cottage of the kiln) which was a field site on the edge of the Denbighshire moors at 1,000 feet altitude and at least a mile distant from a watermill.

Either this kiln at Bryn Bugeilyn was a localised kiln attached to a farm, which makes it something of a rarity in the parish, or it was the kiln for the windmill if the latter existed. Whatever the case, it shows oats were grown in the vicinity at an altitude of between 1,200 feet and 1,400 feet. A windmill would have well suited the farmers of the Ceiriog uplands for they would not have to descend and ascend the steepish slopes to a watermill, with heavy sacks of grain downhill and equally heavy sacks of meal on the upward return. Though these flatish hilltops are now largely given over to pasture, until quite recent years they carried their fair share of cereal crops because the valley bottom land was used for hay and better class grazing.

The review of water flows of the Afon Ceiriog was discussed in Chapter 1 and showed that river levels were low in July, August and September, sometimes embarrassingly low for a watermill. Since several of the medieval or Stage II mills were placed on tributaries of, rather than on, the Afon Ceiriog itself, the problem of water supply in the summer would become all the more accentuated. To build a simple windmill for summer use seems to be a realistic solution to a vexing yearly problem.

If one cautiously accepts that there might have been a windmill in the vicinity of Bryn Bugeilyn, then where was its related watermill? Both were worked by the same miller, so the assumption has to be that the watermill was one of those closest to the windmill. The most likely candidate is the vaguely-known Felin Isaf at Dolywern which stood beside or close to the river site that was subsequently occupied by Felin Lyn's weir; this mill had disappeared by 1800.

A faint echo about the possible existence of this unrecorded weir has come across two centuries and by miraculous chance was 'picked up' by the author himself: In the 1980s he was sorting through some family papers and came across a note written in 1948 by his grandfather (owner of Felin Lyn & weir, 1905-31). What it said was of no consequence to this story but the reverse of the sheet was pertinent. During World War II and the immediate after-years, writing paper was scarce and his grandfather had taken to using the blank sides of sheets of old business letters.

The note he wrote was on the torn half of a carbon copy typed letter and was the upper half of a second page, lacking name of sender, recipient, and date. It is deduced it was written sometime in the 1920s by a solicitor, acting on behalf of the author's grandfather, and was addressed to a landlord or tenant who farmed land adjacent to Felin Lyn's weir, in the vicinity of Llwynmawr. The surviving fragment reads: '*...breach of the peace which your attitude and action threaten to bring about. It appears from your* *letter that the root of the trouble is a misapprehension on your part as to the legal position. It is quite incorrect to treat the weir as if there were or had been* *two* *weirs* (author's emphasis). *There was and is in fact but one weir.'*

One can speculate that the forebears of this irate farmer had certain rights emanating from the pre-1800 weir and related gristmill which somehow disappeared following the building of Felin Lyn's weir – which perhaps used the foundations or site of the older weir. In trying to reassert these rights more than a century later it was inevitable that a clash would occur.

There is a territorial link between Bryn Bugeilyn and this unknown Felin Isaf, in the form of Nant Iorwerth which joins the Afon Ceiriog close by the former weir of Felin Lyn. There is a footpath and lane system on either bank of the Iorwerth of $1^1/_2$ mile length, which could have connected the twinned mills, though it involves a strenuous climb or descent of 850 feet; an interesting feature of this connecting route is that all but a quarter-mile of it runs in an almost straight line.

An attempt should now be made to assess when this alleged windmill was in existence. Working backwards, Hughes must have composed the poem sometime in the mid-nineteenth century, basing it upon a handed-down remembrance. Memory appears to linger in a locality for close to a hundred years – at least that is this author's experience with the history involved in this book. So this takes us back to about 1750. When Felin Lyn was built in the second half of the eighteenth century, it made obsolete any of the older mills in the vicinity which would have included these 'maybe' twinned mills. This suggests the theoretical windmill was in operation prior to about 1775 and could have been much older.

A Welsh windmill of this period usually had a circular stone tower of 15-20 feet diameter and two-storey height. Inside, the machinery would have been that of a Stage II mill consisting of lantern gear transmission and a single pair of millstones of about 3 feet diameter. The monolith stones were only capable of grinding coarse grains (oats, barley, rye) to an indifferent quality of meal. There would be no devices to dress the meal in any way, such as removing the bran or sifting for flour.

A precise location for this possible windmill may never be determined but it it possible that "Ancient Monuments of Denbighshire" provides a lead. In 1850 a tumulus containing a funeral urn was excavated close to Bryn Bugeilyn farm and is listed as Item 188 in the inventory. Item 189 reads: *"Bryn Bugeilyn Fach: 270yds south-west of previous item. Site marked by several large stones embedded in soil and on which have been gathered heaps of smaller stones; visited 1911."* It was quite normal to take building stone from a disused or abandoned building instead of having to hew afresh in a quarry, so this could explain why nothing survives today.

The practice of linking water and wind mills is not as rare as one may think, with examples occurring in Anglesey, the rest of the British Isles, Europe and the eastern United States. There are at least twenty known cases in England. The twinning could take the form of having two mills within a mile of each other as illustrated above or a greater sophistication where there was a single structure housing a watermill and a windmill. The nearest example of the latter type to Llwynmawr was at Hornsmill, ten miles north-east of Chester in Cheshire; this mill is now in a decayed state.

Probably the best known example of the former type of twinning is connected with the famous English painter, Constable. His father owned watermills at Flatford and Dedham and windmills on the adjacent hills at East Bergholt, in Essex.

The first issue of the Journal of the Welsh Mills Society (*Melin, No.1, 1985*) provided an interesting example of where a windmiller lacked wind and went in search of a watermill. This was in Montgomeryshire, 16 miles south of Felin Lyn. The reference states *"a miller who in 1798 had a windmill near Welshpool and for want of wind took corn to grind at Evan's watermill at Pool Quay."* The mill has been identified as Trelydan, two miles north of Welshpool near Guilsfield, and two miles distant from Pool Quay. (Note 5.21)

The investigation required for this section highlighted the not too obvious fact that mountainous Wales with a most adequate annual rainfall has problems with water supply in the high summer, creating embarrassing periods for the watermiller. Short, terse references that had previously gone unremarked now leapt out of the page. Here are some specific Welsh examples: *"There were periods when the Clywedog dwindled to a trickle"; "A Foden steam engine was installed about 1890 for summer work"; "In September the pond had such low water only* $1^1/_2$ *hours milling was done each day"; "the trickle of meal falling into the bin matched the trickle of water falling on the wheel outside"; "In 1852 during a prolonged drought the mill stopped for 6 weeks"; "The chimney beside the mill was for the auxiliary steam engine, used in the summer";* and finally, *"A holding pond was built higher up to help overcome the low summer water".*

Reverting to the subject of these paragraphs, it will be interesting to see if adequate proof ever comes forward to substantiate the folk-memory concept that a windmill might once have stood on a hilltop in the parish of Glyn Traian, Dyffryn Ceiriog, Denbighshire. Even if it does not, it makes for a delightful piece of speculation.

The Canadian Connection

This is included because this book was composed in Canada, and the author and his wife lived in Vancouver, the third largest city in Canada and the largest in the Province of British Columbia, for some 15 years. It does not directly involve Felin Lyn but comes to within yards of it where land stewardship is concerned.

One day in the 1960s the author was browsing in a Vancouver second-hand book shop and came across a rare volume titled "*History of Oswestry*", a 360-page history of a Shropshire town published in 1920. Because Oswestry was the nearest market town to his childhood home and was visited by his family each week, the book became the author's for the proverbial song.

The author was naturally curious as to why such a title would end up in Vancouver. On the inside of the cover of the book was a personalised and highly decorative book-plate which included a spreading tree, stooked grain in a field, a rising sun, the Welsh motto 'Bydd Ffyddlon' (Be Faithful), and the owner's name 'Elizabeth Rogers'.

The name Rogers is quite well known in Vancouver for there are a sugar refinery, downtown office block, and a neighbourhood park, linked to that name. At the time, the author presumed the book had come from an estate sale of this family and after that gave it no more thought.

The story moves forward twenty years to 1986 when the history of Felin Lyn was in first draft manuscript form. Dewi Jones, local historian, who lives in Llwynmawr and not a mile from the now demolished Mill, had sent the author some information about grain markets at Oswestry including quotes from the book "Oswestry". After thanking him for the information, *"I told him I also had a copy of the book and explained how it came into my possession."* Dewi responded saying it must have a connection with the locally famous Rogers of Plas-onn, in the Gwryd, who emigrated to Vancouver in the second half of the last century and made a fortune.

In the Appendices there is a list of dwellings in the territory of Felin Lyn and amongst them is the 60-acre farm of Plas-onn. This development took the author by surprise because for years this small area of land had been put under a microscope and he thought he knew all the salient matters but this aspect had clearly escaped him. Though it in no way advances the story of Felin Lyn, it did and does make the author wonder if he has more than one blind spot that all writers are supposed to have. What was this connection between the Rogers of Plas-onn and the Rogers of Vancouver? The City of Vancouver Archives quickly supplied the linking details.

In 1864 a second son was born to the Rogers at Plas-onn and was named Jonathan; at that time six generations of Rogers had farmed the land there. Young Jonathan, like all his predecessors, grew up speaking Welsh and it was not until he was 16 that he started to acquire some English. At this time he emigrated to Liverpool and lived with an aunt there for seven years, getting involved in the business of rent collecting, tenant house repairs, and perfecting his English.

Living in a bustling seaport, the wanderlust gripped Jonathan and carried him across the Atlantic to Canada in 1887 aged 23. He landed at Montreal and by chance the very first train to cross continental Canada was about to make its inaugural run. He hopped aboard and in great comfort and in a few days he found himself on the shores of the Pacific Ocean at a tiny shanty settlement of about 2,000 people, recently named *Vancouver*. Two weeks after he arrived, Jonathan attended a public auction where parcels of land within the new city were being sold. He purchased four lots in the dense and tall forest and only with difficulty did he reach and locate them later. These 1887 purchases of his now lie in the very heart of downtown Vancouver, a city of one and a half million people.

This emigration interlude has all the hallmarks of 'young man has lucky break' but closer scrutiny shows this not to be the case. The six-day journey on the brand new Canadian Pacific Railway was very expensive, land purchase is never cheap, and the timing was excellent. It is believed his aunt had died leaving him a tidy legacy and he astutely decided to invest it half way round the world. At this time British Columbia was one of the last totally undeveloped areas of North America.

The problem with Jonathan's purchase was that it had potential but he needed to exploit it immediately and neither he nor anyone else had the money, organisation, and equipment, to make anything of it. There followed a depression for ten years, as if the building of the trans-continental railway had exhausted all enterprise. Many land buyers sold out at a loss and moved on, but Jonathan was obstinate and had much faith in the fledgling city. He hung on, gained a precarious foothold in the small community, created a tool and paint shop, and by 1895 had set himself up as a contractor and builder. From then on his rise was swift and he became involved in all kinds of construction work which included manufacturing plants, offices, hotels, banks, and even an electricity generating station. As a result he became a very wealthy man.

One of Rogers' enterprises was the building of a ten-storey office block in 1911 at 470 Granville Street, which was and still is a prestigious location in the heart of Vancouver; to this day it is still called the Rogers Building. In one of its offices an urban encyclopedia of Greater Vancouver, of 900 pages, was assembled and published in 1996. Within this source book is a listing of 500 Vancouver citizens who achieved prominence between 1886 (founding year) and 1994. Each entry contains a photograph and a fifty word biography and amongst these élite is Jonathan Rogers!

Rogers ended that part of his life as an active private entrepreneur during World War I and thereafter became a public figure and benefactor, helping to nurture Vancouver in a variety of ways. He held elected, public, and honourary offices in a diversified group of activities and amongst all of these, his 26 years on the Parks Board was probably his prime interest.

When Jonathan Rogers died in 1945 he was certainly a millionaire (in dollars) and he left a quarter of a million dollars to various deserving causes in Vancouver. It is significant that the largest single bequest ($100,000) was given to the City to create a neighbourhood park in a poorer part of the city which was then without such a facility. Because of delays in property acquisition it was not opened until 1958 and is called Jonathan Rogers Park in his memory. Obviously this son of the Gwryd and the Ceiriog was quite an exceptional man. (Notes 5.22 & 23.)

In 1902 Jonathan married a girl called Elizabeth who hailed from Gobowen, which lies three miles north of Oswestry. This now explains who Elizabeth Rogers was and why she owned the book the author now possesses. They lived in a large, elegant, house in what was then the best residential area of Vancouver close to Stanley Park. They named it 'Argoed' which in Welsh means 'beside the wood'; aptly called because Stanley Park is created out of the virgin forest that once covered all the land now occupied by the City of Vancouver.

Jonathan Rogers had an understanding of watermills. Though he and his family lived in the territory of Felin Lyn, they did not use it. They lived at the crest of the Gwryd side-valley and the way to and from Felin Lyn presented nothing but steep lanes, so they took their milling business to Selattyn, three miles to the east, along roads with more favourable – but still formidable – gradients. As a boy he would certainly have known about

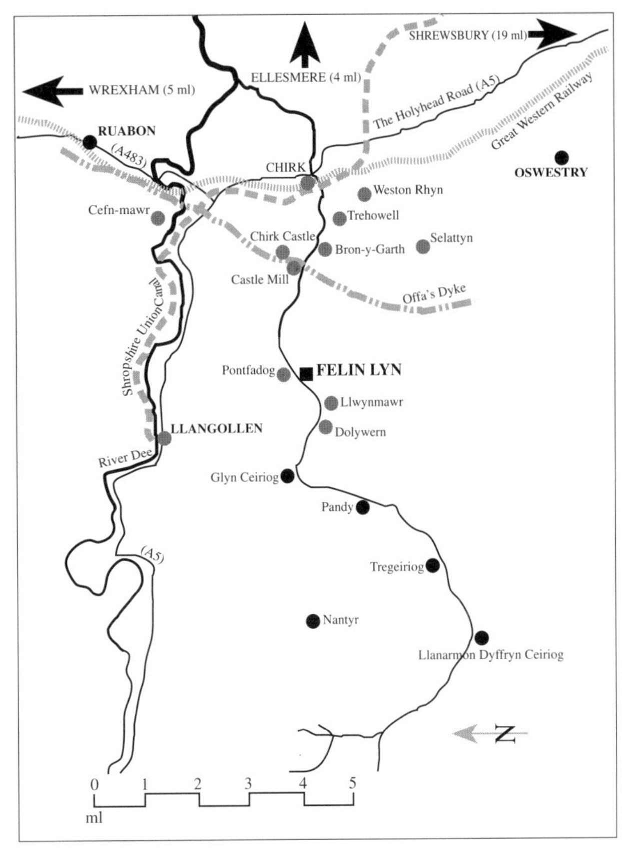

G Nash

Felin Lyn and may have had occasion to visit it. Rogers came from a family of nine children and one of his brothers was the miller of Morda, a village 1½ miles south of Oswestry and it is certain Jonathan visited him there in mid-life. The Rogers family continues to live in the parish of Glyn Traian for one of Jonathan's great nephews currently farms Llangwryd Uchaf and Llangwryd Isaf, living in the latter's farmhouse. These farms, now amalgamated, were the lands closest to Felin Lyn when it still existed.

There is a postscript to this 'Canadian Connection', unrelated to the Rogers family but related to Felin Lyn. The last people to live at Felin Lyn were Bertie and Hilda Jeffreys and their five children during the ten years 1952-1962. One of these children, Stan, married and with a family, emigrated to Canada in 1982 and now lives in the north-western part of the Province of Alberta. It is he who holds the only artistic drawing of Felin Lyn ever made, sketched by the grand-daughter of Ned-y-Felin in the 1950s and given by her to Mrs Hilda Jeffreys as a token of appreciation. So ends the Canadian connection.

NOTES

5.1 **Paper:** *"Lindow Man: The Body in the Bog"*, by Stead, Bourke, & Brothwell, London. Trustees of the British Museum, 1987, 14 relevant pp. See Section 1 re Discovery and Section 26 on Stomach Content.

5.2 **Book:** *"National Trust Book of the Farm"*, Darley, Gillian. National Trust, 1981 256pp. See p.234 in section "Wales"; also 'Barns, Granaries' on pp71-83.

5.3 **List of Farms in the Nantgwryd Township, Parish of Glyn Traian at Census, 1851.** The Census did not ask for acreage sizes but someone added this most useful information to the entries at a later date. Column headings: * = no longer occupied in 1980; T.H. = Total Household; Child = under 13 years; Serv't. = Servants, outdoor to left of oblique and indoor to right.

Dwelling	Surname	T.H.	Child	Serv't	Acres
Llangwryd Farm (A)	Davies	7	1	-	65(40)
Tynygraig (A)	Parry	11	5	1/1	70(40)
Graig Wen (B)	Jones	4	1	-/1	25
Cilnant	Edwards	9	3	2/1	60
Ty Mawr	Turner	6	1	-	49
Ty Draw	Edwards	4	2	-	49
Briwnant	Jones	3	-	-/1	55
Betsi'r y' Nant *	Jones	1	-		
Nant	Jones	7	4	-	-
(indecipherable)*	Roberts	1			7
Graig Pickan (?)*	Jones	2	-	-/1	17
Plas-onn	Rogers	7	1	2/-	60
Caemor (C)	Jones	11	4	3/2	110
Tynygors*	Rogers	5	3	-	1
		78	25	8/7	over 600 acres

Note A – Additional acres shown as if separate hill pastures
Note B – One of household is wheelwright; at Llwynmawr ?
Note C – Household head is widow of 38; dressmaker lodger of 18.

Modern names of dwellings are: 1: Llangwryd-isaf; 5: Nantgwryd-uchaf; 6: Craig yr oryn.

5.4 **Tithe Commutation Act, 1836.** Converted payments of 'kind' into money, with theoretical concept that every field could produce corn. Commissioners used throughout England & Wales a conversion formula of wheat at 7s. 0-1/4d per bushel, barley at 3s.11 $^{1}/_{2}$d per bushel, & oats at 2s. 9d per bushel. London did not have tithes but was levied a rate which was 13.75% of the rental value of property. Tithes were paid half yearly before and after the above Act. In 1891 tithe payments shifted from occupier to landlord and the latter increased rents to cover the new obligations.

5.5 **Ancient System of Ploughing Used by the Welsh.** Ploughing in ancient Wales was a co-operative affair with farmers sharing their oxen and heavy ploughs, using always an eight or more oxen team to make the plough go deep. Ploughing was done in multiples of an acre, which in Welsh is called 'erw'. Ancient Welsh laws fixed the width of an 'erw' to be twice the length of the double ox yoke, and its length was roughly the same as a Saxon acre which was a furrow-long or furlong. In time it was standardised into the British acre which is 220yds long and 22yds wide.

5.6 **Famine and Food for Thought.** Described in dictionaries as 'extreme scarcity of food; starvation'. Usually brought about by drought, but can be caused by insects, plant diseases, and excessive rainfall. Wales has been subjected to occasional famines through the centuries but fortunately they are rare and are usually caused by excessive rain. Russian peasants in the past centuries and the beginning of this one regularly made 'famine bread' or golodnyi khleb. It was usually made from hardy weeds, such as goosefoot, and was mixed with dwindling handfuls of rye meal. At best it was indigestible roughage and at worst it was dangerous to the human system. It had a mouldy smell, and a bitter, sour, taste. It induced diarrhoea, vomiting, and a variety of more serious gastrointestinal disorders; it also produced serious protein deficiency. We take bread and other cereal foods so much for granted that it is worth a moment's reflection to see what would happen to us if the supply was suddenly cut off.

Most recent famine in the British Isles, of catastrophic proportions, occurred in Ireland in 1845-48 when potato crops became diseased. Irish then lived on potatoes, not grain. About one million died, a tenth from actual starvation and the remainder from disease in frail bodies; 'mainland' population hardly aware of the convulsion.

5.7 **Harvesting.** A wistful evocative description of harvesting in this part of Wales is given on p.105 of the book *"Northern Marches"*, London, Hughes Cledwyn, Robert Hale, Ltd 1953.

5.8 **Some Cereal Farming Statistics of 1920s in area adjacent to Felin Lyn.** (Randomly chosen, not a true sampling)

Farm in 1920s	Total acres	Cereal acres	Land altitudes	Acres planted annually Oats	Barley	Wheat
Caemor	160	30 (19%)	900ft & 1100ft	23	7	–
Bonc* (A)	100	10 (10%)	600ft & 1100ft	5	2	3
Llwyn-mawr*	97	16 (16%)	500ft & 1200ft	8	5	3
Brithdir*	90	10 (11%)	800ft & 1200ft	10	–	–
Plas-onn (B)	62	15 (24%)	1000ft only	8	5	2
Briwnant	48	5 (10%)	700ft only	5	–	–
Pwll-hir (C)	32	2.5 (8%)	1100ft only	2.5	–	–
				As percentages of total cereals grown		
Averages	84	12 (14%)		70%	20%	10%

NOTES: • Close to, but outside the Gwryd. 'A' and 'B' known also to have grown 3 acres, and 1.5 acres to 2 acres, of roots, respectively. 'C' Most of farm was rough pasture.

5.9 **Book:** *"History of Oswestry"*. Watkin, Isaac. London, Simpkin Marshall, 1920, 350pp. Details of corn trading on pp. 300-6 and 312. Listings of market and fair days came from May 1980 issue of journal *"Clwyd Historian"* published by Clwyd Local History Council. The Oswestry market continues to flourish today and is held in two locations, one in the inner part of the town with over 120 stalls and the other on the outskirts for livestock-principally sheep and cattle.

5.10 **Bread.** Two publications worthy of notice are: book: *"Food in England"*. Hartley, Dorothy. London, Macdonald & Jane's, 1954, 676pp. Despite the title, is a history of cooking in Britain with historical recipes; Chap. 23 of 42 pages deals exclusively with Bread. Booklet *"Welsh Bread"*, Freeman, Bobby; Y Lolfa Cyf, Talybont, Dyfed, SY24 5HE, Wales, 1981, 47pp.

5.11 **Hearth Baking of Bread in Eire, 1948**. This author (D.Ll.Davies) undertook a 250 mile walking tour in the more remote parts of south-western Eire in 1948, sleeping rough at farms. In three weeks saw only one iron range, all else being open hearths with peat fires, on which the daily bread was baked. An extract from trip diary dated 21st April 1948 reads: "The dough is placed in a large cauldron pan with lid near the fire, with turf ashes placed on the lid. After about three-quarters of an hour the bread is baked. The loaf is circular, about one foot diameter and some 3" in depth. This dark bread is baked every day except Sunday". Unfortunately no note made of grain used but it was a wholemeal. It is most probable in the intervening 50 years that the centuries-old custom of daily home bread baking has died out. Bread was good and substantial, one 'wedge' being adequate at one meal time with two being the the limit. See also booklet *"Cooking on the Open Hearth"* by Minwel Tibbott, Welsh Folk Museum, Cardiff, 1982, 42pp; the author is herself the daughter of a Carmarthenshire miller.

5.12 **Ty Brethyn Woollen Mill**. Three miles north-west of Ty'n-ddol mill lies another former weaving mill, but not of the Ceiriog. Called Ty Brethyn (cloth/tweed house), it is sited on a minor tributary of the Dee on a mountain road that runs between Llangollen and Glynceiriog. The pond and leat are still visible and the 16-foot waterwheel and pitwheel survive in the 3-storey building; but no weaving frames. The place has long been a private residence.

5.13 **Booklet:** *"Horizontal Watermill History and Technique of the First Prime Mover"*, Moog, Berthold. The Hague, International Molinological Society, 1994, 96pp. Extremely detailed and well researched summary of the subject; 50 illustrations. It is the 'Stage I' or 'Irish' mill of this book.

5.14 **The Irish in Wales**. Evidence is mainly archeological though some literary sources exist in Welsh sagas and Irish legend. Main evidence is in ogam stones, ogam being a form of writing using strokes at different angles. By 1970 over 300 ogam stones had been found in Ireland, 37 in Wales, 7 in Devon, 6 on Isle of Man and 11 in south-west Scotland. Roman withdrawal made Irish attacks on Wales possible and profitable and soon plundering excursions gave way to temporary or permanent settlement but none survived long-term.

5.15 **Book:** *"Oxford Dictionary of Saints"*. Farmer, D.H. Oxford, Clarendon Press, 1978, 440pp. See p. 56 for St Bride and p.163 for Germanus. For 'Bride' see also p.183 of *'Celtic Druids' Year'* by John King, Blandford Press, 1994.

5.16 **Milling by Hand Quern**. The following most useful information is quoted from page 186 of *"Islands of Western Scotland"* by W. H. Murray (published by Eyre Methuen, 1973, 328pp): "Grinding was a daily chore for women and querns were in every house. They were usually made of gneiss in two elliptical slabs, the upper having a convex face that fitted the concave lower face. Two women milled, one rotating the upper stone and the other feeding the grain. Four hours were taken to grind a bushel, and the work had its own labour song. Normal daily milling was briefer. A man would carry home as much corn as might be wanted for supper and the next day's food, and this corn, it is recorded, would be reaped, dried, graddaned, ground, and baked into bread, all within two hours."

Early North American settlers also used querns before a settlement grew large enough to warrant a grist mill. One early Canadian wrote: "The wheat was poured by hand through a hole in the upper stone. Between dark and bedtime enough would be ground to provide for the next day's needs".

It should also be remembered that though the quern is an out-moded machine in Europe, it is still very much in widespread use in other parts of the world.

5.17 **Article:** *"Farmhouse Brewing (in Wales)"*. Scourfield, E., Bulletin No 17, National Museum of Wales, 1974,10pp.

5.18 **Inn Names**. A rough and ready analysis of British pub names shows they fit into three major divisions, of which the first is by far the largest. They are: (1) Country life and times over the centuries (e.g.: Barley Mow); (2) Royalty, aristocracy, famous (e.g.; Rose & Crown); (3) All else (e.g.: Rest & Be Thankful). Of the pubs near Felin Lyn, Swan/Butcher's Arms/Star/Plough & Needle fitted into division 1, Queen's Head into 2, and Llwynmawr Inn into 3.

5.19 **Book:** *"Ellesmere and Llangollen Canal"*. Wilson, Edward. Chicester, Phillimore, 1975, 148pp. See pp. 38 and 91-4 for cartage of grain/flour by water. Plan of area immediately surrounding Maesbury Hall Mill is given on p.54 of booklet *"Shropshire Canals"* published by Shropshire Libraries, Shrewsbury, 1980.

5.20 **Lifeless Bread**. One a book reference and the other a comment. Book: *"Food for Nought (Decline in Nutrition)"*. Hall, Ross Hume (Prof.). New York, Random House Inc., 1976, 320pp. Chap. 1, 'Lifeless Bread', of 26 pages, is the most detailed historical and nutritional review of the decline in bread quality in the last 100 years that this author has seen. Extract from book *"The Living Herbalist"* by Jill Davies, Elm Tree Books, London, 1985; page 33 "Our next naughty food category are those foods (cakes,biscuits, white bread, etc.) based on white flours which have 35% of the original grain removed. The bran and surface endosperm are taken away, leaving creamy white granules (the starchy endosperm of the grain) which are then bleached with chlorine dioxide (the one used to clean toilets, etc).

"What in fact has happened to this bread is that all the best bits have gone. The natural vitamins, minerals, protein and roughage are removed, leaving behind a sticky, mucous forming, starchy, unstable, tasteless, binding mass called white bread. Synthetic brown bread, cashing in on the uninformed public opinion that brown bread is better for you than white, is perhaps the most dangerous of all. It is made from bleached white flour with brown colouring – usually caramel."

5.21 **Trelydan Windmill, Pool Quay, nr. Welshpool, Montgomeryshire.** Following further details were gleaned in magazine article appearing in *"Country Quest"*, Mold, Wales, June 1989 issue, p5. Trelydan was a postmill in 1406 and was owned by the monks of Strata Marcella Abbey nearby, itself created in 1170. A successor stone towermill ground meal until the end of the Napoleonic Wars c1815. Presumably fell into disuse. Structure demolished with explosives by the owner in 1914 and the resulting rubble was used to make a farm road.

5.22 **Booklet:** *"Jonathan Rogers (1864-1945)".* Undated typeset 50 page tribute containing photos, achievements and many letters of condolence. Possibly produced for family, friends and business associates in Vancouver about 1946-7.

5.23 **Welsh Society of Vancouver/Cymdeithas Gymraeg Vancouver**; British Columbia, Canada. Formed 1907. Its permanent home came with opening of Cambrian Hall in 1929, which is a substantial two-storeyed brick (where wood is the norm in B.C.) building. There are several Welsh churches in North America but this Welsh hall is a rarity, if not unique. Amongst the nine prominent donors listed on the dedication stone is 'Jonathan Rogers' – no surprise. Currently the Society has 206 members, an active social and cultural life and issues six newsletters per year.

*a*ppendices

I Micro-history of Neighbourhood about Felin Lyn

Local developments

1801	Pont Madoc rebuilt; a stone bridge built prior to 1697.
1806	Non-conformist chapel established in immediate vicinity – Wesleyan Methodists.
1839	First detailed land inventory, by Tithe Commissioners. Tithes, payable in crops/livestock, converted to cash.
1848	Creation of Parish of Glyn Traian with Pontfadog at its centre; church built 1847.
1852	Mill, which had been part of large estate for 500 years, was sold off as a separate property.
c1855	Local threshing of grain by hand flail started to give way to steam-driven machinery.
1863	Beginning of communications improvements with turnpike road constructed along valley bottom.
1867	Miller gets the vote; franchise given to all country males who paid over £12 annual rent.
1873	Horse-drawn narrow-gauge tramway built beside turnpike road. Ordnance Survey takes first accurate survey of Mill property in preparation of large scale map (25 inches to 1 mile).
1870s	Mill premises improved in variety of ways.
1877	First public bakery in Parish opened in Llwynmawr; home baking commences its decline.
1881	Positive evidence that Felin Lyn has become a Trading mill.
1884	Finally, democracy in the countryside. All country males aged 21 and over received the vote, a franchise already granted to urban cousins in 1867. Gentry and labourers now have voting equality.
1888	Horse tramway upgraded and converted to steam.
1891	Electric telegraph erected between Chirk and Glynceiriog.
1894	Ford adjacent to Felin Lyn replaced with steel bridge.
1916	Local malting of barley ceases.
1919	Tithes abolished here and everywhere else in Wales.
c1930	Cessation of local beer brewing at Llwynmawr Inn.
1931	Limited bus service introduced along the valley.
1935	Glyn Valley Tramway closed.
1936	Regular full time watermilling ceases at Felin Lyn.
c1942	First tractors at work in immediate locality.
1943	Damaged weir at Dolywern blown up.
1962	Habitation of Millhouse comes to an end.
1981	Felin Lyn demolished.
1997	Detailed history of Felin Lyn appears as a book.

Sovereigns during Mill life

George III	1760-1820
George IV	1820-1830
William IV	1830-1837
Victoria	1837-1902
Edward VII	1901-1910
George V	1910-1936

This view appeared in the 30th January 1980 issue of the newspaper 'Border Counties Advertizer', Oswestry, Shropshire within an article headed "Children at Risk in Mystery Mill". The disintegrating building to the front is the barn, which obscures Felin Lyn itself.

Explanation of local Welsh place-names

CEIRIOG	Origin lost in the mists of time. May have derived from a chieftan's name *Câr* or similar. Current spelling first seen in 1573 but not stabilised until the late 18th century.
CHIRK	Two theories. One is that it is a Saxon phonetic corruption of *Ceiriog*; another, espoused by the author, is that it is of Norse/Viking origin. These peoples settled in the Wirral in the 900s and later in lower- and mid-sections of the River Dee. Just below Chirk was the

river's head-of-navigation and it is conceivable that a Norse community was established there for a time as a trading post, and later either withered or was absorbed by the Saxons. A primitive 'kirk' was built and in time would have been called a 'church' but was linguistically arrested half way at 'chirk'. (Conversion examples; kid/child, kanal/channel.)

DOLYWERN	Meadow of the alders/alder grove.
FELIN LYN	Glen mill. '*Melin Glyn*' before the mutations take place.
GLYNCERIOG	Abbreviation of the full name of the village of Llansantffraid Glynceiriog which is translated as '*Church (of) Saint Bridget (in the) glen (of) Ceiriog*'. St Bride (AD c450-c525) was one of the founding female members of the Irish Celtic Church. The term '*The Glyn*' loosely applies to that part of the Ceiriog that lies between Offa's Dyke and Glynceiriog.
GLYN TRAIAN	The Parish in which Felin Lyn stood. In 1848 the large parish of Llangollen was split up and a third of it formed the new parish of Glyn Traian, aptly named because in Welsh '*traian*' means a '*third*'.
GRAIG	Crag or rock. Word is '*craig*' prior to mutation.
GWRYD	Some controversy over the meaning, maybe '*valour*'. Possible site of invasion skirmish between Henry II and Welsh in 1165.
LLWYNMAWR	'*Llwyn*' is a grove or bushland and '*mawr*' is '*great*'.
PONTFADOG	Bridge of Madog. '*Fadog*' being the mutation of Madog. Wales was anciently divided into three kingdoms of roughly equal areas and one of them called Powys occupied north-east, and much of mid-Wales. Powys was in turn subdivided into smaller areas of allegiance or administration and one of these was called Powys Fadog after a succession of chieftains named Madog. Powys Fadog was roughly triangular in shape with the corners resting at Chester, Cerrigydrudion, and at a place on the River Severn five miles north-west of Shrewsbury. Llangollen was at the approximate centre of this triangle. It was not known why the 17th century bridge was used to commemorate the ancient name of Madog but it seems a happy selection.

II Corn measures

All civilizations have had need of a measure of volume, both dry and liquid. In the case of grain, it is a container measure and has stood the test of time over several millennia and in all parts of the world.

Measuring grain by pouring it into a container of some agreed volume has two basic, and perhaps not obvious, advantages. Firstly, it requires no weighing device which was, and is, non-existent in primitive farming communities. Secondly, measuring by volume conveniently ignores the moisture content of grain. Kernels may have 10-15% range of moisture within them but this does not affect their size.

Such a system of measurement was universally attractive as it was evidently accurate, almost cheat proof, and cheap to implement.

All units of measurement have evolved from units that were easily understood and accepted by any illiterate man or woman of times gone by. The foot was the average length of an adult foot, the hand was the breadth of a hand (and at 4 inches is still used to measure horses), whilst a furlong was a furrow length when ploughing (and now l/8th mile). Even grain was pressed into service as a measuring device. The English monarch, Edward I, (who caused Chirk Castle to be built and the town of Oswestry to be encircled with a wall) ordained in 1305 that "*three grains of good quality barley when placed end on end shall make one inch*". The apothecary's weight measure of a grain stems from this self-same barley kernel.

In the case of volume units, their origins are far less obvious because nature did not provide ready-made containers, except perhaps hollowed-out gourds in the tropics. It was left to mankind to devise containers, though it is probable that womenfolk actually created the ancient grain measures. Grain keeps better when it can breathe so baskets and primitive sacks were likely preferred to clay pots. It is probable a woman would weave a small basket to hold her kitchen supplies and it would have a pair of handles and be easy to carry loaded for short distances. Such a basket may have evolved into a standardized measure. Her husband would have need of a much larger unit for harvesting, storage, or marketing, and it is likely his wife made him a back-carrying creel or wove him a primitive sack. Again this larger volume of grain must have evolved into a unit of volume for purposes of measurement at the farm, and barter or sale at the market.

Out of these probable origins emerged the bushel, which has been the accepted English (not British) Measure of volume for grain and other dry commodities for the last thousand years. The known genesis is the Winchester Bushel which is close to $1^1/_4$ cubic feet. The name given to this bushel is of significance because Winchester was the capital of England prior to the Norman invasion and as a city reached the zenith of its prosperity at the beginning of the 12th century.

It should be made clear that in earlier centuries the size of the Winchester bushel was something of an ideal and that in practice each market or trading area had its own sized corn measure which it jealously protected. The Winchester bushel was an early example of an attempt at standardization first for southern England, then England, and more recently for the British Isles and the rest of the English-speaking world.

The Winchester bushel was superseded by the Imperial Bushel in 1824, which rationalized some anomalies and increased its size by 3%. However, the Winchester bushel is still very much alive and well in the U.S.A. because the Americans did not adopt the Imperial measure for good nationalistic reasons.

Since this is a book about an upland watermill, it is worth mentioning that there existed at least two other grain measures in the uplands of the British Isles until the very end of the last century. One was of Celtic continental origin and was in used in Wales, whilst the other came from Scandinavia and was found in Scotland and northern England, including Durham, Cumbria and the Isle of Man. The latter system was likely introduced by the Norwegians when they ruled northern Scotland.

The history of these units is extraordinarily complex and confusing because changes in political power, trading areas, and centuries, caused amalgamations and integrations, often of the force-fit kind. Looking backwards much of it seems illogical but at the time it was a practical compromise at a workaday level. An example in our own age is the acceptance of metrication in Britain but the retention of 'miles' as a unit of long distance. An examination of the roots of the surviving Welsh words for measuring grain show that these words came from such diverse languages as Old Irish, Latin, Bretonese, ancient French, and middle English.

It is probable that the coming of the railways brought universal acceptance and usage of one standard of grain measurement throughout the British Isles. The following quotation from a book of 1815 dealing with the agriculture of South Wales gives a good insight into what things had been like before the whole of Britain became a common trading area:

"The Winchester bushel, and its subdivisionary measures have been brought at different times into most of the market towns of Wales; but the peasantry has frequently succeeded in driving the foreign invaders into the citadels of the townhalls, and in bringing back their own favourite measures in triumph into the market places. Of late, the magistrates have displayed more than usual vigor and the Winchester measure is becoming more common, especially in the larger towns and near the coasts."

As to the actual measuring container, in the times of Felin Lyn, every miller had a 1-bushel measure and some also had a 2-bushel measure. These measures usually had straight sides and were always flat-bottomed. Some of them were made of wood with staves, as in barrel construction, whilst others were made of brass or copper and all were fitted with some kind of double handle. Typical dimensions for a 1-bushel measure would be: internal diameter of $18^1/_2$ inches and 8 inch height. When filled, the grain was leveled off with a wooden stick known as a 'strike', and at this point the bushel had been established by volume and was known as having been 'struck'.

The miller was also equipped with a tolling dish which was a curved wood or metal scoop that he used to extract his fee or 'toll' from the farmers' sacks of grain. This tolling dish had to have a precise volume and would have been a fraction of a bushel, perhaps a $^1/_2$ gallon, which is one-sixteenth of a bushel.

The grain unit next in size above the bushel was the 'Quarter'. A confusing term – but typical of the subject – since it was not a quarter of anything in modern times.

Originally it had been the fourth part of a 'wey' or 'load', the latter terms once being units of capacity of Ireland and Scotland and units of weight in England. It was the trading unit for grain and grain prices were usually quoted per Quarter; it was always written with a capital 'Q'. If a grain price is listed without a volume measure beside it, most times it can be assumed to be the price per Quarter.

This Quarter, which is a measure of volume, must not be confused with a unit of weight, which was also called a 'quarter' but spelt with a small 'q'. This was one quarter of a Hundredweight (cwt.) of 112lbs and was 28lbs. The 'C' in cwt was the Latin symbol for 100 and goes back to earlier times when a Hundredweight did contain 100lbs.

Bushel: specification and tables

BUSHEL is the basic measure of capacity or dry volume and is used to measure such things as fruit, grain, hops, potatoes. It is the space occupied by 8 gallons of water. In the change to metrication in recent years, it is now an obsolete measure in the U.K. Its abbreviation is 'bu'.

Imperial Bushel (Britain) 2219 cubic inches. $1^1/_3$ cubic feet approximately

Winchester Bushel (U.S.A.) 2150 cubic inches. $1^1/_4$ cubic feet approximately

Precise	*Less So*
2 pints = 1 quart	3 or 4 bushels = 1 sack
4 quarts = 1 gallon	12 sacks = 1 chaldron
2 gallons = 1 peck	5 Quarters = 1 cart load
4 pecks = 1 bushel (8 gallons)	(approx 1 ton)
8 bushels = 1 Quarter (64 gallons)	1 coomb = 4 bushels
36 bushels = 1 chaldron ($4^1/_2$ Quarters)	

Brewer's bushel (19th century)

1 bushel of barley = 48 lbs;
1 bushel of barley MALT = 36 lbs (25% weight loss)

Welsh Grain Measures

Caution: Product, locality and century, make for different definitions of the same particular measure. Subject is a veritable quicksand and following material is proffered only on the basis of being a 'guide and not gospel'.

Unit of Volume	*Alternative or corrupt*	*Makes*	*Notes*
2 pedwran		1 pecaid bach ($^1/_8$ bu)	A
2 pecaid bach	(pegaid)	1 pecaid ($^1/_4$ bu)	B
2 pecaid	(pegaid)	1 cibyn ($^1/_2$ bu)	C
2 cibyn	(kibbin)	1 bwysel (1 bu)	D
2 bwysel	(pwysel)	1 hestoraid (2 bu)	
2 hestoraid	(stored)	1 hobaid (4 bu)	
2 hobaid	(hobed)	1 peged (8 bu or 1 Qtr) (or pegget)	

Notes: A = 'pedwr' means 4, so suggestion of a fourth, equivalent to 2 English quarts.
B = from the English 'peck'; 'bach' means little/small.
C = 'cib' is a cup or seed vessel.
D = from the English 'bushel'.

There was also a flour measure/weight called a 'ffiolaid/phiolaid' which is thought to be about 8 quarts.
The inclusion of pecaid and bwysel as Welsh translations of English measures suggest that an ancient system of Celtic measures was modified at some stage to make it integrate with English measures. Older measures of perhaps a true Celtic measuring system included: *meiliad* (peck or $^1/_4$ bushel); *llestraid* (about $2^1/_2$ bushels); *telaid* (about 5 bushels or a double llestraid).

Other miscellaneous grain measures

One bushel of wheat holds approximately 600 handfuls or some 870,000 kernels.
Primitive measures of volume still in use at markets up to fifty years ago were: pinch, handful, double handful. A strike was a dry measure, varying locally from 2 pecks (1/2 bushel) to 2 bushels. Another measure was a coomb or coom which amounted to 4 bushels and originated with the Danish occupation of England.
The number of bushels in a square/rectangular space can easily be calculated, being equal to four-fifths of the cubic footage. For example; there is a bin 10ft long by 4ft wide, holding grain to 2ft depth. $10 \times 4 \times 2 = 80$ cub ft = 64 bushels.

Designated Bushel Weights

In the second half of the last century, legislation permitted bushel-to-weight conversions as follows:

Oats		34 lbs
Barley malt		36 lbs
Barley		48 lbs
Rye		56 lbs
Wheat		60 lbs
Maize	on cob	70 lbs
	shelled	56 lbs
	as meal	50 lbs

Approximate conversion of bushel volume to weight

In a legal and a precise arithmetic sense, it is not possible to convert measures of capacity into measures of weight. However it is often necessary to make close approximations, as has been done in this book in several places.
Weights of different cereals per bushel have slowly increased as farming methods have improved. For the last century in England, the following approximations per Bushel can be used:

Barley at 48 lbs;
Wheat at 60 lbs.
Though a bushel is not intended to be a liquid measure, a bushel volume when filled with water weighs 80lb.

Flour (wheat) weights

All the foregoing information has related to grain in its kernel state prior to milling. When converted to flour, the product was measured by weight and never by volume. Weight units were established for sacks and barrels.

A sack of wheaten flour held an unwieldy 280lbs, which is the equal of 20 stones (14lbs = 1 Stone). It was essentially a baker's measure and was unrelated to household use. Not until the 1870s was it retailed in smaller and handier quantities, but always in multiples of a Stone. It was being sold in Oswestry in the 1920s in sacks of 140lbs.

Flour was also sold in barrels holding 196lbs, or14 stones. These barrels were about 30 inches long and of 18-inch diameter. Subsequently, flour was sold in bags holding subdivisions of the barrel quantity, thus $^1/_2$ barrel (98 lbs), $^1/_4$ barrel (49 lbs), $^1/_8$th barrel ($24^1/_2$ lbs). At a still later date, the bag weights were rationalized and became 100 lbs, 501bs, and 25 lbs respectively.

III Welsh, always the millers' mother tongue

Mae'r atodiad hwn wedi ei gynnwys er tynnu sylw darllenlwyr Saesneg i'r ffaith fod y melinwyr a'u teuluoedd yn siarad Cymraeg fel eu mam iaith. Gwnaed eu masnach i gyd yn Gymraeg hyd ddiwedd oes y Felin yn 1936, heblaw am yr achlysuron pan na fedrai brodor lleol neu ymwelwydd siarad Cymraeg. Mae'r rhestr o gyf eithiadau o eiriau malu a geiriau perthnasol yn ymdrechi gynhyrchu i ychydig o naws Gymreig mewn llyfryn sydd wedi ei ysgrifennu yn Saesneg am Felin Gymraeg.

(Translation: This Appendix has been included to draw the attention of English readers to the fact that all millers, and their families, at Felin Lyn spoke Welsh as their mother tongue. All their business was also conducted in Welsh, right to the end of mill working in 1936, except on those few occasions when a local resident or a visitor had no Welsh. This translation list of milling and related words is an attempt to produce a little Welsh atmosphere into a book written all in English about a Welsh watermill.)
Welsh is a member of the Celtic group of languages, these being the indigenous languages of Scotland, Ireland, Isle of Man, Wales, Cornwall, and Brittany in northwest France. The Celts, a once powerful and thrusting race, established themselves in Britain in about the fifth century B.C. and presumably spoke a common language. In turn they were embattled by others and were pushed to the less desirable parts of the British Isles. A few of their words still survive in England, for example 'avon' which has the same meaning as the Welsh 'afon'.

Because of this partial fragmentation of the British Celts, it is assumed their common language became distorted by local dialects. By about AD 800 the Celts located in what is now known as Wales became a linguistically isolated people with a distinctive language - in today's world. The language lacks the letter J, K, Q, X and Z; vowels are identical to English plus W and Y.

The present language has a rich and expressive vocabulary and, though still in everyday use, is slowly losing ground to the all pervasive influence of English. At the beginning of this century a third of all the inhabitants of Wales spoke Welsh in the home but now only a fifth do so. It is a sad thing to have to say that if this linguistic decline is not arrested, Welsh will cease to be a working language by the year AD 2,300 or earlier.

The Welsh call themselves 'Cymry', their country 'Cymru' and their language 'Cymraeg'. Because Wales has been administered by England for close to half a millennium the country's proper name of 'Cymru' has become obscured. All maps and most references call it Wales, which is the English translation of Cymru. The names WALES and WELSH derive from a pre-AD 900 Anglo-Saxon root word 'walh/waelisc' (or similar), meaning stranger or foreigner and especially one of Celtic origins. The WALLOONS of Belgium and the British surnames WAILES, WALLACE, WALLIS, WALNUT, WALSH, WALTON and WELCH all derive from the same root word.

It is also interesting to note that the Welsh word for an English person is 'Sais' (plural: Saeson), the literal translation being 'Saxon'. This came about because the Saxons were the only later-to-be English with whom the Welsh had direct contact. The Welsh word for England is 'Lloegr'.

Welsh milling (and related) terms

Note: All words are nouns, except for verbs shown as (v). Where Welsh words or spellings have regional differences, North Wales takes precedence. Spelling is for the 19th century.

arian money

bara	bread
berfa sachau	sack barrow
blawd	meal
blawd coch	animal feed
brâg	malt
bragwr	malster/brewer
bwyd	food
bwysel	bushel
cae	field
cafn	launder/trough
cartwr	carrier(retail)
carreg fflur	hard stone
carreg silian	soft stone
carreg melin	millstone
ceffyl	horse
ceiniog	penny
ceirch	oats
cibyn	half bushel
clorian	weighing scales
cnewyllyn	kernel
cod	bucket (of waterwheel)
cog	cog/tooth
cogyddio(v)	stone dressing
cored/argae	weir/dam
corlac	wood shovel
craswr	kiln operator
cwru	beer
cwsmer	customer
cynhaeaf	harvest
da byw	stock/cattle
dannedd	cog wheel
deiliad	tennant
dwr	water
dyrnaid	handful
dyrnu(v)	to thresh
eisin	husk/shell/bran
felindre	mill house
fferm	farm
ffermwr (ffermwyr)	farmer
ffiol yd	grain scoop
ffiolaid	flour measure
ffordd	road
ffos ddwr	millrace
gerwyn	stone vats
gôf	blacksmith
gronyn	grain
gwair	hay
gweisgian	husks, hulls
gwenith	wheat
had	seed
haearn	iron
haidd	barley
hobaid	four bushels
hopran	hopper
llygad y maen	eye of stone
llawr	floor
llif	flood
llifddor/fflodiart	sluicegate
llifo(v)	to flow
llwy	bucket (of wheel)
lon	lane
maen isa	bedstone
maen melin	millstone
maen ucha	runner stone
mal	grist
malu(v)	to grind
march	horse
marchnad	market
mashin fflwrio	bolter
masnachu(v)	to trade
meistr tir	landlord
melin	mill
melin ddwr	watermill
melin flawd	grain mill
melin wlan	woollen mill
melin wynt	windmill
melinydd	miller
mesur	measure (e.g. grain)
mesur wyth galwyn	bushel
mochyn	pig
neithiwr	grain cleaner
nenlofft	attic
odyn	kiln
olwyn ddwr	waterwheel
palad	shaft
pecaid	peck ($^1/_4$ bushel)
pedwran	$^1/_{16}$ bushel
peillied	bolted meal/flour
peillio(v)	to bolt/sieve
peilliwr	dressing m/c
peiriant	machine
peiriannau	machinery
peiriant fflwrio	bolter
poban/popty	oven
pren	wood/timber
pris	price
pwn/sach	sack
pwys	pound (lb)
pwyso(v)	to weigh
rhedfa felin	mill watercourse

rhod/olwyn	waterwheel
rhuchion	husk
rhyg	rye
rhynion	groats
sach/sachaid	sack/sackful
saer cerrig/melin	stone dresser
saer melinau	millwright
shiliad	farmer's parcel of grain
silio(v)	to hull grain
silied	hulled corn
siliwr	winnowing m/c
siprys	oat/barley mix
swm/mesur	quantity
tal/toll	payment/toll
torth	loaf
troi(v)	to turn, rotate
trol	cart
trwsio(v)	to repair
tyddyn	smallholding
yd	corn
ysgub	sheaf of corn
ysgubor	barn

Translation of local placenames

Note: Letters in brackets show mutated form, eg *c(g)och* is *coch* or *goch.*

afon	river
arddu	dark/black
bach	little/small
b(f)edw	birch
bod	dwelling
bonc	rising ground
brith	speckled
briw	wound, broken
b(f)ron	slope/hill top
b(f)ryn	hill
bugail	shepherd
bugeilyn	sheep pasture
cae	field
c(g)anol	middle
cefn	back/ridge
celyn	holly
cil	recess/nook
clawdd	ditch (Offa)
c(g)och	red
c(g)oed	wood
c(g)ors	bog/swamp
c(g)raig	rock/crag
(c)oryn	hill top
cychwyn	rise/stir
c(g)yll	hazel tree
dentyr	tenter frame
derw	oaks
dol	meadow
d(t)ir	land
du	black
dwr	water
dyffryn	wide valley
erw	acre
ffordd	way/road
ffynnon	spring/well
garth	enclosure/ridge
gelli	grove of trees
glan	river bank
glyn	glen/valley
gwern	swamp/alder grove
gwryd	valour
gwyn	white
gyll	ravine/cleft
hafod	summer place/pasture
helyg	willows
hen	old
hendre	permanent farm(winter)
heulog	sunny
hir	long/tall
hwnt	beyond
hyfryd	pleasant
isaf	lower
llan	church/village
llech	slate/flagstone
llety	lodgings
llwyn	bush (land)
m(f)aen	stone
maes	field
m(f)awr	big
m(f)elin	mill
min	edge/brink
mynydd	mountain
nant	brook
newydd	new
obry	beneath/below
oen	lamb
onn	ash trees
pandy	fulling mill
pant	hollow/side valley
pen	end/head
pennant	valley head
pentre	hamlet
plas	big house

p(b)ont	bridge
pwll	pool
rhiw	ascent/slope
rhos	wet moorland
rhyd	ford
stryt	road/lane
tal	head/front
tan	under
t(d)ir	land
twll	hole/dimple
ty	house
Proper names	
tyddyn/ty'n	small farm
Crogen	see below
uchaf	upper
Dafydd	David
wen	white
Ffowc	Foulkes
wyn	lambs
Ifan	Ivan
y, yr, 'r	the, of the
Iorwerth	Edward
ysgythrau	carve/prune
M(f)adog	Welsh prince

Crogen Iddon and *Crogen Wladys* are supposedly associated with an inconclusive battle fought in 1165 between Henry II and the Welsh. (See Chapter 2 in book 'Chirk Castle and Chirkland' referenced in Appendix X)

IV Characteristics of grain

Cereal grains are self-pollinating dry fruits of grasses such as oats, rye, and wheat. The kernels of the various grains are similar in structure but differ in size and shape.

The kernel is contained within a fruit wall attached to the rachis, which in turn is attached to the plant stem. The outside of the kernel is the husk or pericarp.

The three structural parts of a grain are:

Bran: outside protective covering, 13% by weight.

Endosperm: the food supply for the new seed when it germinates, 85% by weight.

Germ or Embryo; new seed or germination portion, 2% by weight.

A food analysis of a wheat, barley or oat grain shows it to contain: Carbohydrates = 66% to 74 %; protein = 12% to 16%; water = 8% to 13%; fat = 1.7% (wheat) to 7.3% (oats); minerals = 1.7% to 1.9%.

Man has always grown grain in order to eat the

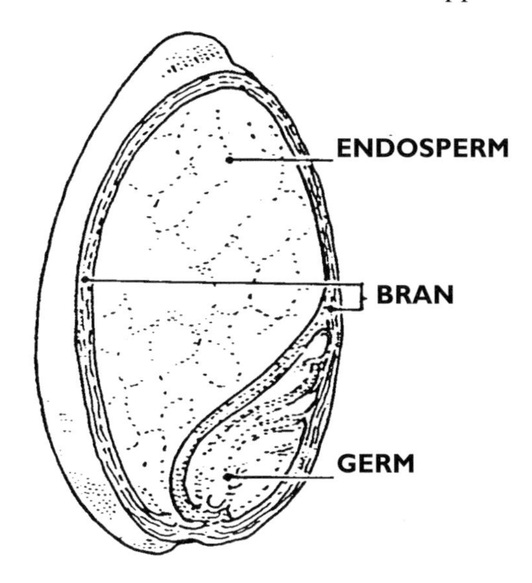

endosperm which consists of starch and gluten. These two substances can easily be separated by a simple experiment. Place a quantity of fine flour in a porous bag and repeatedly knead and squeeze the bag in a bowl of water to create a milky solution. Eventually pour off the water and what remains is starch, whilst the sticky gel in the bag is gluten.

Nature endowed these grasses with protective spikes to prevent browsing animals eating the 'fruit'. These are called awns and are attached to the husk. They are very evident in barley and less so in wheat. Until about 1880 oats had them too, and could be seen on the Welsh varieties of Ceirch du Bach and Ceirch Llwyd Cwta. In the wild these awns moved the ripened and detached seed along the ground in a most agile way, as if it possessed an inner power. Present-day oats have a protective covering called a hull or shell which is not easy to separate from the kernel.

Oats, barley and wheat have about equal nutritional value, and are judged as having good calorific (energy) levels when compared to most other basic foods. This must be so because since man has started to eat cereals, it has become his staple food and around the world he has never switched to some other primary foodstuff.

Wheat grown experimentally in Britain in the last century, without benefit of manure and with little attention, produced 13 bushels per acre; this may be regarded as the 'natural' yield in temperate zones and is the same as present day wheat yields in Asia and Africa. In areas where rainfall is inadequate and land is poor, yields may fall as low as 5 to 8 bushels an acre. This was the situation encountered by the first settlers in parts of north and south America and Australia in the nineteenth century. Medieval wheat in England often was only ten inches tall and yielded about ten grains to a head.

This suggests grains grown on suitable lands with compatible climate can have their 'natural' yields doubled or more with good husbandry.

The following table summarizes the principal characteristics of the three grains grown in the Parish of Glyn Traian and ground at Felin Lyn, from 1800 onwards. In earlier years rye may have been grown in the vicinity but it was replaced by wheat.

Characteristic		Oats	Barley	Wheat
First cultivated		2000 - 500BC	6000-3000BC	9000-5000BC
Growth		Grows on damper & more acidic soils than other two grains. Disease resistant.	'In-between' plant but hardy Shallow-rooted. Faster grower at c. 90 days.	Fussier in all regards when compared with coarse grains. Deep-rooted.
Seeding rate per acre, (for 'A')		$2^1/_2$ to 4bu	$2^1/_4$ to $3^1/_2$ bu	2 to 3 bu.
Yield per acre	'A'	28 to 35 bu. or $^1/_2$ ton.	26 to 32 bu. or $^2/_3$ ton	21 to 27 bu. or $^2/_3$ ton.
	'B'	39 bu. or $^1/_2$ ton.	33 bu. or $^3/_4$ ton.	30 bu. or $^3/_4$ ton.
	'C'	38.1 to 44.5 bu. 11.3 cwt	31.2 to 36.2 bu. 13.5 cwt	26.3 to 34.7 bu. 15.1 cwt
British average bushel weights				
1800s		about 34 lb	about 48 lb	about 60 lb
1900		about 39 lb	about 50 lb	about 60 lb
1970		about 42 lb	about 56 lb	about 63 lb
Grain use		Oatmeal dishes for humans. Feed for horses, cattle, sheep and chickens.	Malt for beer brewing. Pig and cattle feed.	Best of bread with better gluten content. Never fed to animals.
Straw use		Good quality animal feed.	Animal litter & indifferent feed.	Animal litter; thatching.

Notes:

A Ceiriog, Denbighshire, North Wales, 19th Century, estimated.

B Great Britain, 20 years, 1885-1904, national statistics.

C Wales, 10 years, 1914-1923, national statistics.

V Water-driven machinery in the Ceiriog since 1700

Explanatory: (a) * = buildings still standing in 1990. (b) All mills took their water from Afon Ceiriog except for 1, 2, 4, 6, and 17, which were on tributaries. (c) 'Miles' means river-miles from source, which is on the east side of the Berwyns at 1825ft altitude and four straight-line miles N.W. of Llanarmon Dyffryn Ceiriog. (d) Fuller notes follow with mill No. and note No. corresponding.

Water-driven machinery on Afon Ceiriog

No. & Notes	Name & location	Miles & altitude	Purpose	Built	Closed
1	*SARPHLE; $^3/_4$ mile upstream LLanarmon	$4^1/_2$m 975 ft	Grist-farm	unknown	c1870
2	LLANARMON; Llanarmon Dyffryn C	$5^1/_4$m 875ft	Grist	pre-1329	pre-1820
3	*TREGEIRIOG; Tregeiriog	$6^1/_2$m 800ft	Flour	pre-1750	1926
4	*PENRHEWL FARM; Tregeiriog	$6^1/_2$m 850ft	Farm work	1908	1952
5	*HENDRE; at site of old granite quarrey	8m 710ft	Manufacture of gunpowder	c1870	1879
6	MELIN DEIRW & PANDY; Pandy	$8^3/_4$m 660ft	Wool fulling	1300s	c1800
7	LOWER PANDY QUARRY; below Pandy	$9^1/_4$m 610ft	China stone	1894	1908
8	GYNFAWR or UPPER; Glyn Ceiriog	10m 560ft	a fulling b flannel	1600s 1815	c1800 1951
9	GLYN FECHAN, *MASON or LOWER; Glynceiriog	$10^1/_2$m 530ft	a flour b flannel	pre-1545 1818	c1880 c1923
10	HEN BANDY (Old Pandy) Pont Bell.	$10^1/_2$m 530ft	a fulling b flannel	unknown 1883	c1880 1905
11	*TY GWYN, *FELIN NEWYDD; below Glyn Ceiriog	$10^3/_4$m 505ft	a flour b flannel	pre-1703 1883	1920s 1898 or c1920
12	*GLAN-Y-WERN; Dolywern	$11^1/_2$m 480ft	a grist b corn/ malt	pre-1700 1837	c1795 c1916
13	**FELIN LYN**, Pontfadog	$12^1/_2$m	grist flour	Medieval late 1700s	late 1700s 1936
14	PANDY TYNDDOL, 3/4m below Pontfadog	$13^1/_4$m 395ft	a fulling b weaving	unknown 1803	1800 c1818
15	MELIN-Y-CASTELL, Castle Mill	$14^3/_4$ 340ft	corn	pre-1398	pre-1800
16	*CHIRK, Chirk	$16/_4$m 255ft	flour	pre-1498	(i) 1914 (ii) 1964
17	PONT-Y-BLEW, $1^1/_2$m east of Chirk	$18^1/_4$m 200ft	Iron forge	1710	mid-1800s

Two slate mines (Cambrian & Wynne) immediately to west of Glynceiriog used water power to drive machinery, at first by waterwheel and later Pelton turbine; used primarily to trim slates. These mines were not on Afon Ceiriog but at 750ft and 1000ft levels and worked at varying periods between 1857-1947. On the upland waters of Nant Teirw at 1050ft elevation was a pond and gristmill half mile downstream from Plas Nantyr; ceased working 1822-5. Its predecessor was probably a Stage I mill.

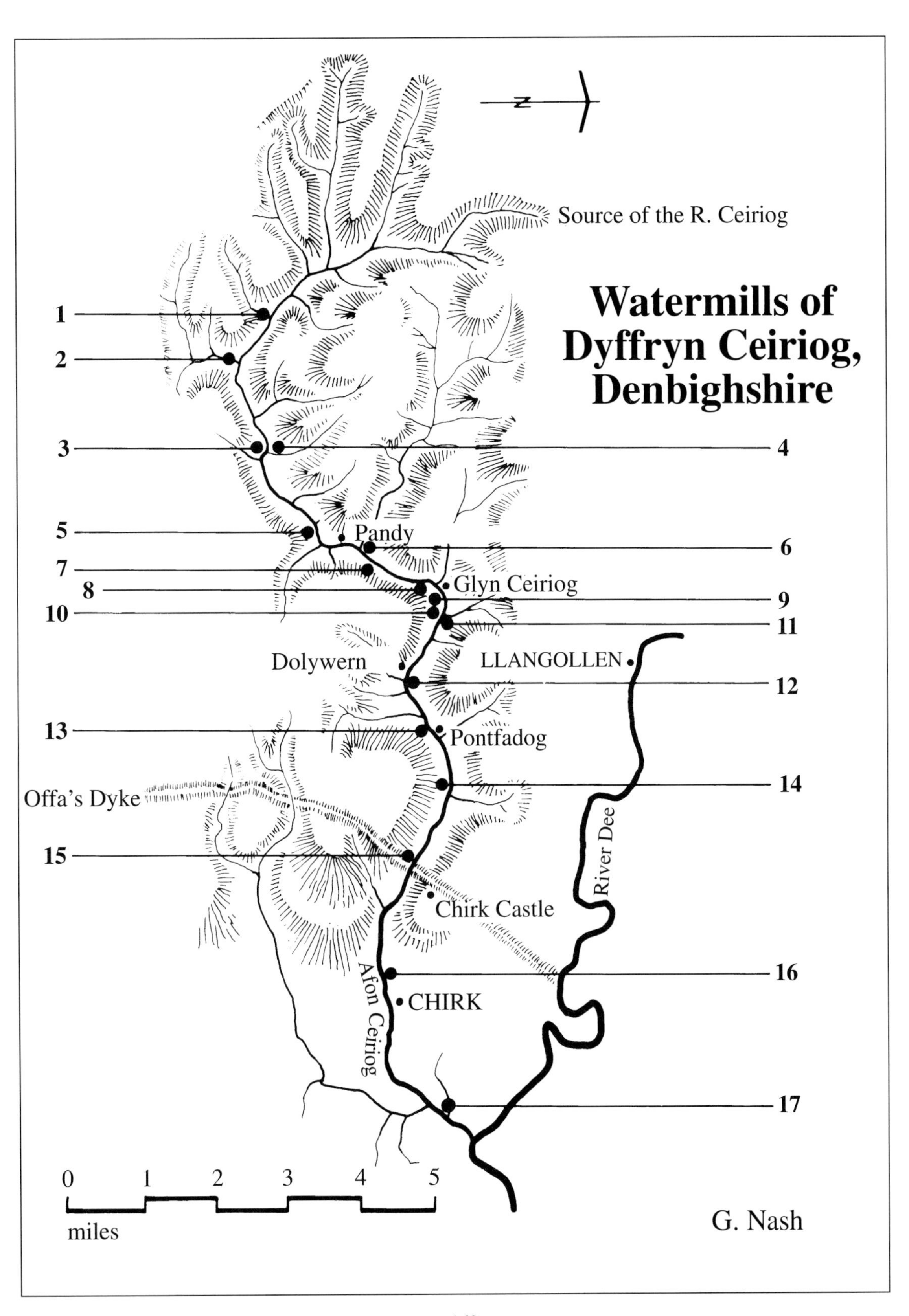

N
Source of the R. Ceiriog
Watermills of Dyffryn Ceiriog, Denbighshire
1
2
3
4
5
Pandy
6
7
8
Glyn Ceiriog
9
10
11
Dolywern
LLANGOLLEN
12
13
Pontfadog
14
Offa's Dyke
15
River Dee
Chirk Castle
16
Afon Ceiriog
CHIRK
17
0
1
2
3
4
5
miles
G. Nash

Notes to preceding table

(1) Presumably a 'farm' mill built on Nant Sarphle; probably 1 pair of small stones, perhaps run seasonally. Hoard of 500 Roman coins dated 42 A.D. to 226 A.D. found on this farm in 1918.

(2) Mentioned in Chirk Castle account book of 1329. Llanarmon is an ancient settlement and was converted to Christianity about AD 440, well before most of England. Mill thought to lie on Nant Gwrachen, not far from centre of present day village.

(3) Undershot waterwheel, 55" diameter millstone extant in 1983. George Borrow described it in 1854. (Wild Wales, Chap. 64).

(4) Sited on Nant Tregeiriog at N. end of village. No millstones. Used year-round for chaff cutting, swede/turnip pulping and oat/barley kibbling (form of coarse grinding). Overshot iron waterwheel of 10ft diameter & 34 inches width; underground shafting laid to nearby barns. Last waterdriven machinery to work in Dyffryn Ceiriog.

(5) Short-lived Wood Blasting Co, ground the raw materials to make the blasting powder. Good quality granite was discovered when making millrace and this led to creation of vast quarry at this site. 1881 Census records '*John Briscoe, aged 30, gunpowder manufacturer*' lived at Glynceiriog.

(6) Principal fulling mill on the river. Chirk Castle records mention a fulling mill in 1329 without giving a location but this mill has always been regarded as ancient by local people. Two named mills lay on Nant Teirw tributary, one above the other. A watercourse still leads into the existing Woolpack Inn suggesting this was one of the mills; it may have been converted from fulling to gristing prior to 17th century.

(7) Sited $^1/_3$m. below hamlet of Pandy on S. side of river. At this, and three neighbouring quarries, feldspar was extracted. This crystalline rock is found in granite and when it decomposes it forms clay and contains basic fluxes, alumina and silica. Used in pottery moulding and as a glaze flux at 1300°C. Presumably waterwheel operated a crusher, details unknown. Product shipped to Stoke-on-Trent via G.V. Tramway to Chirk and thence by canal narrow-boat.

(8) Was a fulling mill prior to c1810. Demolished and replaced with 3 storey flannel factory which commenced c1815. First looms were half mechanical, half manual; machines modernized in stages, last c1896. Measured in square-footage, was by far the largest of all the mills in this listing.

(9) Original cornmill of village of Glynceiriog; worked until c1880 and was then absorbed into adjacent woollen mill. Latter mill was 3 storey, built and operated by John Mason (see also Chapter 5) until his death in 1862. The following year power looms were installed. Worked spasmodically between two World Wars.

(8 & 9 combined)
An 1838 Parliamentary Report showed Glynceiriog, measured in terms of persons employed, as fifth largest woollen centre in Wales, and the largest in Denbighshire (followed closely by Llangollen). Report stated 2 mills employed 94 persons and produced 11 horsepower-combined. In 1896 both mills were purchased by the local Ffoulkes family and by 1905 production was rationalized with Lower mill spinning and Upper mill weaving. Products were flannels, shirting and tweeds. After 1920 production became intermittent and ceased for ever in 1951. Both mills supplied first electricity (D.C. only) used in Glynceiriog during 1930s. Externally generated A.C. current reached the village in 1934 and for next ten years or so both systems co-existed.

(10) Fulling mill till about 1885, then used for some ancillary operation in processing flannel till about 1905.

(11) Ty Gwyn was a 3 storey corn mill rebuilt c1820; 3 pairs stones; undershot iron waterwheel of about 12ft diameter. Disused as a cornmill by 1920. M. Abraham reported all machinery intact in 1940, but removed shortly afterwards. Felin Newydd (New Mill) was a single storey flannel mill built alongside in 1883; with the latest machinery installed, it employed 25 persons. Had failed by c1898 but may have been reopened in World War 1. One of these mills subsequently generated electricity in the 1930s for the Dolywern & District Electricity Supply Co. until national distribution became available.

(12) See Chapter 5.

(13) **FELIN LYN**

(14) See Chapter 5.

(15) Mentioned in Chirk Castle records of AD 1398 as *Mill of Crogen*. George Borrow said in 1854 that a long low neat house at this hamlet, later an inn, was formerly the mill of the castle and was still called Melin-y-Castell. (*Wild Wales*, Chap 54). This mill must have always been a small one, for Castle records of 1465 show its rent as 10s. a year, whereas by comparison the mill of Glynfawr was charged 75s 4d.

(16) Preceded by medieval mills. Largest of all cornmills on Ceiriog. Building of three storeys and attic

contains oak beam dated 1693 and corner stone dated 1780; further extensions in brick c1850 and between late 1890s and 1908.

Closed as a flourmill in 1914 but may have been reopened in World War 1. Waterwheel replaced by turbine which generated electricity for Chirk village c1920 to1928, when regional power arrived. Premises used for grinding assorted products in early 1930s, then closed. Worked by diesel as an animal feed mill from 1938 to 1951, and then used solely as a feed store until 1964 closure when all grain related work finally ceased. (Details kindly supplied by Rev. A. Davies who, with his brother, worked the mill from 1938 to 1964.)

(17) Sited above River Ceiriog and fed by pond, outlines of which can still be seen. Wheel drove bellows for blast and tilt hammers for forging. Produced charcoal iron between 1710 and 1795; premises enlarged and puddled iron, using coal/coke, was made in 19th century. In 1830 twenty men produced 20 tons of iron per week. Methods were obsolete by mid 1800s; believed closed 1850-70. Locality still known as Forge.

VI Territory of Felin Lyn – list of dwellings

As discussed in the text, it is impossible to be precise about the boundaries of the *'territory'* of Felin Lyn. The following list is therefore an approximation and is not complete in that it shows some 85 dwellings when in fact there were 110 or more. The discrepancy is partly explained by the fact that cottages in hamlets were not named.

An attempt has also been made to classify the properties by size, at the middle of the19th century. This has been achieved by using several sources but mainly the 1851 Census and an 1852 'Particulars for Sale'. The list should be 90% accurate or better. Acreages shown are believed not to include mountain pastures. Present day Llangwryd-isaf and Llangwryd-uchaf were then known as Nantgwryd and Tanygraig, respectively.

List of most of the dwellings in the territory of Felin Lyn, at mid-19th Century

Houses/cottages without land and small-holdings of less than 5 acres are marked with an asterisk (*). Places marked # indicate they were known to be customers 70 years later in the 1920s.

Bedwlwyn cottages*	Bonc (82)#
Brithdir (60)*	Briw-nant (55)
Brongyll (55)	Brongyll cottages*
Bron-heulog*	Bron-y-garth (18)
Bryn#	Brynarddu (30)#
Bryn-bugeilyn	Bryn-y-ffynnon (44)#
Bryniau (60)#	Butcher's Arms*
Caecoed	Caeiocyn (55)
Caemor (110)#	Cefngoed (36)
Cilcychwyn (90)#	Cilnant (60)
Croggen Iddon isaf (103)	Croggen Iddon uchaf (100)
Croggen Wladys (70)	Dolywern Farm (26)
Dolywern cottages*	Dyffryn#
FELIN LYN (6)	Frondderw
Garth-obry cottages*	Glan-yr-afon (14)
Glan-y-wern (maltings?)	Graig cottages*
Graig Pickan (17)	Graigwen (23)
Gwyn-y-gar cottage*	Hen-gelli*
Henmer House (100)	Herber cottages*
Llangwryd isaf (65)#	Llangwryd uchaf (40)#
Llety Ifan (32)	Llwynmawr cottages*
Llwynmawr Farm (80)#	Llwynmawr Inn *
Nant cottage*	Nant Ffowc
Nant Gwryd (18)	Nant Iowerth cottages*
Pandy-bach (20)	Pant Dafydd goch
Pant-du (20)	Pant-du-uchaf*
Pen-craig (100)#	Pen-isa'r glyn (136)
Pen-llwyn (48)#	Pen-y-bryn (70)#
Pen-y-frongyll#	Pen-y-gelli (46)
Pen-y-stryt*	Pennant (100)#
Pentre Cilgwyn (13)#	Pentre Cilgwyn cottages*
Pentre Pontfadog cottages*	Plas Croggen
Plas-onn (60)	Pwll-hir (15)
Queen's Head Inn*	Smithy, Llwynmawr*
Swan Inn*	Talfryn
Tai'n-y-mynydd (103)	Tan-y-dentyr
Tan-y-garth (100)	Ty Bricly*
Ty-helyg*	Ty-hwnt i'r nant
Ty-isaf brongyll	Ty-mawr [Cilcychwyn] (16)#
Ty-mawr [Gwryd] (49)	Tynant cottages*
Ty-newydd cottages*	Ty'n-y-celyn (13)#
Ty'n-y-coed	Ty'n-y-ddol (108)
Ty'n-y-fedw	Ty'n-y-fron (80)#
Ty'n-y-graig (75)	Ty'n-y-groes*
Ty'n-llwyn (27)	Ty'n-y-mynydd (160)#
Ty'n-twll#	Wern Tower isaf
Wern Tower uchaf	Ysgythrau isaf
Ysgythrau canol	Ysgythrau uchaf (16)

Trading-mill Customers

When Felin Lyn changed from a Toll-mill to a Trading-mill, the pattern of its customers changed somewhat. No longer were they, by necessity, people who lived within a mile or two of the Mill.

The late Mrs Gwladys Jones (FL) provided valuable information about the names of some of Felin Lyn's customers just prior to 1920 when she was a late teenager. She said: *"The places listed below were well known to me because I used to go to all of them either with bills (invoices) or to tell them that their order was ready for collection. Not all of them brought grain for grinding but many of them were good customers for Indian meal (maize), thirds and bran."*

This is indeed an interesting list, even if it is not a complete one. There are 34 customers and of them, 31 are farms and three are stores; significantly there is not one that is just a house or cottage dweller.

In terms of area, a mile downstream or to the east has been lost from the former 'territory' but this has been more than made up by a gain of six miles up-valley as far as Llanarmon. However, it is worth noting that 60% of these trading-mill customers belong to the old toll-milling territory. The list of customers supplied by Mrs Jones is as follows:

FORMER 'TERRITORY' OF FELIN LYN	BEYOND FORMER TERRITORY
Bonc	*Between Dolywern & Glynceiriog*
Brithdir	Bryn-arddu
Bryn (nr Llwynmawr)	Fron-frys
Bryn-y-ffynnon	Pen-y-frongyll
Bryniau	Tal-y-garth Isaf
Caemor	Tal-y-garth Uchaf
Cilcochwyn	Ty'n-y-celyn Brongyll
Dyffryn	Ty'n-y-fron
Llangwryd Isaf	
Llangwryd Uchaf	*Village of Glynceiriog*
Llwynmawr farm	Berwyn Stores
Pennant	Cross (Roads) Stores
Pencraig	
Pen-llwyn	*Pandy*
Pentre Cilgwyn	Aberweil farm
Pen-y-bryn	
Ty-mawr [Gwryd]	Woolpack Inn store*
Ty'n-y-mynydd	
Ty'n-twll	*Rhiwlas*
	Bwlch-y-dongiau
	Ty Ucha
	Llanarmon
	MacAlpine Estate

Notes:

(1) All three Stores were supplied with a mix of products.

(2) Significantly, no customers are listed for the hamlet of Tregeiriog, which had a watermill in operation until 1926.

[*] In 1987 the derelict and former Woolpack Inn still showed an upper-floor storeroom marked in faded lettering 'Flour & Meal', with a wall crane beside it. The building is now a restaurant.

VII Grain prices for England & Wales

Average annual prices of cereals per hundredweight (i.e. shillings and pence per 112lb).
Prices: 1770 to 1940

Year	Oats	Barley	Wheat
1770	6/2d	7/5d	11/4d
1780	4/9d	4/11d	8/7d
1790	7/0d	7/4d	12/9d
1800	14/1d	16/9d	26/7d
1810	10/3d	13/6d	24/0d
1820	8/8d	9/6d	15/10d
1830	8/9d	9/1d	15/0d
1840	9/3d	10/2d	15/6d
1850	5/11d	6/7d	9/5d
1860	8/9d	10/3d	12/5d
1870	8/2d	9/8d	10/11d
1880	8/3d	9/3d	10/4d
1890	6/8d	8/0d	7/5d
1900	6/4d	7/0d	6/3d
1910	6/3d	6/6d	7/5d
1920	20/5d	25/0d	18/10d
1930	6/2d	7/11d	8/0d
1940	13/4d	18/2d	10/0d

Note: These prices are not decade averages but are for the 12 months of the year shown. They are also prices 'at the time' and have not been adjusted to reflect inflation and deflation; they are therefore not strictly comparable but do reflect trends.

Best and worst individual years in the 19th & 20th Centuries (for the 20th century to 1940 only).

	19th Century				20th Century		
Best	1812	1801	1812	Best	As for 1920 above		
	16/0d	19/2d	29/6d				
Worst	1895	1895	1894	Worst	1933	1904	1934
	5/2d	6/2d	5/4d		5/7d	6/3d	4/10d

To convert these prices per *hundredweight* (cwt) to prices per Imperial *Quarter*, multiply by the following factors:
Oats by 2.785
Barley by 3.571
Wheat by 4.285

It has been assumed that the Imperial Quarters of oats, barley, and wheat hold 312 lbs, 400 lbs, and 480 lbs, respectively.
Source: *Century of Agricultural Statistics in Great Britain*, published by H.M.S.O., 1968, pages 81 and 82.

Grain acreages in Wales: 1875-95
(in thousands of acres)

Grain	1875	1880	1885	1890	1895
Oats	237	240	**247**	241	242
Barley	**154**	143	126	120	112
Wheat	**112**	90	74	69	44

Peak average in **bold.**

VIII Local annual tax valuations of felin Lyn

Surviving valuations, for the purpose of levying local taxes, come from three sources, and are dated 1839, 1867, and 1916 respectively. They are all housed at Clwyd County Record Office at Ruthin.

Local authorities value properties so that they may levy local taxes or 'rates'. The valuations listed below were assessed on the basis of how much income any property would produce annually and were mainly based on how much rent could be obtained.

For the years 1867 and 1916 the records also obligingly supplied the '*Gross Estimated Rental*' of the property, presumably an amount close to what a landlord was charging at the time. In the compilation below, RV = *Rateable Value* and GER = *Gross Estimated Rental.*

Year 1838: (Source: Tithe Commissioners Survey) Covers house, flourmill and garden (but no fields). Area: Nil acres, 1 rood, 36 perches. Tithe payable of 2 shillings and 3 pence.

Year 1867: (Ref: RDD/C/3/l Glyntraian Parish Valuation) Cornmill & Sawmill and land. Area: 3 acres, 1 rood, 32 perches. RV = £27.4s.1d. GER = £31.15s.0d.

Year 1916: (Ref: RDD/C/3/2 Glyntraian Parish Valuation) Consists of three parts.

(a) Mill & Buildings: Area: Nil acres, 1 rood, 24 perches. RV = £13.0s.0d. GER = £19.0s.0d.

(b) Mill Fields: Area: 5 acres, 1 rood, 22 perches. RV = £5.10s.0d. GER = £6.0s.0d.

(c) Minafon Field: Area; 1 acre, no roods, 18 perches. RV = £1.0s.0d. GER = £1.5s.0d.

Total Property of (a,b,c): These three 1916 entries are not totalled in the Valuation and are considered as different lots. Aggregate = Area: 6 acres, 3 roods, 24 perches. RV = £19.10s.0d. GER = £26.5s.0d.

The Valuations indicated that the rateable value for agricultural land, per acre, in the vicinity of Felin Lyn had the kind of pattern shown below. Monetary amounts are approximations.

Year	Bottom lands	Halfway hillsides	Top lands
1867	£1.12s.6d	£1.1s.0d.	11/-
1916	£1.0s.0d.	———	11/-

IX Country mill values, 1860-1880

Just as we are interested in comparing values and costs today, so it would be interesting to see the kind of costs a miller had to contend with in running his mill a hundred or two hundred years ago, especially if it related to Felin Lyn. Unfortunately this kind of information is very hard to come by.

The author, in his research, came across miscellaneous prices, jotted them down and found he had the greatest number of entries for the period 1860-80, which explains why it was chosen. The sources related to places all over Britain, so the review can only be regarded as a rough and ready indicator, but nevertheless revealing.

It is believed that in this period the average family income for England and Wales was about £80 per annum. Most of this was earned by the husband but often the wife and older children contributed by such work as clothes washing, caring for sick persons, field work and odd-jobbing.

One has to be cautious about thinking these were cash wages. For the country worker probably the majority of his wage would be in 'kind' and the minority in 'cash'. For a bachelor labourer living and working on a farm, perhaps one third of his earnings came in cash, another half was in food and the rest covered his crude accommodation. A married farm worker living in an estate cottage might have it rent free but the landlord took this into account when determining the man's wage, so the accommodation was neither free nor subsidized. The wages quoted immediately below are assumed to be the 'cash' component of the total wage.

Jobs

Welsh border farm labourer	1860	10 shillings per week
Female under 20, UK average	1867	7s.10d. per week
Male under 20, UK average	1867	7s.3d. per week
Welsh border farm labourer	1870	11 shillings per week
Hired miller, south England	1871	19 to 21s. per week
Mill carting lad	1871	10 shillings per week
Odd job man around mill	1871	2s.6d. per day

Mill carter	1874	13/- and 1 gallon flour per week
Pembrokeshire girl servant	1879	£8 10s. 0d per year, live-in, free board/bed
Shropshire canal warehouseman	1879	14/- to 16/- per week
Ploughman (his lad @ 6/-)	1880	18/- per week

Mill Machinery and Equipment

Iron waterwheel, 20ft diameter, 24" wide	1861	£340
Pair Derbyshire 'soft' stones, dia. unknown	1861	£30 (used)
Pair French burr stones, dia. unknown	1861	£70 (used)
100 sacks (2/6 each)	1871	£12-10-0
Pair Derbyshire 'soft' stones, 48" dia.	1873	£88 (new)
Pair French burr stones, 48" dia.	1875	£114(new)
Metal bushel measure	1877	10/4
Miller's weighscale (4 cwt capacity)	1881	£3.10.0
Dressing 1 pair millstones, 3 days	1885	30/-

Property Values

Woodbridge Tide Mill, Woodbridge, Suffolk, S.E. England. 1875. Total of £1,700.

Mill itself assessed at £500 and subdivided as follows: structure (wood) at £200, machinery at £250, tenant's fittings at £50. Construction of canal agent's cottage near Chirk 1874 for £200; rented at £8/p.a. or 3s. 7d/week. Scottish estate, 116,000 acres, average annual rent per acre in 1873 was 10/8d.

Other items

Simple iron plough	1860	£2-2-0.
Weekly cost of food for labourer, N. Wales	1863	3s.8d.
Weekly food cost for whole family re above entry	1863	15s 3d.
Hotel/inn room for 1 night/1 person, no food	1865	2/-
Man's overcoat	1865	£1-15-0.
Book 'Wild Wales' by G. Borrow, 347pp.	1868	6s. 0d.
Tea or tobacco, per ounce (duty of 6d/lb)	1870	ld.
Welsh ewe	1870	£2-4-0
Lamb	1870	14/6
2-wheeled cart to carry 20 cwt.	1871	£14-10-0
Pair of cart wheels, 4'6" dia.	1871	£6-10-0
Meat, averaging per lb	1875	9d per
Double bed with mattress	1875	£2-10-0.
Slaughter pig at 220 lbs	1877	£1-2-0.
Goose, for eating	1879	2s.6d.
Man's pair of boots	1880	16s. 0d.
Cow in calf	1880	£13-£16
Maintaining inmate in asylum	1880	1/5d per day
Best grade coal at Chirk pithead	1885	8/4d ton

X Medieval references to Ceiriog corn

The farming and milling of corn in the Ceiriog belongs to antiquity. It has been recorded for 600 years but of course is much older than that. The Felin Lyn that has been described in this book was, as it were, a member of a milling relay team that carried the baton in the final stage of the race.

Thanks to the proximity of Chirk Castle, its medieval record keeping, and the preservation of documents, an extraordinary amount of detail is known about the lower Ceiriog in earlier times. Two books recording a fraction of the archival material are listed here to indicate resource material.

Book *"Chirk Castle and Chirklands"*, Margaret Mahler, London, Bell & Sons, 1912, 231pp.

Mrs Mahler lived at Pen isa'r Glyn which lies between Felin Lyn and Chirk Castle. The following extracts illustrate cereal growing and grist milling; page location within the book is given in brackets after a date. Details in square brackets are not part of the original text.

1329 AD (p. 48)
And in repair of the woodwork of the mill of Llanarmon... and in one mill-stone bought for the same mill, 2s.

1330 AD (p. 53)
And in repair of the tools (ferramentum) of the said Mills for the year, 10d., from the lord's iron.

1330 AD (p. 54)

Proceeds of wheat to Michaelmas [29 Sept]	£20-15-0
Proceeds of oats to Michaelmas [29 Sept]	£1-2-8
Proceeds of pigs to St Martins [11 Nov]	£2-1-9

1331 AD (p. 61-2)
And of 4s.7d. of all customary tenants for reaping the corn in the autumn, namely 487 reapers. And of 4d. of Crogan Ithan [Crogen Iddon] for reaping beyond the reaping aforesaid. And of 16d. of certain reaping beyond the reaping in Glyn Vaur.
Of 65s.4d. of custom of free tenants of the whole Lordship for Trethmelyn. [Treth melin or mill tax was paid by those who were not forced to have their corn ground at the mill and who did not supply manual labour for upkeep work.]

1398 AD (p. 78)

Of £9.0s.10d. the price of 27 quarters and 1 bushel of corn and oatmeal flour, of rent there, at the term of All Saints [1 Nov] price of a bushel this year 10d. [In South Wales a year later price was 6d-8d / bushel] Of 7s.3d. the price of 3 quarters 5 bushels of oats, of rent there, at the feast of the Apostle Philip and James [1 May]. Price of a bushel this year 3d. [In South Wales a year later price was 6d / bushel for oats and 1/- per bushel for wheat]

1465 AD (92)
Of £4 of the tenants of Glyn of their purparty of £8 for turning the water to the lord's mill. [This '*turning the water to...*' is a recurring phrase through the centuries.] And of 75s 4d of rent of the mill of Glynvaur. And of 2s. of increase of rent of same mill. And of 10s, of rent of the mill of Crogen.

1526 AD (p. 113)
And took of the King one parcel of waste land to build a fulling mill in the towne of Chirk, to wit in length from le Pant Kerigk up to a place where the water, turning the mill of the Lord King [Chirk Castle was at this time owned by the Crown] called Melin y Waun [Chirk mill] falls into the river Keiriog...

1529 AD (p. 124)
Sawyares: Item payed to Ieuan ap Hoell ap Robert and his brother for sawyng of halfe a roode of Tymber. [Included to relate to sawmillng in Chapter 4]

1590 AD (p. 142)
[The lease agreement for a watercourse to a fulling mill at Bron-y-garth has an interesting penalty clause. Should the tenant default on his rent payments, then the landlord may] entre and breke downe to the myddyste of the said Ryver Keriog all the said watter corse and all maner hedges, stakes, and stones, whyche be ther sett for the turnyng of the said watter corse.

1620 AD (p. 160)
Paid to Ned Fenton for 6 measure of wheate to sowe in ye [Chirk] Castle park-19s.0d. Payd for da gwynpowder to kyl crowes-8d.
1689 AD (Chirk Castle Accounts)
Thomas Sympson received £1-2s-0d. for 15 thraves of rye straw to repair his outhouses. [Quoted to show that rye was grown in the area; a 'thrave' was a measure of straw and fodder and contained 24 sheaves of corn or pulse.].

Book- "*The Extent of Chlrkland, 1391-93*", G.P.Jones, London, University Press of Liverpool (Hodder & Stoughton), 1933, 103pp.
This book is an exact reproduction, in Latin, of all the holdings in the Lordship of Chirk in the last decade of the 1300s. For each holding it lists: gavella size, tenant name, amount and type of taxes to be paid – in much detail. A 'gavella' was a land unit, theoretically of some 64 Welsh acres, but in practice had variable size.

The author neither translated into English, nor analyzed and summarized the data. Chirkland then consisted of about 100 square miles of which half was settled and half was mountain 'waste'. It was divided into four parts for rent and legal administration and one of these was 'Glynn', which was the land between Chirk Castle and Glynceiriog. The upper parts of the Ceiriog appear not to have been settled but this is contradicted by Mahler's book that shows a mill at Llanarmon 80 years earlier.

Within the 'Ringildry of Glynn' there are 75 holdings listed by size of gavella, namely: 1 double-gavella, 35 gavella, 25 half-gavella, 11 quarter-gavella, and 3 lesser.

The farm of 'Nant Goryt' will be taken as an example of the ledger detail and because it was then the largest farm in the 'Glynn'. Its joint tenants were Jeuan ap Ithell, Eigon ap Madog, and David ap Eigon. They paid 17 annual taxes and levies totaling 211 pence and four items of farm produce. These comprised: rent of 80d, 28d for "*de operibus molendini de Chirc*" (Chirk mill expenses), 103d for 11 other levies, plus 8 measures (gogr) of barley, $^1/_2$ bushel of oats, 2 lambs and 2 hens.

XI Harvest extremes 1790 to 1890; prodigious and ruinous

Until about 1880 harvests were of the utmost importance to each and every living person in Britain. A bountiful harvest meant good eating for the year, a bad one spelt anything from belt tightening to subsistence living. To the miller and farmer it could mean a dramatic difference to their annual incomes.

In spite of the importance of the subject, there appears to be no literature about harvest extremes. This Appendix has been included to provide some needed focus and to show in what years people were affected, especially in regard to the Ceiriog and Felin Lyn.

It has been assumed arbitrarily that in 100 years there will be ten exceptionally good harvests and ten exceptionally bad ones, leaving the residual 80% to be considered 'normal'.

Investigation of the subject soon disclosed three problems. The assessment of harvest quality is largely subjective and judgments are scarce and random. They also range over several generations in a 100 year period, so there is no absolute consistency of judgement. It was also found that there were as twice as many reports about bad harvests as there were for good. Reflection tells us this is normal because we can usually recollect when we were seriously ill but not when we were extremely well. Finally, in some cases there were contradictory assessments about a given harvest over a 24-month period. This was because a farmer would give his opinion just after the harvest, but consumers, corn factors and others, would likely voice theirs in the following summer.

Notwithstanding these minor obstacles, it was possible to make a tentative plot of harvest extremes for the 100 years, 1790-1890. These apply to the whole of Britain and not just Wales. A word of caution about the table below. It is experimental and is intended to help others investigating local or national harvest extremes, and be subject to future refinement by others. Years shown in bold type indicate greater certainty.

Prodigious	Ruinous
1802	**1795**
1807	1799
1813	1800
1815	**1810**
1822	**1816**
1834	**1818**
1842	1828
1849	1836
1854	**1839**
1863	**1848**
1868	**1853**
1874	**1879***
	1888

(*) The Guiness Book of Records states that the coldest and wettest summer in Britain between 1728 and 1978 was 1879.

In addition to these extremes, it was noted there were also periods of successive above-average or below-average harvests. They were: *Good:* 1831-36; 1883-90. *Bad:* 1792-1812 [*"In this period of twenty years there were 14 poor seasons of which seven were shockingly bad."*]; 1828-30: 1837-39; 1852-56; 1865-69; 1874-82.

Other incidental information surfaced during the survey and is worthy of inclusion. The harvest extremes seemed attributable in all cases to weather and not to crop disease. The weather pattern needed to produce an extreme seemed to be one that blanketed Britain in sunlight and judicious amounts of rain or perpetual rain or very prolonged drought. In normal harvests the weather appeared to be more fitful and regionalised.

Quantitative terms were rarely mentioned but when given were: Prodigious = plus 25%; Ruinous = minus 20%, 33%, 37%, 50%.

Harvesting commenced with the first field to be cut and ended when the last wagon trundled into the rickyard. How long did this operation take ? A few harvesting dates were given but all relate to England. They were:- 20 July to 3 Sept; 26 July to 6 Sept; 31 July to 26 Aug; 3 Aug to 28 Aug; 6 Aug to 8 Oct. One Gloucestershire farm maintained a record of harvest duration for the years 1830 to 1865. The median duration was 31 days, with a range of 22 to 49 days plus one abnormality of 71 days; the 'normal' band seemed to lie between 29 and 36 days.

Potential book sources: "Agricultural Records" (AD 220-1977); "Seasons and Prices" (18th & 19th C.); "History of Prices" (1750-1855).

XII Weights, measures and money

This appendix lists the weights, measures, and money in use when Felin Lyn was in operation from the late 18th century to 1936. Very little change occurred in this period. The only significant change that directly affected the Mill was the Weights and Measures Act of 1824 which altered the bushel size by 3%. Prior to this time there were different measures for dry and liquid capacity and the legislation simplified the situation by creating a new gallon and making dry and liquid measures identical. The new 'Imperial' gallon was 20% larger than the old one and contained 10lbs of water. For several hundred of years a bushel had contained eight 'dry' gallons and this concept was continued. The new 'Imperial' bushel held the space that was occupied by 80lbs of water, which came to 2218 cubic inches. More exacting calculations in 1932 altered it to 2219.37 cubic inches. The older 'Winchester' bushel became obsolete in the British Empire but continues to be used to this day in the USA.

There was a further Weights and Measures Act of 1835 which tightened control and gave further protection to the buyer. For the first time Felin Lyn and other mills had to ensure their bushel measures were of exact capacity and were *'denominated, stamped or marked on the outside in legible figures and letters'*. The Act also set the Stone at 14 lbs, the Hundredweight at 112 lbs and the Ton at 2,240 lbs, and outlawed Stones of other poundages. The Act also authorised Counties to appoint Inspectors who would have copies of the London Parliamentary weights and measures, and would have powers to enforce this and earlier Acts.

The Weights and Measures Act of 1878 dealt mainly with administration and changed none of the essentials.

In matters of currency there was less change, except that the worth of a coin diminished over 150 years due to creeping inflation. A farthing that was a meaningful coin in 1775 had become worthless by 1935.

It is quite probable most of the money that changed hands at Felin Lyn were in the form of coinage, for paper money in the form of 10/- and £1 notes was not introduced by the Bank of England until 1928.

Coins seen at Felin Lyn would have been: penny (and, in earlier times, 3d, 4d), sixpence, shilling, half-crown, half-sovereign and sovereign. For values of these coins see table below. Pennies were made of copper, the medium value coins in silver, and the sovereigns in gold. The inherent value of these coins, which had been untampered with for several centuries, underwent change because of problems created by World War I. In 1914 the sovereign was withdrawn from circulation to create stocks of gold bullion and in 1920 silver coinage was debased by making such coins have 50% silver and 50% alloy content; not since Edward IV had such debasement occurred.

Nowadays we readily accept that notes and coins are acting as tokens for money values but in the days of Felin Lyn everyone knew that any coin held its value within itself in the form of semi or precious metal.

The following tables present units in use when Felin Lyn was at work. Symbols or abbreviations for units are given in square brackets.

Length

12 inches [inch]	= 1 foot [ft]
3 feet	= 1 yard [yd]
220 yards	= 1 furlong*
8 furlongs	= 1 mile [ml]

Area

9 square feet	= 1 square yard
4 roods (1210 square yards)	= 1 acre or 4840 square yards
640 acres	= 1 square mile

Acre was originally defined as being 1 furlong in length by 1 chain (22 yards) in width.

Capacity

2 pints [pt]	= 1 quart [qt]
4 quarts	= 1 gallon [gal]
2 gallons	= 1 peck [pk]
4 pecks	= 1 bushel [bu]
8 bushels	= 1 Quarter [Qr]

Weight

16 ounces [oz]	= 1 pound avoirdupois [lb]
14 lbs	= 1 stone [st]
8 stones	= 1 hundredweight [cwt] 112 lbs
20 cwt	= 1 ton (2240 lbs)

Money

2 farthings ($^1/_4$d)	= 1 half-penny ($^1/_2$d)
2 half-pennies	= 1 penny (1d)
12 pence	= 1 shilling (1s. or 1/-)
20 shillings	= 1 pound sterling (£1)

Coins used at various times, whose values were not self-evident, were: *florin* (2/-), *half-crown* (2/6), *crown* (5/-), *half-sovereign* (10/-), *sovereign* (20/-) and *guinea* (21/-).

Percentage parts of a £ were: Penny = 0.4%, 6d = 2$^1/_2$%, 1/- = 5%, 2/6 = 12$^1/_2$%. 5/- = 25%, 10/- = 50%, 15/- = 75%.

Imperial to metric conversions

1 inch	= 2.54 centimetres
1 foot	= 0.305 metres
1 yard	= 0.914 metres
1 furlong	= 201.2 metres
1 mile	= 1.609 kilometres
1 rood	= 1012 square metres
1 acre	= 4047 square metres or 0.405 hectares
1 square mile	= 259 hectares
1 pound weight (lb)	= 0.454 kilograms
1 hundredweight (112 lbs)	= 50.80 kilograms
1 ton (2240 lbs)	= 1016 kilograms
1 gallon	= 4.546 litres
1 bushel	= 36.37 litres or 0.0364 cubic metres
1 cubic yard	= 0.765 cubic metres

Glossary

Cereal terms used by farmer, miller and customer

Most milling glossaries cover the technical details of mill machinery. This one aims to be complementary by ignoring the mechanical aspects and touching on much else. Words in **bold type** within a definition, indicate that the word itself is defined elsewhere in the glossary.

ANIMAL FOOD Country cornmills in last 150 years of their existence probably produced as much food for animals as they did for humans, if not more. This would be bruised oats, barley, and maize but never wheat, and 'dross' of all grinding. See **provender.**

AWN One of bristly hairs forming beard on head of grasses; for British grown grains is prominent in barley. Better recognized in word 'awning', a protection.

BARLEY Hardiest of temperate cereals and will grow as far north as 70° latitude in Norway. Shallow rooted. Grown everywhere in Wales but densest in south-west and in early part of this century was grown twice as extensively as wheat. Used from early times to make beer and provide animal fodder. In Welsh called 'haidd'.

BARN Building where sheaves of **corn** were stored and then subsequently threshed in batches through winter and spring.

BERE Four rowed barley, once widely grown in eastern and lowland Scotland; origin of word **barn** and beer.

BIN FLOOR Temporary storage for sacked or loose grain in uppermost floor of mill prior to processing. Divided by partitions into bays or 'bins'; also called 'garner'. See **parcel.**

BOLT (v) To sift meal by mechanical means through wire or cloth sieves to produce fine to coarse gradings. See **dressers.**

BREAD Dough made of some type of flour, fermented and baked into flat breads (oatcakes, barley) or risen breads (rye, wheat). In Wales formerly made using one or more types of grain but since 19th century almost exclusively of wheat. See **leavening.**

BOLL Former basic grain measure of capacity in Scotland and northern England. Scandanavian origins. Related to words *bowl* and *beaker.*

BRAN Outer protective covering of **kernel** containing valuable food trace elements but largely indigestible to humans. Comprises about 15% of kernel.

BUSHEL Measure of dry capacity formerly used in most English speaking countries, but which is now being displaced by metric units. See Appendix II for details.

CEREALS Grains used as human and/or animal foods throughout the world, e.g.; rice.Word itself is derived from 'Ceres', Roman goddess of agriculture.

CHAFF Short **straws, hulls/husks.** Properly is husk or dry calyx of cereals.

CLEANER Machine used to remove **chaff,** dirt, dust, and weed seeds from **grain,** prior to milling. Uses principle of sieving in rotating wire mesh drum and air current. Cleaner used horizontal drums, whilst **smutters** had vertical ones. Smut is black fungus which attacks cereals.

COARSE GRAINS Include oats, barley and rye, all capable of being ground on soft **millstones.**

COOM Measure of 4 bushels; Danish origins. Also spelt *comb* and *coomb.*

CORN Dominant **cereal** crop(s) of particular country or region, e.g.; in Wales was oats until this century and in much of England has always been wheat. For Britain as a whole, wheat, barley and oats, can be regarded as its 'corn'. Originally was bread-making grain of a locality and was spelt with a 'k' as in korn, kaum, koren, kern, etc. When second or third grain was introduced to area, name distinction had to be made but use of word 'korn/corn' persists to this day. Winter corn is sown in autumn and harvested following year, whilst Spring corn is sown and harvested in same year. In North America the word has entirely different meaning and refers only to **maize** or its alternative name of Indian Corn. Americans use the term **grain** where the British would use corn.

CORNMILL Place where machinery was powered by water or wind to **grind** corn or **pulses** to **meal** or **flour.**

CORN CHANDLER Corn dealer; chandler is corruption of Teutonic 'handler', meaning trader.

CORN EXCHANGE Place where grain was sold or bartered and samples shown and examined; 19th century innovation.

CORN LAWS Series of laws dating back to 1436 which regulated import/export of grain in Britain. Largely repealed in 1846; this date marks the shift of prime power in Britain from agriculture (landowners) to industry (business).

CORN SCOOP Shovel made of wood with slightly concave blade about 15 inches long × 12 inches wide; shortish handle. Metal tools were not used in grain handling.

DREDGE CORN Sowing of two or more grain as oats and barley; often **forage** or **fodder** crop. In Welsh 'siprys'; see also **maslin.**

DRESSERS Machines used for **bolting** meal into various grades of fineness. *'Bolter'* or *'silk reel'* uses cylinder of cloth; *'wire machine'* has wire sleeve; *'Jog-scry'* and *'plansifter'* use oscillating sieve trays.

EAR Fruiting spike of any **cereal** holding from 10-100 individual grains or berries.

EMBRYO Also called 'germ'. Life starter when seed is planted, rich in nutrients including oil. Comprises one-fiftieth of whole seed.

ENDOSPERM Starchy white part of cereal grain which man is anxious to eat. Constitutes 85% of a grain by weight. Nourishes **embryo** when first planted.

FARMING (cereals) Consult old dictionaries for such terms as: Barn, Binder or Bindster, Bird-scaring, Flail, Glean, Grange, Harvest-home, Hummeller, Mow, Reap, Rick, Scythe, Seed broadcasting, **Sheaf,** Shock or Stook, Sickle, Smut, Staddle-stone, Thrave, Thresh, Winnow.

FIELD (arable) Obvious but essential feature of grain production. In Wales enclosure surrounded by hedge or stone wall and prior to this century averaged 3-5 acres. Ploughed by oxen until 1700s when horses introduced. Altitude, soil type & quality, drainage, sun exposure, wind shelter, and husbandry all affected grain yield.

FINNINGS Best and finest grade of **flour.**

FLOUR Finely ground **meal**, nowadays invariably **bolted.** In previous centuries was preceded by adjective to describe type, e.g.: rye-flour, wheaten flour. Nowadays presumed to be always made from wheat. 'Flour mill' originally meant mill equipped with 'hard' stones and so therefore capable of grinding wheat satisfactorily.

FODDER Entire cereal plant, excepting its roots, fed in **sheaf** form to animals.

FORAGE Animal food. Mills supplied substantial amounts of forage for fattening animals for slaughter or providing energy for draught animals.

GEARING Transmission of power by rotative force, by means of shafts and gear wheels.

GERM See **embryo.**

GLEANER Originally person who took stalks cut by reaper and fashioned them into a **sheaf**. Later, poor person who searched cornfield, after all stooks removed, for loose grain for free.

GLUTEN Sticky protein substance found in wheat (10% by weight of kernel) and to lesser extent in other grains. Gives **bread** dough its elastic qualities and ability to retain gases.

GRAIN Seedlike fruit of any cereal grass, rich in easily digested starches. In the singular, one cereal berry, grain or fruit. In bulk called **corn**. In North America used in place of word 'corn'.

GRANARY Room expressly allocated to storage of grain, after threshing, on a farm. Mostly sited above cart shed with external access. Grain was stored in sacks or loose on floor.

GRANGE Originally farm primarily devoted to cereal growing. Grange, garner and granary stem from Latin *granum* (grain).

GRAVITY HEAD Vertical distance water falls from headrace to tailrace; also called 'Head of water'.

GRIND (v) To crush substances between **millstones,** such as apples, components of paint, earthenware or gunpowder. For cornmill this was limited to grains and **pulses.** Synonymous with **milling** but appears to be verb commonly in use prior to 1900.

GRIST Comes from Old English word 'grind'. Before 17th century all corn mills were called grist mills. Has had meanings of (a) corn or pulses before milling, (b) meal after milling; now refers to animal feed/coarse meal.

GRISTMILL More primitive type of **cornmill,** usually having ability only to grind **coarse grains** and performed no **bolting.**

GRITS Corn which is **hulled** and very coarsely ground.

GROAT Naked **oat** with **husk** removed but not yet ground. Also called **hulled** or **shelled** oats. For the two other cereals, term is 'wheat berry' and 'pot barley'.

HEADRACE See **millrace.**

HORIZONTAL WATERMILL This and sail-boat claimed to be world's oldest prime movers. Turbine attached to vertical shaft drove set of millstones, without intermediary gearing. Also called a 'Norse' wheel.

HULL/HUSK Protective and separate outer covering of **kernel.** Also called 'shell'. Verb is *hulling* and *shelling*.

HUMMELLING Manual process of separating **awns** (spikes or beards) from heads of barley with iron striker.

HURSTING Strong timber framework supporting the **millstones** and **gearing** and independant of mill walls.

INDIAN CORN See **maize.**

KERNEL Whole grain but excluding **husk.** In everyday speech often used to describe one whole grain in its natural state with husk attached - no one word exists for this. Etymologically is diminutive of 'kern' or 'korn' – see **corn.**

KIBBLE (v) To grind coarsely for animal food.

KILN Room heated with hot air draught which toasted **oats** to make **husk** brittle and so easier to remove, and to substantially reduce moisture content; also used in **malt**ing process. Root word is Latin 'culina', kitchen.

LAUNDER Trough made of metal or wood to drop water onto top of overshot **waterwheel**; also called flume, fleam, pen-stock, pen-trough, sluiceway. Prefix 'pen' derives from penning a stream; pent-up. It is one of few Celtic words absorbed into the English language and in successor tongue of Welsh means 'head' or 'end'.

LEAT See **millrace.** Never spelt 'leet' which has entirely different meaning.

LEAVENING Yeast or other agent added to bread dough to create fermentation and so produce a risen loaf.

LEDGER Book kept permanently in one place, usually close to main door of mill; all transactions were recorded in it.

M-root A word has been needed, ever since man has harvested wild or tamed grain, to describe pulverizing action needed to crush open grain **kernel**. In some ancient now-lost language of western Asia it had an 'M' sound and has descended in all Romance, Slavonic, Germanic and Celtic languages as word beginning with 'M' and having all forms of the obligatory vowel following it. Synonyms would be: *beat, bray, bruise, crush, grind, mash, mill, pound, pulverize, smash*. Examples of the word, as noun or verb, in various languages: *macinare* (Italian), *melin* (Welsh), *moudre* (French), *molino* (Spanish), *muhle* (German), *mlyn* (Polish), *moller* (Swedish). In English the sense of 'to pound' survives in several 'M' words; e.g.: *mall* (beaten path), *maul* (heavy wood hammer), *mallet[te]* (small wooden hammer), *molar* (tooth for grinding), *meal* (repast of bruised grain); all have their origins in this ancient 'M' sounding word.

MAIZE Cereal not native to Britain but introduced as import in mid 19th century for animal feed. Also called Indian Corn. Has three staes; on the cob, shelled and meal. Mainstay of most country mills in first half of 20th century. Currently ranks second as a world cereal. In Welsh formerly called 'gwenith yr India' but nowadays 'corn melys'.

MALT Partly germinated grain, usually barley, dried and cured. Used in making beer. Has nutritional value. Loses quarter of its weight when **kiln**ed**.**

MASLIN Mixture of grains, especially rye and wheat. Also written *'mashlin', 'mashlim'*, or *'mashlum'*. Derives from word *'mash'* which in turn comes from old English word meaning to mix. Most grains grow better when mixed than as single grain crop. *'Mash-haver'* was dialect word for hot-water mashed oats used as animal feed, *'haver'* being German/Scandanavian for oats.

MEAL Result of grinding **grain** or **pulses** between **millstones,** prior to further refinement. Contains all the **bran.** When sifted produced **flour.** Wheatmeal and barleymeal are now obsolete terms but **oatmeal** continues to be used. 'Whole wheatmeal' means wheat ground to meal but from which nothing has been abstracted. 'Wheatmeal' means much of the bran has been removed (5-10% of total grain). Meal monger was a trader.

MEAL FLOOR Ground floor of mill containing transmission machinery and products of first grinding, i.e.; meal.

MIDDLINGS That part of kernel between bran covering and starchy central interior which is tough and resists grinding. Coarser parts of flour, an intermediate grade. See also **offal** and **shorts.** Animal food.

MILL (grain) Device to make human and animal food more edible.

MILLER As a surname, heavily represented by Miller, and to a lessening extent by Miles, Mills, Millar, Miln(e), Milner, Millward and Melin. Many men and boys with the surname Miller have had to carry the nickname Dusty.

MILLING In narrow sense, synonymous with **grind**ing. In wider sense, whole art of managing a mill.

MILLRACE Ditch to carry water from source to **waterwheel** varying from 50 yards to one mile length. If there was a millpond, short section between it and mill could also be built of wood, brick/stone, concrete, iron, and either be open or piped. Inference that millrace is artificial cut and millstream is natural adaptation. Also called: goyt, lade, leat, millrun, water-course. Divided by mill into two parts: *headrace/headwater* and *tailrace/milltail/millwash.* Lower end of headrace is connected to waterwheel with **launder.**

MILLSTONES Pair consists of 'upper or runner' revolving stone, and 'bed/bottom/nether' stationary stone. Stones themselves were rated as 'hard' or 'soft' and were used for different grinding operations.

MILLSTREAM See **millrace.**

MILLWRIGHT Craftsman who designed and/or repaired mill machinery. A 'wright' (as in shipwright or wainwright) was to wood as a 'smith' was to metal.

OAT Was traditional and dominant grain of Wales until this century because it was suited to soil and climate. Was grown extensively in all 13 former counties of Wales from sea-level to 1,200 ft; prime oat counties in descending order were: Pembrokeshire, Anglesey, Denbighshire, Flintshire, Montgomeryshire and Cardiganshire. It belongs to botanical Family of 'Grasses' and Genus of 'Avena' (this was the Roman's name for plant). In Welsh it is called 'ceirchen'.

OATCAKE Thin flat cake made of oatmeal mixed with water, milk or buttermilk and baked on a griddle or in an oven.

OATMEAL Result of grinding **groats** to a meal and bolting. Contains natural antioxidant that prevents staleness for several months.

OFFAL Milling process produces two basic commodities – flour and offal. Offal is less desirable residue after meal has been bolted and is fit only for animal food. Consists of parts of **bran, shorts** and **middlings,** and totals nearly a quarter of the whole kernel.

PARCEL Small delivery of grain to mill for grinding, which by segregation retained its identity and ownership as it was processed. End products returned to owner. Feature of **toll** milling. In upland mills, varied in size from single sack to contents of two-wheeled cart with processing time ranging from half-hour to half day.

PIG See **swine.**

POLLARD Finer grade of bran containing some flour; animal food. Also called gurgeons.

PROVENDER Dry food for domestic animals, such as hay, straw, and coarsely ground grain; especially mixture of meal and chopped straw and hay. Almost all corn watermills in Britain became provender mills in the 20th century. See **animal food**.

PULSE Edible seeds of leguminous plants, such as peas and beans. Until beginning of 19th century these were frequently taken to gristmills to be ground to **meal** for human consumption. It was one of the components of *"all grist to the mill"*.

QUARTER Confusingly, measures of both volume and weight. For volume, spelt with capital 'Q' and contained 8 bushels; for weight, spelt with small 'q' and was a quarter of a hundredweight (cwt.) at 28 lbs.

QUARTERN Loaf of 4 lbs.

QUERN Primitive hand-held stone mill in universal use in Britain prior to 10th century and in slowly diminishing use till its virtual extinction in about 17th century. A woman's tool and part of her household duties. Quern and churning may be related to the Welsh word 'chwyrn' meaning whirl or rapid motion.

RANCIDITY Milling releases fats in cereals which turns flour rancid within 2 weeks to 3 months. Wheat most, and oats least, affected. Explains why **embryo** was removed in factory flour milling from late 19th century onwards.

RIPARIAN RIGHTS Legal water rights held by owner of land that borders **waterway.**

ROLLED OATS **Groats** that have been passed through rollers to produce flakes. Regular and quick-cooking rolled oats differ only in thinness of flakes.

RYE One of quarter of European cereals. Does well on poor sandy soils and is admirably suited to infertile plain of north central Europe where it is chief cereal crop and bread flour. Has always been little grown in Wales and largely disappeared by 1800 when wheat was becoming dominant bread stuff. Subsequently grown only as occasional green **fodder.**

SACK Universal handling container on farms and in small mills. Made of stout woven material. Usually held 4 bushels of grain, meal or flour.

SAWMILLING (Refers only to when timber and grain milling are found at the same site.) Function added to probably less than 5% of all cornmills in 19th century. Used 'up and down' saw blade(s). Late innovation outmoded before 1900 by specialist steam-driven sawmills using circular saws. A few survivors were still at work in the first half of the 20th century.

SEMOLINA Hard particles of wheat that resist grinding and are collected as rounded pieces. Can be ground to coarse flour. Mixture of **sharps** and **middlings.** Derived from Italian 'se-molina' meaning half-ground.

SHARPS Hard pieces of **endosperm** that defy first grinding. Either ground second time or set aside as animal feed. See **middlings.**

SHEAF Bundle of cereal plants bound together after reaping, about 12 inch diameter at waist. Originally amount of stalks cut in one sweep of sickle. Farmers' basic unit of grain crop handling for at least 3,000 years until eclipsed by combine harvester in this mid century. Plural: sheaves; verb: to sheave. Stood upright in fields, for grain heads to dry out, in clusters of six and upwards, called stooks; variants shock, shook.

SHELLING Removal of **hull/husk** by millstones leaving **kernel** intact; usually associated with **oats.** Also spelt: *shealing, sheeling, sheiling, shilling, skilling.*

SHORTS Mixture of fine **bran, embryo** and coarse parts of **meal.** Shorts and **middlings** account for about 12% of kernel.

SLUICE GATE Vertical sliding gate in frame which is used to regulate water volume flow. Sluice is a constriction. Occassionally called staunch.

SMUTTER See **cleaner.** Smut is fungus infection of grain heads.

STIVE Floating dust within mill; archaic root word meant to stifle/suffocate.

STONE DESSSER District or itinerant tradesman who re-sharpened cutting surfaces of **millstones;** also called stone picker, cadger.

STONE FLOOR Floor on which grinding is done. Above is **bin floor** and below **meal floor**.

STONE FURNITURE Wooden components over and around millstones including hopper, horse and tuns/vats.

STRAW Stalk of plant on which ears of grain grow. Refers to state when cut and dried out.

STRIKE/STRUCK To ensure correct bushel measure, measure itself was filled to overflowing and then stick or roller was drawn across its rim. At this point fair measure had been obtained and bushel was 'struck'.

SWINE The miller's animal. Precise terms were: piglet= newborn; gilt= young female; boar= breeding male; sow=mature female; drove= collective noun.

THIRDS What is left after milled wheat has had its flour and bran extracted by bolting, i.e: third part. It is dross of refining operation and makes very palatable animal feed. See also **middlings, offal, sharps** and **shorts.**

TITHES Annual payment of one-tenth of land's produce in form of corn, wool, etc. to medieval church and later Church of England. Converted in 1836 to cash based upon prevailing corn prices and soon became known as Corn Rent. System subject to later amendments and was abolished by 1925.

TOLL MILL Mill in which miller performed service but took no financial risk. Ground corn of neighbouring farmers, processing each customer's **parcel** separately. Charged fee or 'toll' which was usually ranged between one-eighth and one-tenth of grain to be ground. This was measured in toll-dish or multure bowl.

TRADING MILL One operated as business venture with associated profits and risks. Miller bought grain, usually in quantity from few sources, processed it and then sold products locally. Development of late 19th century for country cornmills.

WATER 'Fuel' of watermill. One gallon weighs 10 lbs and occupies 277 cubic inches; one cubic foot of water weighs 62.4 lb and holds $6^1/_4$ gallons.

WATERWAYS Terms for natural water gatherers are imprecise but can be categorized as follows. Those too small to turn waterwheel are Drain, Gutter, Level, Rhine, Rill, Rivulet, Runnel, Runlet. Small tributaries that can turn breast or overshot wheel are Allt, Beck, Bourne, Brook, Burn, Clough, Gill/Ghyll, Pant, Stream. The lesser or principal trunk with more even grade and suited to undershot wheel is Afon, River, Water.

WATERWHEEL 'Overshot' type is where water discharges onto top of wheel and turns it by initial impetus and weight; common to hilly districts and often found in British uplands. 'Undershot' type has stream water directed at bottom of wheel which is always submerged; common to flatlands. 'Breastshot' type is where water enters wheel at about axle level.

WEATINGS Inseparable mixture of bran and flour; used for animal feed.

WEIR Permanent dam across river or stream to capture water for **millrace** or pond. 'Spillway' or 'apron' takes surplus water over top of weir. There is also English regional word 'lasher' which can mean weir itself, water falling over it, or pool below weir.

WHEAT Very much grain crop of England, but in Wales least grown of all cereals. In Wales confined to lowland plains and deep river valleys with largest concentration in north-east. Suited to clay soils or rich heavy loams, wheat requires mean summer temperature of at least 55°F for 3-4 months to ripen, plus minimal rain. In Welsh called 'gwenith'.

WHOLEMEAL Unadulterated fine meal or coarser flour from which nothing has been removed (except large flakes of bran) and nothing added. No bleaching.

WIDDERSHINS Counter-clockwise (which is counter-sun) rotational direction of millstones. Scottish derivation.

Sources

Primary

Hughes, John (1802-89). Carries identifier (Dol) in text. Brought up at Dolywern gristmill and finished working life as woollen manufacturer at Llangollen. Man of natural curiosity with a talent for illustrating what he was describing. Produced two notebooks (Vol. 1 is 336pp, Vol 2 is 86pp) in Welsh, and some English, of memoirs and ephemera. Held by Welsh Folk Museum as MS 3021 and 2872. Contains slight but valuable direct or related references to Felin Lyn.

Jones, Gwladys nee *Evans* (1902-92). Carries identifier (FL) in text. Eldest daughter of Edward & Jane Evans II. Born and brought up at Felin Lyn. Recollections contained in several letters written to author in 1981-85.

Borrow, George (1803-81). Traveller and author with publications spanning period 1841 to 1874. Ceiriog references appear in his book "*Wild Wales*" published in 1862 and resulting from 1854 walking tour. They are, moving upstream: *Chirk & Castlemill*, Chapter 54; ***Pontfadog & Graig***, Chapter 11; *Glynceiriog*, Chapter 17; *Pandy*, Chapter 20 & 21; *Tregeiriog & Llanarmon*, Chapter 64.

Roberts, Thomas (1906-87). Farmer, Bonc Farm, Llwynmawr, Denbighshire. Memories. By 1985 was last surviving former farmer-customer of Felin Lyn.

Phillips, Jonah (1858-1929). Joiner & wheelwright, Glynceiriog, Denbighshire. '*Account Book*' written in Welsh and covering period 1913-20, of about 120 pp. Four references to work done at Felin Lyn; held privately in Ceiriog.

Heald, George (1922-91). Born and brought up at Pentrevoelas Mill, Denbighshire. Took to banking and retired as a manager. Lifelong interest in milling resulting in knowledgeable articles in retirement. Inspected many mills, including Felin Lyn, in early part of WWII (for Denbighshire War Agricultural Committee) to see if they could be used for war effort.

Abraham, Mitford (1885-1959). Lifetime hobby of studying and recording corn mills in mid & northern England, Covered 700 windmills and 250 watermills mainly in the years 1925-40. By rare circumstances he recorded Felin Lyn. His collection of 1,080 photographs and negatives and related notes are held by John Rylands Library of Manchester University. 224 glass plate slides are held by Society for Protection of Ancient Buildings, London.

Tithe Map & Apportionment, 1839, Llangollen Parish. Townships of Hafodgynfor, Nantgwryd, & Talygarth. Specifically, parcels 346, 347, & 561. Valuer was Edward Tench, Junior, of Plas Newydd, Ruabon. Parish copy held by Denbighshire Record Office, Ruthin.

British Census Returns, 1851, 1861, 1871, 1881, 1891.

Property Tax Valuations. Listed in detail in Appendix VIII.

Ordnance Survey Maps. (a) 25 inch/mile, Denbighshire, Sheet XXXIX-12, 1899 and 1912. (b) 6 inch/mile, Denb. Sheet XXXIX-S.E., 1880,1900 and 1914. (c) 2$^{1}/_{2}$ inch/mile, Sheet SJ23,Chirk, 1957. First two sets of maps give good detail, last map provides hill contour profiles.

Conveyances of Property. Two, dated 10th July 1931 and 20th July 1962. Held by author.

Invoices: Glyn Valley (horse) Tramway, Sept 1881-April 1883. Ledger book, size 25" x 22", of 170 pages holding 1,960 pasted-in copy invoices; 135 invoices relate to Felin Lyn. Held privately in Dyffryn Ceiriog.

Illustrations. All known surviving photos of acceptable quality and one watercolor have been reproduced in this book. A c1908 photo showing outbuildings of Felin Lyn appears on page 65 of '*Glain-y-Glyn*', Handbook of Ceiriog Memorial Institute, Glynceiriog, 1933, 72pp.

Mills on the Ceiriog, by J.W. Davies (1906-73). Series of seven newspaper articles in *Border Counties Advertiser*, Oswestry, Shropshire, under sub-heading '*Bye-gones*'. Printed between 16th April and 28th May, 1941, inclusive. Felin Lyn entry appears in issue dated 23rd April.

Newspaper Articles, *Llangollen Advertizer*: (a1) 'Opening of Iron Bridge at Pontfadog', 17 August 1894; (a2) 'Accidental Death of Miller's Wife, Pontfadog', 16 February 1900. *Oswestry & Border Counties Advertizer*, Oswestry: (b1) 'Death of John Jones, Surrey', 15 September 1909; (b2) 'Tenancy of a Pontfadog Small-holding', 29th August 1951. [Kindly supplied by late Richard D. Thomas of Ontario, Canada, in 1985, who had retained it since time of clipping]; (b3) 'Children at Risk in Mystery Mill', 30 January 1980; accompanying photo shows ruined barn.

Survey and Measurements of Mill. Taken by late Ifor Edwards (1915-92), well known Denbighshire historian, and his Wrexham students in 1980, and by author in 1981.

Aerial Photo of lower half of Ceiriog. Print nos. 5043-46 & 5149-51. Taken by RAF c1945-50. Useful for visualizing topography and examining field crop patterns. At this period there was still an intensity of arable farming (due to WWII) in the district so it demonstrates what is possible.

Demolition Order. Felin Lyn, per Section 25, Public Health Act of 1961, Glyndwr District Council, Ruthin, effected 21st September, 1981.

Meal chest

Secondary sources have already been listed in Chapter Notes. This part of the bibliography details some sources which may prove useful to readers who are researching the Ceiriog, upland watermills or country life.

Welsh Dictionary. Spurrell's *Cymraeg-Saesneg & English-Welsh.* London, William Collins Ltd, 1960, 317 pp., which is a pocket edition. Spurrell dictionaries have been in use in Wales for over a century.

"Encyclopedia Britannica". An overlooked but useful source, the older the edition the better, preferably pre-1930. The 12th Edition is 1922 and the 9th is 1875. See such entries as – *Corn Laws, Diets, Flour, Grain Trade, Granaries, Oats*, etc.

"Local Historian's Encyclopedia", John Richardson, Hertfordshire, Historical Publications Ltd, 1977, 312pp. Heavy on data, short on prose. Covers 18 aspects, e.g.: *Taxes/Rents/Rates/Dues, Law & Order, Social Welfare, Education, Land/Agriculture.*

Weights & Measures. Most useful source is *Second Report of the Commissioners appointed to consider the subject of Weights and Measures*; 1820. House of Commons, London. Appendix 'A' of 35pp lists virtually all units then in use throughout England, Wales and Scotland.

General introduction to milling. For anyone wishing to learn more about the subject, many books, booklets and articles have been published in the last quarter century. The various milling enthusiast societies and groups in Britain (see last two entries in this Section) will be happy to advise.

Grains – Characteristics & Harvesting. Two beginner sources are books: *"Grains, Illustrated World History with Recipes"*, Elizabeth Burton Brown, London, Prentice Hall International Inc.,1977, 261pp, and *"Growing Cereals"*, anon, I.C.I. Ltd, London, 1982.

"Windmills and Watermills". John Reynolds, London, Hugh Evelyn Press, 1970, 196pp. Excellent book but recommended here for its drawings and glossary. Author has produced some beautiful isometric drawings which illustrate the type of mills once found on the Ceiriog, i.e.; *Cornmills,* p23; *Fulling mill,* p118; *Woollen mill,* p127; *Iron forging,* p161; *Gunpowder,* p168. Technical glossary is most comprehensive and carries some 330 entries on pages 183-91.

"Watermills of Cumbria". Mike Davies-Shiels, North Yorkshire, Dalesman Publishing, 1978, 120pp. Largely deals with upland mills. DLD has only had his attention drawn to this excellent book recently and regrets not reading it sooner. Recommended for all upland mill enthusiasts. Chapter 7 deals most usefully with *'Researching Your Mill'*.

Recording the physical aspects of an old watermill. Good practical advice is given on pages 104-129 and 151-153 of the book ***"Feldwork in Industrial Archaeology"*** by J.K. Major, Batsford Ltd, 1975. Using derelict Devon mill as an example, shows 11 fieldwork sketches and 7 finished drawings.

"Scottish Country Miller – 1700 to 1900". Enid Gauldie, Edinburgh, John Donald Pub. 1981, 254pp. Useful source because Scotland & Wales are Celtic lands with similar terrain and climate, which produced comparable farming, milling & dietary characteristics. More revealing than examination of lowland English practices.

"Water Power in Scotland, 1550-1870". John Shaw, Edinburgh, John Donald Pub. 1984, 605pp. Includes discussion on horizontal mills, cornmills, fixed threshing machines and sawmills.

Booklets on the subject of upland working watermills. Useful and well-illustrated guides for visitors.

(a) Felin Geri, Cwm Cou, Newcastle Emlyn, Dyfed. 9pp, 1977.
(b) Melin Bompren, Welsh Folk Museum, Cardiff, 27pp, 1982
(c) Pentre Mill, Loggerheads, Mold, Clwyd, 19pp, c1990.
(d) Leap Mill, Burnopfield, Gateshead, Co Durham, 12pp, 1994.
(e) Felin Newydd, Crugybar, Llanwrda, Dyfed. 23pp, 1995.

Watermills of Radnorshire & Border Country. (This author's composite title) Panoramic & detailed guide to river systems and their mills from stark uplands to Welsh Marcher lowlands, contained in three separate publications; *Melin 1 (1985), Melin 5 (1989)* – [see Welsh Mills Society below] – and booklet *"Some Watermills of S.E. Shropshire"*, published by Midland Wind & Watermills Groups, 1991, All carefully researched and written by late Professor Gordon Tucker, totalling 161pp and 120 photos/drawings.

"The Ceiriog – One Piece in Historical Jigsaw puzzle of the Welsh-English Border", Booklet. David Llewelyn Davies (same author as this book), Chirk Local History Soc., Chirk, Clwyd, 1991, 42pp, two maps but no illustrations. Summary from pre-historic times to present day first published 1963. Separate and detailed bibliography covering area, and containing 130 references, is also obtainable from Society at extra cost.

"Economic History of the Ceiriog, Denbighshire, 1775-1950". 150pp typescript. Microfilm record of incomplete researches made by David Llewelyn Davies (author of this book) in 1960-63, from which emerged booklet immediately above and booklet *"Glyn Valley Tramway"*. Held by National Library of Wales, Aberystwyth, as MSS

18444D.

"Lost Country Life". Dorothy Hartley, London, MacDonald & Jane's, 1979, 374pp. Veritable encyclopedia of country life, in minute detail, prior to industrial revolution. Most helpful in writing this history. By coincidence the late Miss Hartley lived at Froncysyllte (also home of famous Welsh choir), three miles north-east of Felin Lyn.

"Old Farms, An Illustrated Guide". John Vince, London, John Murray Publishers, 1982, 160pp. Good visual reference source for buildings, implements, and methods prior to days of mechanization. In keeping with title 'Old', all wording is hand lettered with not one piece of typesetting. Apart from content value, book itself is minor work of art.

"Horse Power". Marylian & Sanders Watney, Hamlyn, London, 1975, 96pp. Explains horse employment throughout the world but mainly in Britain in nineteenth century. Useful background material considering that major market for Welsh oats was the horse.

"What Jane Austin Ate and Charles Dickens Knew". Daniel Pool, London; Simon & Schuster, 1993, 416pp. The social aspects of daily life in 19th century England. Third of book consists of glossary; remainder deals with all manner of topics: clothing, gentry, servants, the poor, living conditions, women, etc.

"Byegones (relating to Wales & Border counties)". Weekly column in newspaper *Oswestry Advertizer,* Shropshire, which was subsequently issued as bound biennial by Woodall & Co., Oswestry. Dealt with minor events, customs, the odd and the remarkable; now valuable resource for local historians. 1st series: Vol 1-9 (1871-1888); 2nd Series: Vol 1-14 (1889-1910); New Series: Vol 1-7 (1925-39). Indexed and full set held by Oswestry Public Library.

Denbighshire Record Office. Archives held at Ruthin. Repository is located in former Victorian prison closed in 1916 and is worth a visit on that score alone, with some of the records stored in the old cells. Archives include: County admin. records, parish registers, papers of large estates, maps, directories, local history in all aspects, etc. Microfilm room provided for newspaper and census searches and photocopying service for most documents. Has own *'Publications for Sale'* leaflet listing over 100 items. Its four-page pamphlet *"Tracing the History of Your House"* (Student Aid No 5, 1975) is most helpful. Address: 46 Clwyd St, Ruthin, LL15 1HP. Phone 01824-703077 for hours of opening.

Denbighshire Historical Society. Covers old county of Denbigh.l Founded 1950 and has some 300 members. Holds lectures, field trips and publishes its annual 'Transactions'; latest issue Vol. 45, has 136pp and six articles. Vol. 32 (1983) contains cumulative title index of Vols. 1-31. Enquiries to: Hon. Sec., Cefn Ceirch, Betws Gwerfil Goch, Corwen, Denbighshire, LL21 9PG.

Cymdeithas Melinau Cymru/Welsh Mills Society. Formed in 1984 to study, record, interpret, and publicise the water and wind mills of Wales; also to advise on preservation and uses. Holds twice yearly meetings/field trips. Produces quarterly newsletter, annual Journal, and yearly tourist leaflet listing Welsh mills open to the public. Currently has 220 members. For further details write c/o Museum of Welsh Life, St. Fagans, Cardiff, CF5 6XB.

Other Milling Enthusiast Groupings. There are two. In 1877 the Society for Protection of Ancient Buildings was formed, and in 1929 a specialist group was created within it, called the **Wind and Water Mill Section**. This is a voluntary organization which attempts to save existing mills, and encourages the study of milling and the history of individual mills. It organises meetings, conferences, and mill visits, and produces a newsletter for the benefit of its members. It also has a library and sells milling publications on behalf of itself and others. The **Section** also acts as an umbrella for about a dozen regional mill groups in England, e.g. *Friends of Norfolk Windmills.* Address: 37 Spital Square, London E1 6DY; Tel. 0171-377 1644.

The other body is the **The International Molinological Society** which was founded in 1975, after a preliminary meeting held in 1965. TIMS (its acronym) fosters worldwide interest and understanding of wind, water, and animal powered mills and encourages research, knowledge and restoration. It has a membership in 28 countries and is strongest in the USA, Netherlands and Britain. It issues two newsletters a year and holds a week long symposium every four years in different countries. The 1993 symposium was hosted by the Welsh Mills Society at Aberystwyth, Wales. Further information can be obtained from TIMS Hon. Sec., c/o 269 St Fagans Road, Fairwater, Cardiff, CF5 3DW, Wales.

Watermills of (pre-1974) Denbighshire

This list has no connection with Felin Lyn. It has been added to assist any reader who is studying all, or some, of the mills in Denbighshire and Flintshire. It is not intended to be exhaustive but rather to indicate potential sources.

Clwyd Mills Survey. On-going accumulation of data

covering site visits, sketch plans, historical detail, photos, etc. About 250 mills in the former county of Clwyd have received some mention todate. No intent to publish but available for perusal. Located at Archaeology Service, Clwyd County Council, Shire Hall, Mold, CH76 NB.

King's Mill Visitor Centre, Wrexham. Situated on town's south-eastern outskirts and is featured within the Clywedog historical trail. Erected in 1769, ceased work in 1930s and became derelict. Wrexham Maelor Borough Council commenced restoration in 1970s and opened it to public in 1991. Not a working mill but has running wheel. Bilingual interpretive centre with displays and much general information about cornmilling. Open Easter to end of September. Address: King's Mill Rd, nr Hightown, Wrexham. Tel: 01978-362967.

Pentrefoelas Mill, 1920 to 1949. (article) Heald, G.W.; *Trans. Denb. Hist. Soc.*, Vol 25, 1976, p.211-26. Good detailed technical description. This was last working commercial watermill in former County of Denbigh and, prior to closure in 1982, sold health food flours and meals. Was restored by Clwyd County Council as part of Pentrefoelas Heritage Village and is open to public at certain times.

***E. Mitford Abraham Collection*:** (see Primary Sources) Two to seven line entries of dates 1933/6 & 1943 re: Bache (Llangollen); Llangollen town; Loggerheads (nr Mold); Marford (nr Wrexham); Plas Ucha (Abergate); Rossett (nr Wrexham); Trevor (nr Llangollen).

Rossett Mill. (5m. N.E. of Wrexham) Dates from 1661, much photographed. Appears in *"Discovering Watermills"* booklet and on p.70-1 of Chap. 'Wind & Water Power' in *"B.P. Book of Industrial Archaeology"* by Neil Cossons, Newton Abbot, David & Charles Ltd, 1975, 496pp. Also in 'Liverpool Daily Post' article of August 1953.

"Grinding Corn in Days of Good Queen Bess". Article about Adenbury Mill, Wrexham, in periodical *'County Quest'* (Mold), Oct. 1972, p.26-8.

Pentre Mill, Loggerheads, near Mold. This was combined saw and cornmill which worked until 1942. Was restored by Clwyd County Council and is feature of Loggerheads County Park and runs occasionally for demonstration purposes. Two sale booklets about the Mill are available from Shire Hall, Mold; they are *'Pentre Mill'* (descriptive),19pp and *'The Last Miller'* (biography by grandson), 27pp; both 1986.

Random Articles in 'Liverpool Daily Post' in 1953. All by Charles Quant. (a) Afon Ystrad Mills (between Nantglyn & Denbigh, 4 Sept 1953; (b) Brook House mill (nr Denbigh), September 1953; Bwlch Mill (nr Cerrigydrudion), 27 Aug 1953; (c) Erbistock Mill (nr Overton), August 1953; (d) Ruthin Mill, October 1953.

Cobden Mills (1865-1929), Wrexham. Steam powered industrial cornmill. Articles in newspaper *'Wrexham Leader'*, dated 7 Sept. & 9 Nov. 1984.

Millstones of Halkin Mountain, Flintshire. Reference & listing within article 'British Burrstones,1799-1821' of *Melin No 1* (1985), Journal of Welsh Mills Society.

Fulling Mills of Chirk. Article within National Library of Wales Journal, Vol. XXIII, 1984-5, 8pp.

INDEX

Subjects in **bold type** are the sub-headings to be found in all chapters and appendices. (FL) is the abbreviation for *Felin Lyn*.